Childhood Dreams

Childhood Dreams

A Book of Crib Quilt Projects

Susan Bennett Gallagher

A Sterling/Main Street Book
Sterling Publishing Co., Inc. New York

For H.C.M.

Text Design by Ronald R. Misiur

10 9 8 7 6 5 4 3 2 1

A Sterling / Main Street Book

Published by Sterling Publishing Company, Inc.
387 Park Avenue South, New York, N.Y. 10016
Distributed in Canada by Sterling Publishing
℅ Canadian Manda Group, P.O. Box 920, Station U
Toronto, Ontario, Canada M8Z 5P9
Distributed in Great Britain and Europe by Cassell PLC
Artillery House, Artillery Row, London SW1P 1RT, England
Distributed in Australia by Capricorn Ltd.
P.O. Box 665, Lane Cove, NSW 2066
Manufactured in the United States of America

Sterling ISBN 0-8069-7343-9 (Trade)
0-8069-7342-0 (Paper)

Contents

Introduction

QUILTED MATERIALS are as practical as they are elegant. Two layers of cloth, carefully stitched together and lightly stuffed, make a strong, warm, and decorative fabric. It is not surprising that such materials have a long history and many uses. They show up as robes in ancient Egyptian carvings, as rugs in prehistoric Russian tombs, as coverlets on medieval Sicilian beds, and as underskirts in Elizabethan petticoats.[1]

Patchwork quilts—those bedspreads composed of small scraps of cloth—have a much shorter history. They are an American achievement, closely tied to America's history and reflective of its customs and values. The evolution of these patchwork quilts, and especially of the small ones made just for babies, is an interesting and evocative story.

Colonial Quilts and Their English Origins

American quilts have direct ancestors in seventeenth-century England. There, Elizabethan merchants imported a fine printed cotton cloth called *chintz* from India. Its colors were brilliant and its dyes were colorfast. Chintz was fashionable and expensive.[2] Even the scraps left over after a dress had been cut were hoarded. Enterprising seamstresses soon came up with a use for the leftovers. They cut out the printed figures—the flowers, birds, and animals—and stitched them onto whole pieces of plain-colored local cloth. The largest element would go in the center, with the smaller pieces, usually garlands and birds, framing it in a hierarchical composition. This technique, known as *broderie perse* (Persian embroidery), fulfilled two goals at the same time. The costly decorated chintz was extended to cover a full blanket, and a sort of shortcut instant embroidery was accomplished.[3] These blankets were early versions of appliquéd quilts, appliqué being the technique in which a small piece of material is sewn directly on top of a larger one.

Other seamstresses devised another use for their chintz scraps. They gathered them up, trimmed them into triangles and squares, and sewed them together to make large mosaic-like sheets. The large sheets were backed with full lengths of plain material, stuffed with bits of wool, and the whole ensemble stitched together. These bedcovers were pieced quilts. Piecework is the technique in which many small cloth elements are sewn together to produce a larger piece.

While these chintz spreads were fashionable, they were never essential. The cotton trade with India was always secondary to England's own well-developed wool industry and to Europe's ample linen production. Lacking the push of necessity, England's quiltwork never developed far beyond those Elizabethan efforts.

Early America took its cues from England. Colonial housewives, like their English sisters, saved their scarce imported fabrics. Since England controlled the lucrative textile trades among its colonies, and since the Americans were forbidden to make their own cloth, the fabrics were even scarcer and more costly in America than they had been in England.[4] A broderie perse crib quilt, c. 1825 (figure 1), shows the arrangement established by English traditions—a basket of flowers is ringed by garlands. Another quilt, from the same period, is an example of the piecework style (figure 2). Typically, quilters of these bedcovers used their fancy fabrics on the front and backed them up with a common woolen homespun material.

Only their small size identifies these as children's quilts. Some scholars, including Philippe Ariès and Anita Schorsch, have suggested that the

FIG. 1. Flowers and Birds, c. 1825, probably from Baltimore, 34″ x 36″. Printed chintz and muslin. (*Photo courtesy of the Baltimore Museum of Art; Gift of Linda and Irwin Berman, St. Simon Island, Georgia.*)

FIG. 2. Variable Star, c. 1825, found in New York, 43″ x 32″. Eighteenth-century printed fabric and glazed chintzes. (*Photo courtesy of the Baltimore Museum of Art; Gift of Linda and Irwin Berman, St. Simon Island, Georgia.*)

seventeenth- and eighteenth-century societies of England and America considered children to be just like adults, only smaller.[5] They propose that a combination of factors, including high infant mortality, lack of public education, and the early preparation of children for adult jobs, prevented the sentimental indulgence that has been associated with childhood from the nineteenth century on. Whether or not it is possible to read such cultural attitudes from simple artifacts, it is nonetheless true that these small quilts are nearly identical to the adult versions—no particular themes, techniques, colors, or designs mark them as children's pieces.

Pioneers and Settlers in the Nineteenth Century

American independence was followed by a century of exploration and growth. Pioneers and travelers pushed against the edges of the wilderness to settle in the midwestern and western territories. On their way, these settlers and farmers faced frequent hardship and abundant toil. Women worked alongside men at the plow and in the field. In the evenings, they cooked, cleaned, and raised children. At night, when the day's work was done, the women pieced together fabric from their scrap bags to make quilt squares, and sewed the squares together to make quilt tops. The final step, joining the top to the backing with thousands of tiny stitches, might be done by the woman alone, or it might be done by a party of women in a social event known as a quilting bee.

In this culture, quilting was a necessity, a virtue, and an opportunity. The cold nights and scarcity of material made quilts indispensible. Beyond that, quilts expressed a combination of traits prized by the frontier settlers. Economy, frugality, and efficiency met with patience, charity, and community in the task. And for women quilting was an opportunity to mingle tradition and invention in an artifact of enduring practicality. So often women's work was short-lived. Meals were eaten the same day, and gardens were gone in a season. Women did not usually make buildings or furniture. So the quilt, which might be passed through several generations, or even through a community as a form of payment,[6] acquired a certain permanence and continuity.

Most pioneer quilts were geometrically patterned piecework, made up of square, rectangular, and triangular elements (figures 3 and 4). Sometimes curved elements were used (figure 5), but, as they required more material to make and more skill to sew, they were less common. Piecing was the most economical of all techniques. In its use of repeated identical blocks, it was also the most simple and democratic. By themselves, the square units were small and could be made one at a time, in even the most cramped quarters. An elaborate overall design could be achieved through the manipulations of adjacent blocks.

The patterns were referential. They alluded to pioneer life and artifacts,

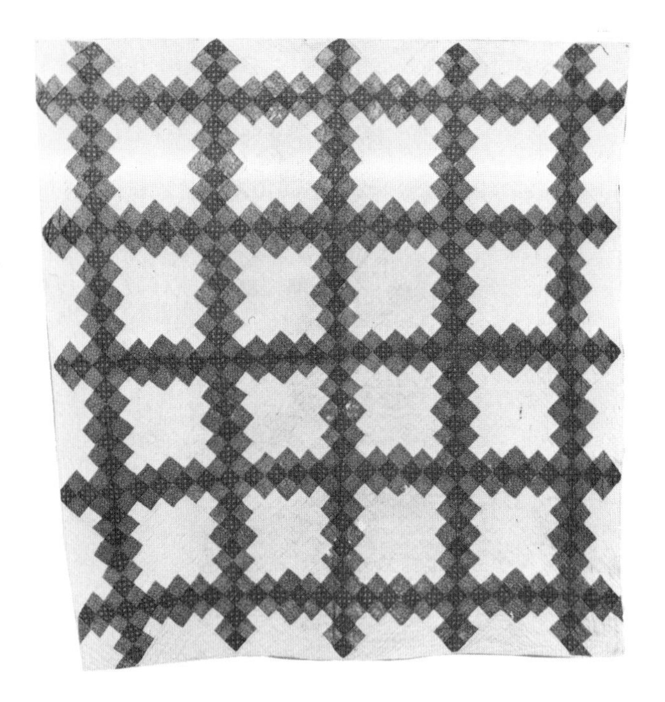

to tools and construction, to food and travel.[7] Log Cabin (figure 6), Carpenter's Square (figure 7), and Corn and Beans (figure 8) were just a few of the designs drawn from everyday life. Occasionally the designs were representational, but the constraints of the technique limited pictorial work to a few patterns. Stars (figure 9) were the most common representational motif, and baskets must have been second, but clever seamstresses also devised a rather graceful flower, the Carolina Lily (figure 10). Frequently, a pattern would have different names in different regions. Thus the arrangement known as Duck's Foot to Long Island's shore communities was called Bear's Paw by Ohio's forest settlers and Hand of Friendship by Philadelphia's Quakers.

The patterns were usually executed in contrasting colors—dark and light patches alternating in stark arrangements. Blue and white pairings are particularly common, white being the natural color of the wool, cotton, or linen fabric, and blue the result of the successful indigo dyes. Other colors were harder to achieve. Green and yellow dyes were unstable and red dyes, expensive. But the simple colors were used to great effect. The bluntness of the combinations recalls the light and shadow of outdoor work and the pleasures and adversity of the pioneer effort.

Some pieced quilts have special optical properties. They are illusionistic. They may imply that the surface of the quilt is three-dimensional, that it has depth and shadow. Or they suggest motion and turbulence. With these quilts, the pattern is ordinary: it is the asymmetric arrangement of color or tone that creates the illusion. Tumbling Blocks (also named Baby Blocks, figure 11) is probably the best known optical design. In it, dark,

FIG. 3. Double Irish Chain, 1840, 48″ x 49″. (*Photo courtesy of the Brooklyn Museum; Gift of the Jason and Peggy Westerfield Collection.*)

FIG. 4. Wild Goose Chase, nineteenth century, 40″ x 39.5″. Printed cottons and brown chintz. (*Photo courtesy of the Smithsonian Institution.*)

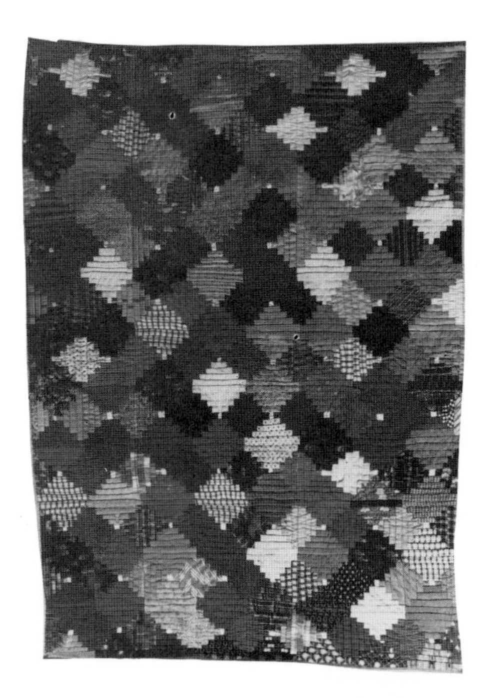

Fig. 5. Orange Peel, mid-nineteenth century, 44″ square. (*Photo courtesy of the Brooklyn Museum; Gift of the Jason and Peggy Westerfield Collection.*)

Fig. 6. Log Cabin, c. 1860, 43″ x 30″. (*Photo courtesy of the Smithsonian Institution.*)

Fig. 7. Carpenter's Square, 1844-1854, made by Esther Wileman for Flora, 50.5″ x 47.5″. (*Photo courtesy of the Smithsonian Institution.*)

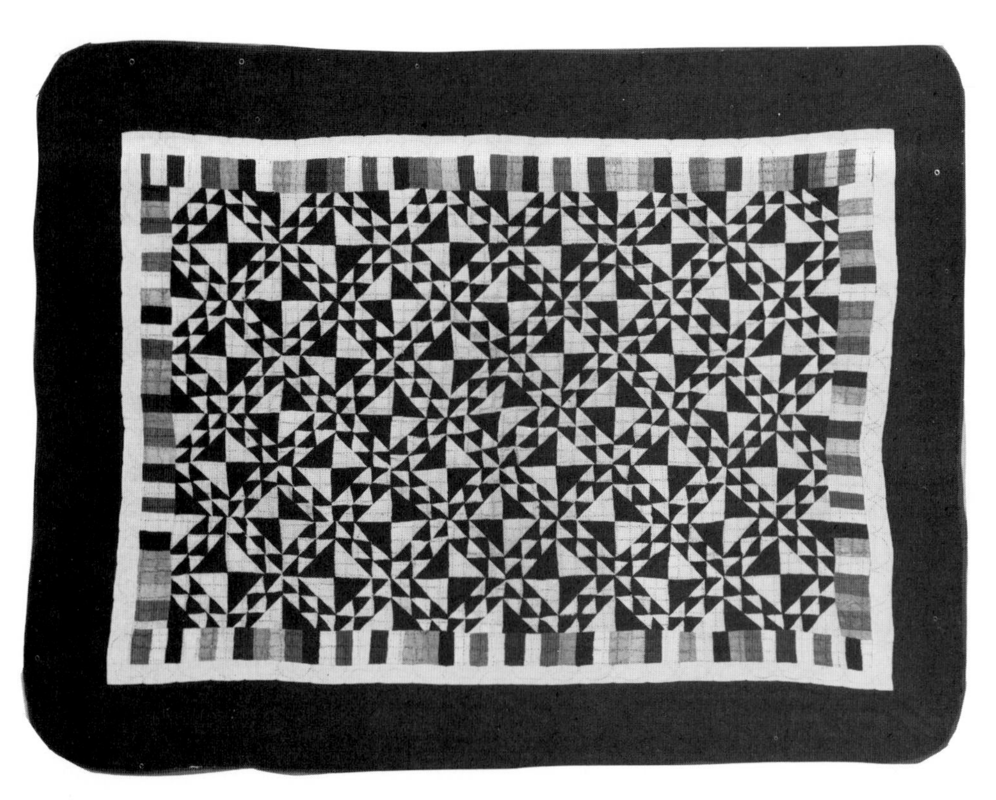

Fig. 8. Corn and Beans (also called Lady in the Lake), c. 1915, 41″ x 30″. Cotton sateen cloth. (*Photo courtesy of the Baltimore Museum of Art; Gift of Linda and Irwin Berman, St. Simon Island, Georgia.*)

Fig. 9. Ohio Star, c. 1913, made by Polly Bontrager, Yoder Corner, Indiana, 48″ x 38″. Pieced and hand quilted cotton. (*Photo courtesy of the Permanent Collection of the Museum of American Folk Art; Gift of David Pottinger.*)

Fig. 10. Carolina Lily, c. 1920, Amish, Holmes County, Ohio, 47″ x 32″. (*Photo courtesy of the Baltimore Museum of Art; Gift of Linda and Irwin Berman, St. Simon Island, Georgia.*)

Fig. 11. Tumbling Blocks, 1882, dated and signed I. A. D., 24″ x 36″. Wool. (*Photo courtesy of the Baltimore Museum of Art; Gift of Linda and Irwin Berman, St. Simon Island, Georgia.*)

medium, and light tones are arranged to suggest a three-dimensional surface. If the diamond-shaped blocks were colored differently, the quilt might resemble stars or flowers instead. Other optical designs, like the one in figure 12, rely on only two colors to create an ambiguous and tense surface.

Along the frontier, infancy was almost too brief to celebrate. Crib quilts were always a bit of a luxury, always rare. Most babies slept in their cradles under folded blankets, or cut-down sections from larger quilts (figure 13). The pieced crib quilts that *were* made, however, are extremely interesting. Most often they are perfectly scaled miniatures. Both the quilt and the constituent blocks were shrunk to infant size. The Tiny Triangles quilt (figure 14), with 1,008 triangles, illustrates this: it shows many scraps were incorporated in a single crib quilt and how tiny the scraps were. No particular patterns or colors were favored for children. Log Cabin, Bethlehem Star, and Bow Tie appear in both large and small versions.

Appliqué quilts were less economical than pieced ones. When money, time, and space allowed, appliqué work might be used for a "best" quilt. In general, appliqué designs are more flexible and more pictorial than others. There are some standard elements, such as double hearts, plumes, wreaths, and leaves, which appear on many quilts. There are also recurring themes which appear with a wide range of individual variation. Flowers, stars, and patriotic motifs are characteristic. Religious subjects occur occasionally. Mostly from the South, and often the work of slave women, these highly individual pieces feature crosses, crowns, and other Biblical references.

Appliqué crib quilts shared some design elements with adult quilts—

FIG. 12. Orange and Black, unknown pattern, 1920-1940, Amish, Mrs. Jacob Miller, Shipshewana, Indiana, 40″ x 30.5″. Pieced and hand quilted cotton. (*Photo courtesy of the Permanent Collection of the Museum of American Folk Art; Gift of David Pottinger.*)

FIG. 13. Cut down quilt, nineteenth century, 40″ x 32″. Cotton. (*Photo courtesy of the Germantown Historical Society, Philadelphia, Pennsylvania.*)

FIG. 14. Tiny Triangles, c. 1850, Lehigh Valley, Pennsylvania, 39″ x 35″. Cotton. (*Photo courtesy of the Baltimore Museum of Art; Gift of Linda and Irwin Berman, St. Simon Island, Georgia.*)

for example, hearts and flowers (figure 15). The technique was accommodating, and many pieces incorporate personal messages and announcements. The Stars and Stripes quilt from Kansas (figure 16) features popular patriotic devices, indicators of both the awakening national identity and the growing influence of national politics on frontier communities. But it also has the word "Baby" written in its largest star. It raises the obvious question, Who was "Baby"? Even more obscure is the message on the Heart and Hat quilt (figure 17). Below the appliqué heart, written in ink, is the following verse:

A heart I send, Young Squire Baldwin
Reject it not I do implore thee
A warm reception may it meet
My name a Secret I must keep.

The appliqué technique lent itself to pictorial work, and, for the first time, special children's themes can be identified in quilts made after the middle of the nineteenth century. Alphabets and schoolhouses, perhaps reflecting the growth of public education, are common. Sometimes the lettered blocks are combined with simple pictures of common objects, like saws, ladders, and scissors. The quilt in figure 18 is almost like a lesson, with its alphabet and images resembling a reading primer. Other quilts used the alphabet alone or were finished with a heart or some other device.

FIG. 15. Floral appliqué, c. 1845, probably from Pennsylvania, 33″ x 34″. Cotton. (*Photo courtesy of the Permanent Collection of the Museum of American Folk Art; Gift of Joel and Kate Kopp.*)

FIG. 16. "Baby," c. 1861, 37″ square. (*Photo courtesy of the Permanent Collection of the permanent collection of the Museum of American Folk Art; Gift of Phyllis Haders.*)

Fɪɢ. 17. Heart and Hat, c. 1850, 35″ x 33″. Cotton and wool with black ink inscription. (*Photo courtesy of the Baltimore Museum of Art; Gift of Linda and Irwin Berman, St. Simon Island, Georgia.*)

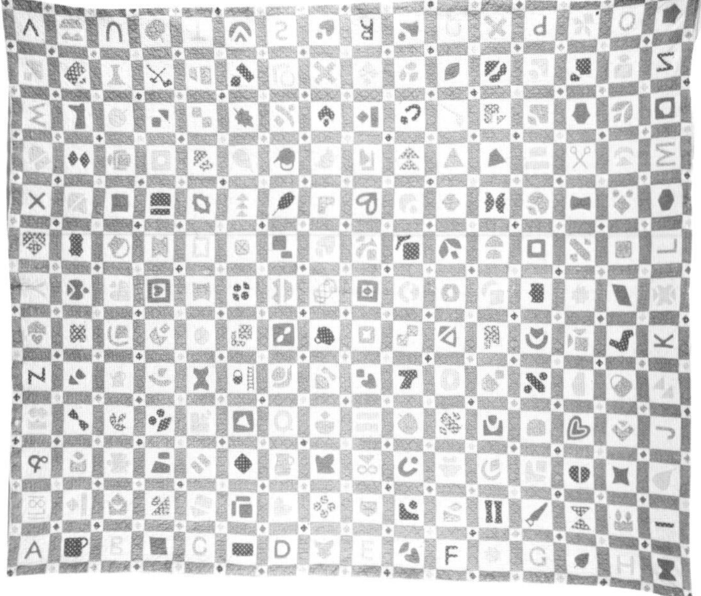

Fɪɢ. 18. Alphabet, 1871, 77″ x 62″. (*Private collection; photo courtesy of Thos. K. Woodard American Antiques and Quilts.*)

Amish Quilts

The quilts of Amish women, which were produced concurrently with the examples already mentioned, stand out as a special category. They distinguish themselves with a plainness of pattern that is made electric by a richness of color. In addition, they sometimes feature exceptional stitching.

Deliberately plain, intensely private, and very religious, the Amish settled to farm in Pennsylvania, Ohio, Indiana, and Iowa. They were content to work their quilts with the simplest of elements: large rectangles (figure 19), plain squares, or broad stripes (figure 20). In general they avoided the fancier diamond- and hexagon-shaped elements used by non-Amish quilters; they also avoided the minuscule repetition and ornamentation that characterized certain other pioneer quilts.

The glowing colors are the most striking aspect of the Amish works. Without prints, which the Amish regarded as vain and unnecessary, the solid colors take on a new dimension, depth, and resonance. The Amish

FIG. 19. Inside Border Pattern, 1913, Amish, probably from Ohio, 48″ x 35″. Pieced and hand quilted cotton. (*Photo courtesy of the Permanent Collection of the Museum of American Folk Art; Gift of David Pottinger.*)

FIG. 20. Amish Bars, c. 1925, Mifflin County, Pennsylvania, 53″ x 51″. *(Photo courtesy of the Baltimore Museum of Art; Gift of Linda and Irwin Berman, St. Simon Island, Georgia.)*

were not afraid to use very dark colors—navy blues, browns, and purples are standard — realizing that the darkest colors can make the lighter ones more vibrant. In some cases, the lighter elements even appear to float above the darker field.

Industrialization, Cities, and the Victorian Tradition

While the nineteenth century saw exploration and settlement in the West, it was also a time of industrialization and urbanization. Industrialization gathered people into cities, where they lived and worked indoors.

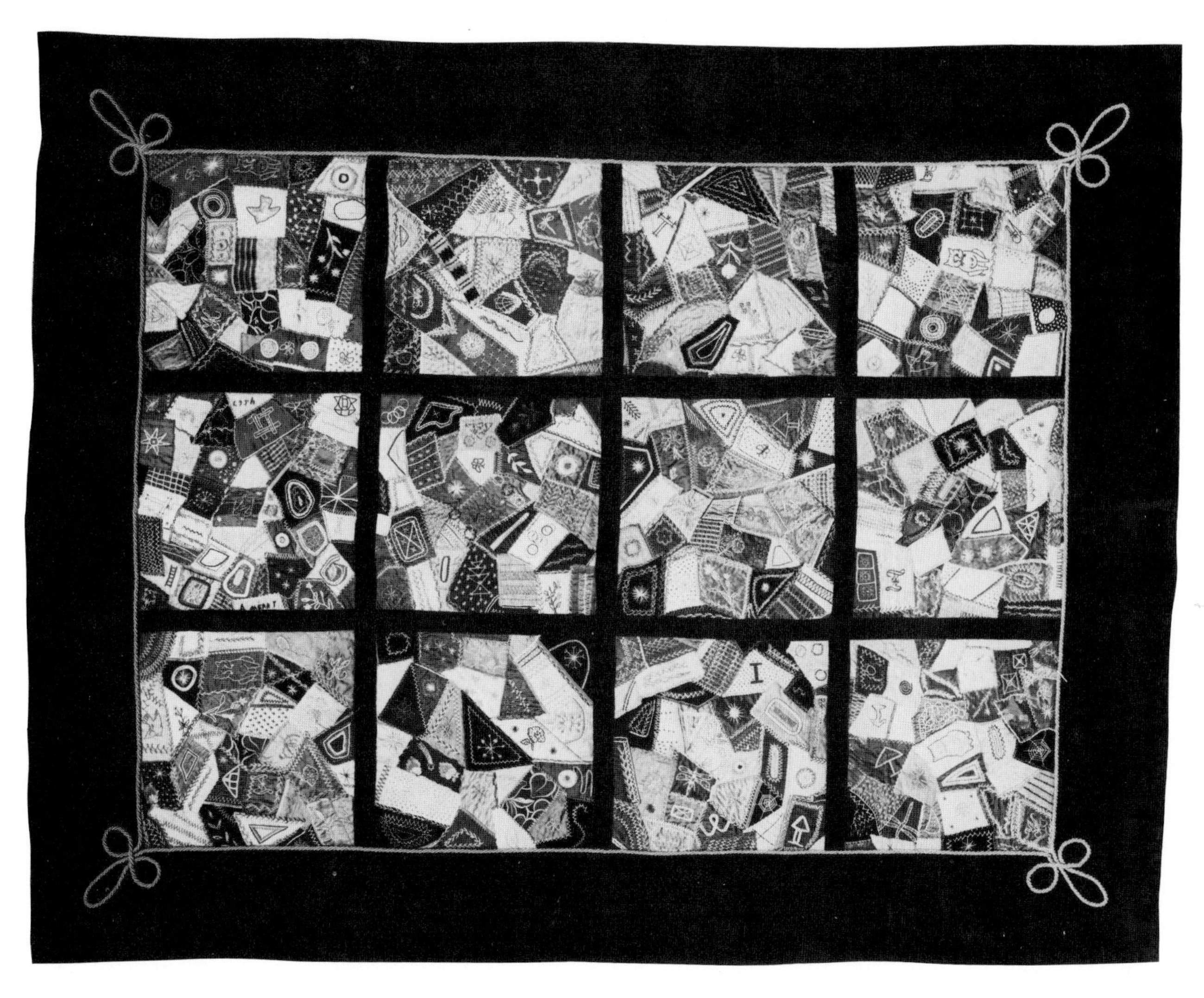

Fig. 21. Crazy Quilt, 1882, 60″ x 76″. Feather stitching and embroidered emblems. (*Photo courtesy of the Smithsonian Institution.*)

The Victorian ideal was an urban life, comfortable, warm. It was epitomized by the parlor, a decorated, ornamented room for small social gatherings and afternoon entertainments.

Machine-made blankets and bedspreads were available, and quilting was no longer a necessity. Instead, it was cultivated as a hobby, something that ladies might do for their amusement and improvement. Quilts became parlor dressing, ornamental pieces of needlework. Fragile fabrics—satins, velvets, and brocades—were favored, and a whole assembly might be embroidered with flowers, spiders, and other emblems (figure 21). The harsh contrasts of dark and light, and the strict geometrical organizations so critical to pioneer efforts, were avoided. The quilts were collections of dark tones and shades: black, wine red, dark blue, and gold swatches shone and glistened beside one another. Oriental fans, associated with the contemporary fascination with Japan and China, were common (figure 22). Crazy quilts, made from wild arrays of overlapping irregular elements (figure 23), were also in vogue.

FIG. 22. Oriental Fans, c. 1880, made by Martha Ada Mumma, Sharpsburg, Maryland, 52.5″ x 51″. Silk and velvet. (*Photo courtesy of the Smithsonian Institution.*)

FIG. 23. Crazy Patchwork with Boxer Dog, 1890-1910, 31″ x 24.5″. Silk, velvet, and lace with silk embroidery. (*Photo courtesy of the Permanent Collection of the Museum of American Folk Art; Gift of Margaret Cavigga.*)

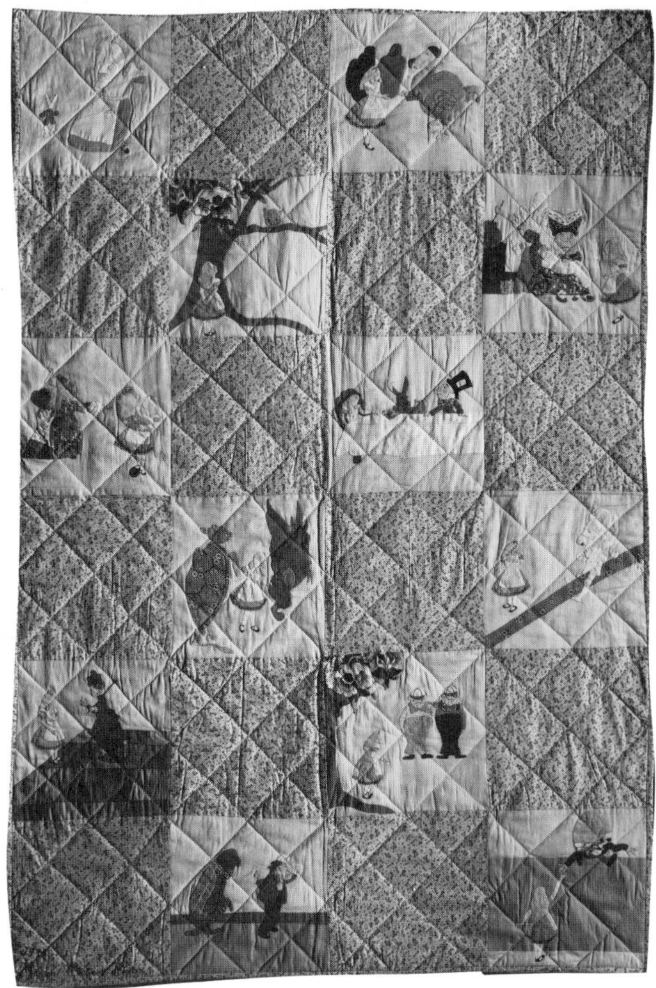

FIG. 24. Alice in Wonderland, 1945, Marion Whiteside Newton, New York, 36″ x 54″. Cotton. (*Photo courtesy of the Metropolitan Museum of Art, Edward C. Moore Fund, 1945.*)

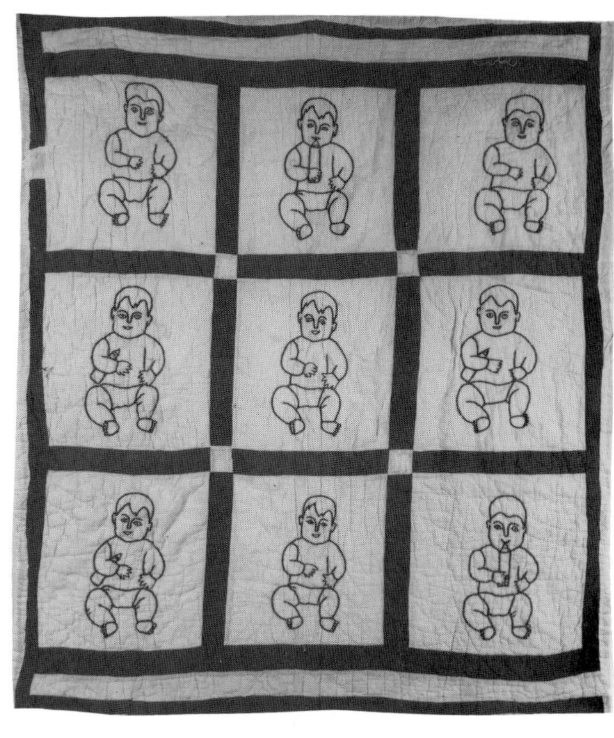

Fig. 25. Gingham Dog and Calico Cat, c. 1910, probably from Pennsylvania, 34.5″ x 28.5″. Appliquéd and pieced cotton. (*Photo courtesy of the Permanent Collection of the Museum of American Folk Art; Gift of Gloria List.*)

Fig. 26. Baby Boys with Bottles, c. 1930, probably from Texas, 48″ x 56″. Cotton cloth with yarn embroidery, hand quilted. (*Photo courtesy of Laura Fisher.*)

The Victorians regarded childhood as a time of innocence and purity. The nursery was an important room, a sanctum filled with lace and embellished linen. Childhood had its own books, themes, and secrets, which were expressed in nursery rhymes and fairy tales. Figures from these tales show up on crib quilts from this period, and continue to appear in twentieth-century works. Thus Alice, the quintessential Victorian child, appears with Wonderland characters on one quilt (figure 24), while the Gingham Dog and the Calico Cat sit side by side on another (figure 25).

Some designs were influenced by newspapers and advertisements—both achieving wide circulation for the first time. The baby boys from Texas (figure 26) represent a new direction in quilt design: they are line drawings, not appliqué or piecework. Executed in red yarn, the figures resemble those that appear in the comic pages. Advertising images, taken from billboards, labels, and magazines, also appear in works from the early part of the twentieth century. The quilt in figure 27 features Grace Drayton's Campbell Kids in a variety of innocent adventures—the same kids who appeared in advertisements for Campbell's Soup.

The Twentieth-Century Decline

In the early twentieth century there were more factories, more goods, more money, and fewer reasons to make quilts than ever before. Quilts, like other homemade products, were sometimes associated with poverty and

Fig. 27. Campbell's Soup Kids, c. 1920, probably from Massachusetts, 42″ x 32″. Cotton cloth with cotton embroidery, hand quilted. (*Photo courtesy of Laura Fisher.*)

Fig. 28. Red Crazy, 1987, made by Jan Myers, 41.5″ x 54.5″. Cotton. (*Photo courtesy of Jan Myers,* © 1987.)

CCNY

backwardness, a source of shame or embarrassment.[8] Grandmothers and great-grandmothers continued the traditions that they had learned as girls, but quilting was in decline.

There was a sputter of enthusiasm in the 1930s, perhaps related to the poverty of the Depression and to the theme of the heroism of labor which was part of the recovery. The National Park Service even developed a quilting program to assist rural women. Quilt patterns were recorded in several books at the time and quilt kits were introduced.[9] But the enthusiasm faded quickly and vanished by the time of World War II.

FIG. 29. The Men: Mask Face Quilt #2, 1986, made by Faith Ringgold, 70″ x 62″. Painted and pieced fabric. *(Photo courtesy of Bernice Steinbaum Gallery, collection of Mr. & Mrs. Robert James.)*

Contemporary Quilting

Only recently have old quilts been recognized as the great and original works that they are. A seminal show at the Whitney Museum of Art in 1971 pushed hundreds of the finest quilts into the public eye.[10] Other museums arranged exhibitions. Collectors took note and scholars did research. Books and articles appeared. The Whitney show also contributed to a surge in quiltmaking, modern and experimental. The constraints that earlier quilters had endured were no longer applicable. Modern quilters enjoy an abundance of fabric and other materials; they have ample working space; they have helpful machines. They also benefit from scientific processes and techniques which could not have been imagined by our quilting ancestors. They can use photographic transfer technology to print photographs on cloth; they can use airbrushes, paints, and reliable dyes for color; they can even use graphic computers to fine-tune their patterns and designs.

Many new quiltmakers are studio artists who abandoned painting or sculpture in favor of quilting. They treat quilts like canvases done in fabric, and they try to locate their works in the artist's domain.

Modern quilting themes vary widely. Some quilts explore the old issues of contrast, light, and shade, but they replace the repetitive blocks that characterized earlier quilts with changing blocks. Their makers are colorists, working with finely graded and subtle color distinctions. Other quilters use collision and impact in their work: different traditional patterns collide and recombine to create new designs. Still others, like Jan Myers, create modern crazy quilts, with very tightly controlled and organized "crazy" elements (figure 28).

Other quilters make figurative quilts. The figures range from the abstract and allegorical to the intensely personal. The artist Faith Ringgold's "100 Pounds Weight Loss" quilt documents her own struggles with diets: she uses it as an element in a performance she gives on the same topic. Her other works deal with her family and the Harlem neighborhoods in which she grew up. The Men: Mask Face Quilt #2 (figure 29) combines painting, silkscreen, and quilting in one such piece.

A Personal Approach to Quiltmaking

The challenge of history is to learn from it, to experiment with it, to build on it. The history of quilting is so rich in technique and so varied in content that there is limitless room for invention. A quilt can be a literal true-to-tradition piece; it can use a modified or reinvented design; or it can be completely experimental, incorporating new materials and technologies.

I like to work with simple elements and materials, so most of my quilts are fairly straightforward. They use standard materials, printed and solid cotton cloth, joined by hand and by machine. (I use a sewing machine whenever I can, and I feel quite certain that my quilting ancestors would have done the same if machines had been available to them.) Most of my quilts are rectangular, but some are square. Many are inspired by traditional designs, but they are not slaves to historical precedent.

I am particularly interested in three traditions of quilts—the geometric, the pictorial, and the crazy—and it is to these types that I have directed most of my efforts. I should say right away that not all my efforts have been successful: my closets are filled with single squares, small panels of designs, or combinations that just did not work.

The geometric tradition is the most celebrated of the quilting categories. In general, geometric designs are the easiest to make and therefore are a good place for a beginning quilter to start. The clean lines and strict patterns allow the designer to explore some of the basic ideas of pattern and color.

In my geometric quilts I have investigated some of the following questions:

Should the quilt be dark or light? The Pinwheels quilt (Project 15) is a dark one, but most of my quilts fall into a middle ground, neither light nor dark. Does the quilt have high-contrast colors, or does it use a range of evenly graded tones? My Leaves quilt (Project 7) uses tones, while the Nine-Patch design (Project 3) works with contrasting colors. I find contrast easier to establish than a tonal pattern.

Why are the traditional two-color blue and white quilts so successful? In a two-color arrangement, do the two colors appear in equal or unequal amounts? What effects do printed fabrics have on the overall pattern? Does the quilt design make a continuous net over the quilt surface, as in the Waves quilt (Project 14), or are there clearly defined, independent units as in the Apple Pie quilt (Project 12)? What about geometric quilts with three or four colors, like Fence Rail (Project 11)? Can the colors be used to create the illusion of depth, or of light and shadow? How do the colors work together? What about curves? How do curves meet each other, how do they join? In the Watermelons quilt (Project 10), each block has three concentric curves, but the curves do not join across the blocks. In the Waves quilt, the undulating pattern depends on the continuity of adjacent arcs across the surface.

What about those odd geometric quilts that actually look like objects? As has been previously noted, picture quilts are rare in the geometric tradition, but both the Waves and the Watermelons quilts are pictorial.

And finally, are there simpler ways to make complicated patterns? Which designs can be assembled from a series of fabric strips? In this collection of quilts, the Nine-Patch lends itself to strip assembly, but the other projects do not.

The pictorial tradition relies chiefly on appliqué work. Appliqué requires more hand sewing and is usually slower and more difficult than geometric quilting. Like the geometric quilts, my appliqué projects study a range of questions.

Is the quilt one picture, like an oil painting, with a top and bottom, sides, and a single subject? Or is it a pictorial pattern, an arrangement

FIG. 30. Moon and Stars, 1985, made by Susan Bennett Gallagher, 36″ square. Cotton. (*Photo courtesy of Susan Bennett Gallagher,* © 1985.)

of repeating elements on a neutral surface? Contemporary quilts, especially those designed to hang on a wall rather than lie on a bed, often adopt the former attitude. I prefer the latter, and all my appliqué quilts have arrangements of repeating blocks. How do the blocks relate to each other, and to the whole quilt? Are the blocks square? Rectangular? Is the quilt square or rectangular? Most of my quilts are rectangular—Grapevines, Ducks and Umbrellas, Hearts and Hands (Project 5, 6, and 8)—but occasionally the theme dictates a square shape. The Moon quilt (figure 30) is square because the phases of the moon follow a regular, even cycle.

FIG. 31. Crazy, 1985, made by Susan Bennett Gallagher, 36″ x 48″. Cotton. (*Photo courtesy of Susan Bennett Gallagher,* © 1988.)

What about colors for the pictorial elements? Do the pictures rely on color and line for definition, or are they just silhouettes? Silhouettes, like the rabbits in Rabbits and Carrots (Project 2) and the hands in Hearts and Hands, are the easiest to appliqué. Figures with internal seam lines (color lines) are harder to make. For example, the ducks in Ducks and Umbrellas have white bodies with yellow beaks and feet. Should the figures be colored "naturally," or can other colors be used? I have found that if the figure is going to be a silhouette, it can be done in almost any strong color. If the figure is to be subdivided into separate color areas, realistic colors work best.

Crazy quilts are my current interest. I find them the hardest to understand, the most challenging of all the quilts to design.

What makes a quilt crazy? Is it a profusion of colors? The Crazy Blocks quilt (Project 4) cycles twelve different colors through a single irregular block, but the Crazy Quilt (Project 9) limits itself to a minimal palette of four colors. Can a two-color quilt be a crazy quilt? The quilt in figure 31 is just that: a two-color crazy quilt, done in traditional blue and white fabrics. Does a crazy quilt need a wide range of element sizes? Is asymmetry important? Do the elements overlap each other, as they do in classic crazy designs, or can they be pieced together like geometric patterns? Does the randomness of the pattern recognize any borders or edges, or does it just slam into the quilt boundaries? What about printed materials in crazy quilts? Do they strengthen or weaken the effect?

And what about the ornamental stitching and embroidery that show up on so many Victorian quilts? How is the embroidery designed, and what do the figures mean?

What challenges, what opportunities!

Each question raises another, and each completed quilt generates ideas for ten new designs.

Quilting is wonderful. Enjoy it.

Susan Bennett Gallagher
December 1, 1989

Notes

1. See *Crib Quilts and Other Small Wonders,* Thomas K. Woodard and Blanche Greenstein (New York: E. P. Dutton, 1981).
2. See *English Chintz,* Frank Lewis (Essex, England: F. Lewis Publishers, 1973).
3. See *The Pieced Quilt,* Jonathan Holstein (New York: Galahad Books, 1973).
4. Ibid.
5. See *Centuries of Childhood, a Social History of the Family,* Phillipe Ariès, translated by Robert Baldick (New York: Vintage Books, 1962) and *Images of Childhood,* Anita Schorsch (Pittstown, N.J.: The Main Street Press, 1985).
6. See *The Quilters: Women and Domestic Art,* Patricia Cooper and Norma Bradley Buferd (New York: Doubleday and Company, 1977).
7. See "The Quiltmaker's Landscape," Dolores Hayden and Peter Marris (*Landscape* Magazine, New York: December, 1981).
8. See *The Perfect Patchwork Primer,* Beth Gutcheon (Baltimore: Penguin Books, Inc., 1973).
9. Ibid.
10. See *Abstract Designs in American Quilts,* Jonathan Holstein (New York: The Whitney Museum of American Art, 1973).

Metric Equivalency Chart

INCHES TO MILLIMETRES AND CENTIMETRES

MM—Millimetres CM—Centimetres

INCHES	MM	CM	INCHES	CM	INCHES	CM
1/8	3	0.3	9	22.9	30	76.2
1/4	6	0.6	10	25.4	31	78.7
3/8	10	1.0	11	27.8	32	81.3
1/2	13	1.3	12	30.5	33	83.8
5/8	16	1.6	13	33.0	34	86.4
3/4	19	1.9	14	35.6	35	88.9
7/8	22	2.2	15	38.1	36	91.4
1	25	2.5	16	40.6	37	94.0
1 1/4	32	3.2	17	43.2	38	96.5
1 1/2	38	3.8	18	45.7	39	99.1
1 3/4	44	4.4	19	48.3	40	101.6
2	51	5.1	20	50.8	41	104.1
2 1/2	64	6.4	21	53.3	42	106.7
3	76	7.6	22	55.9	43	109.2
3 1/2	89	8.9	23	58.4	44	111.8
4	102	10.2	24	61.0	45	114.3
4 1/2	114	11.4	25	63.5	46	116.8
5	127	12.7	26	66.0	47	119.4
6	152	15.2	27	68.6	48	121.9
7	178	17.8	28	71.1	49	124.5
8	203	20.3	29	73.7	50	127.0

YARDS TO METRES

YARDS	METRES	YARDS	METRES	YARDS	METRES
1/8	0.11	3 1/2	3.20	6 7/8	6.29
1/4	0.23	3 5/8	3.31	7	6.40
3/8	0.34	3 3/4	3.43	7 1/8	6.52
1/2	0.46	3 7/8	3.54	7 1/4	6.63
5/8	0.57	4	3.66	7 3/8	6.74
3/4	0.69	4 1/8	3.77	7 1/2	6.86
7/8	0.80	4 1/4	3.89	7 5/8	6.97
1	0.91	4 3/8	4.00	7 3/4	7.09
1 1/8	1.03	4 1/2	4.11	7 7/8	7.20
1 1/4	1.14	4 5/8	4.23	8	7.32
1 3/8	1.26	4 3/4	4.34	8 1/8	7.43
1 1/2	1.37	4 7/8	4.46	8 1/4	7.54
1 5/8	1.49	5	4.57	8 3/8	7.66
1 3/4	1.60	5 1/8	4.69	8 1/2	7.77
1 7/8	1.71	5 1/4	4.80	8 5/8	7.89
2	1.83	5 3/8	4.91	8 3/4	8.00
2 1/8	1.94	5 1/2	5.03	8 7/8	8.12
2 1/4	2.06	5 5/8	5.14	9	8.23
2 3/8	2.17	5 3/4	5.26	9 1/8	8.34
2 1/2	2.29	5 7/8	5.37	9 1/4	8.46
2 5/8	2.40	6	5.49	9 3/8	8.57
2 3/4	2.51	6 1/8	5.60	9 1/2	8.69
2 7/8	2.63	6 1/4	5.72	9 5/8	8.80
3	2.74	6 3/8	5.83	9 3/4	8.92
3 1/8	2.86	6 1/2	5.94	9 7/8	9.03
3 1/4	2.97	6 5/8	6.06	10	9.14
3 3/8	3.09	6 3/4	6.17		

Designs for Fifteen Crib Quilts

General Notes

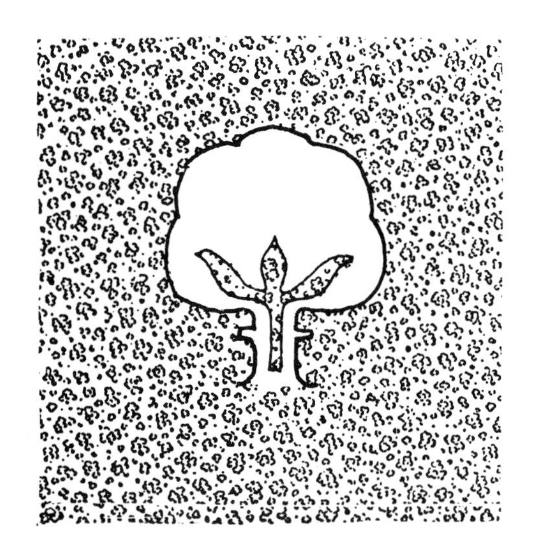

1. Use 100 percent cotton fabrics. Synthetic materials and blends can be unpredictable and may deteriorate over time.

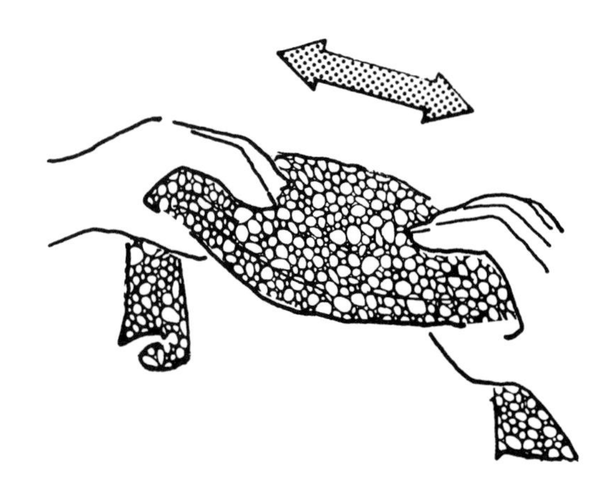

2. Test material by pulling on it (gently) in several directions. It should hold its shape well. If it stretches, the quilt pieces will stretch before they are sewn, and it will be harder to sew them together.

3. Pick prints carefully. Small calico prints, like #1, are the easiest to work with. One-way prints, like #2, can be difficult. If they don't all point in the same direction (and in a quilt, they probably won't), they can be visually disturbing. Try to use materials with different tones or values. Print #3 is considerably darker than print #4. Combining these two fabrics should make the quilt surface more interesting and lively.

4. Wash and iron all fabrics before cutting or sewing.

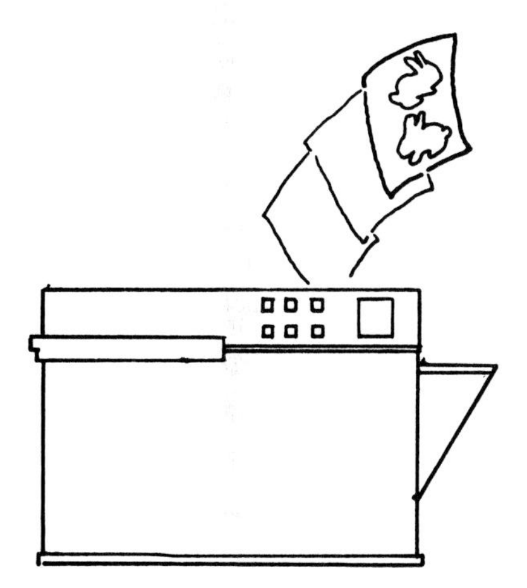

5. Copy patterns from the book. They can be traced onto cardboard or duplicated on a copier machine. Some of the older copier machines distort images slightly; be careful that the machine reproduces images accurately.

6. Cut and measure all pieces carefully. The more accurately the material is cut, the easier it will be to assemble the quilt.

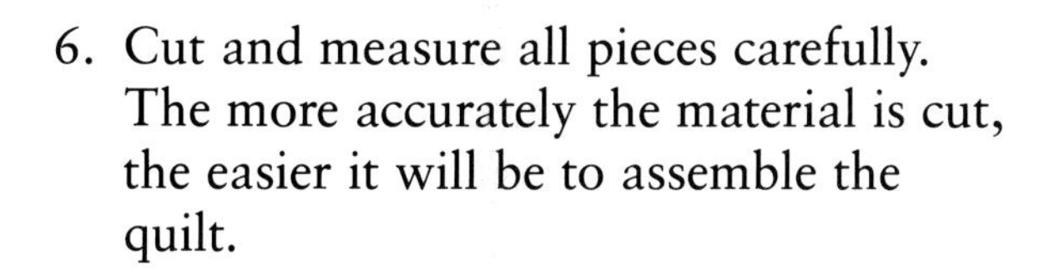

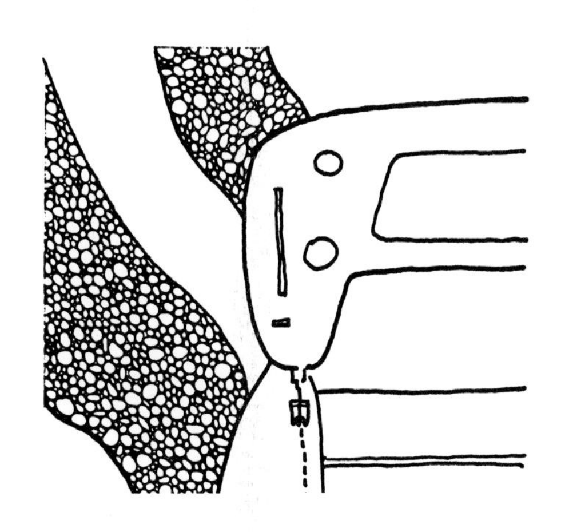

7. Appliqué work is generally done by hand. Piecing can be done by hand or with a machine. Seam allowances are ¼″ unless noted otherwise. Seam allowances can be trimmed or clipped if the pieces are small or very curved.

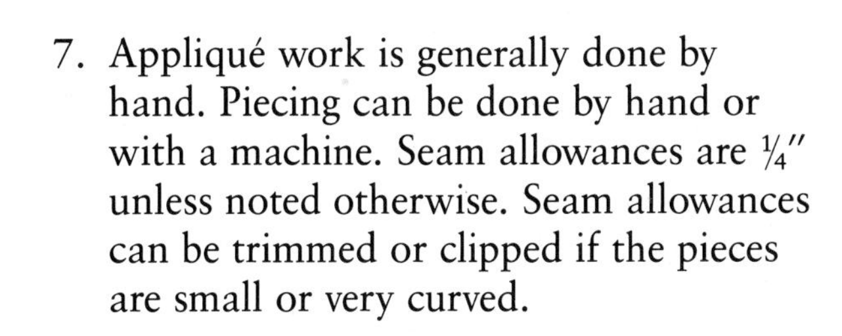

8. The quilt can be filled with either cotton batting or polyester batting. Cotton batting is thinner, flatter, and a bit easier to work with. Polyester makes a puffier, thicker quilt. The choice between polyester and cotton is mostly a question of preference, although if the surface becomes too puffy, it may detract from the overall quilt design.

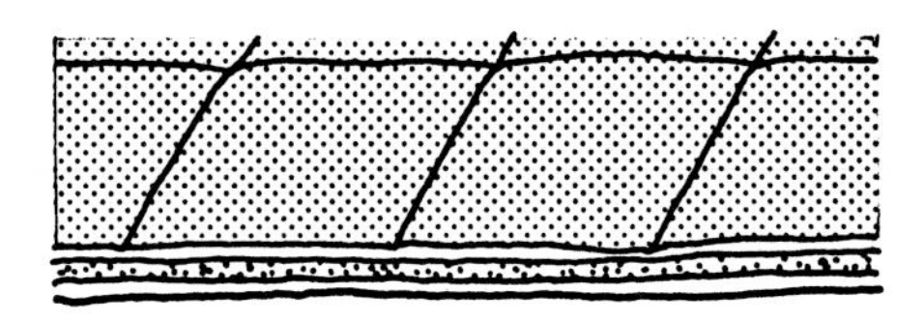

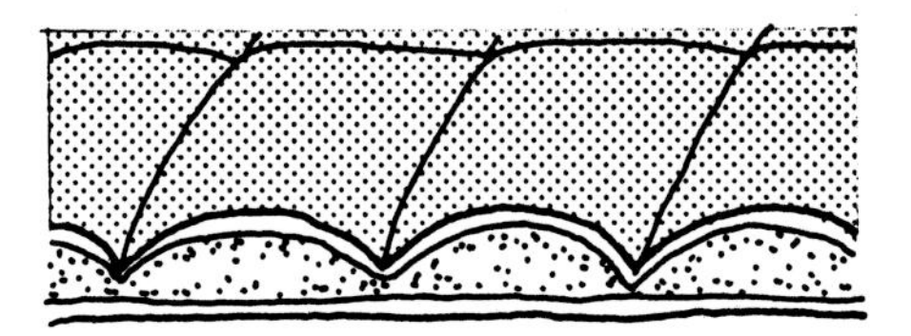

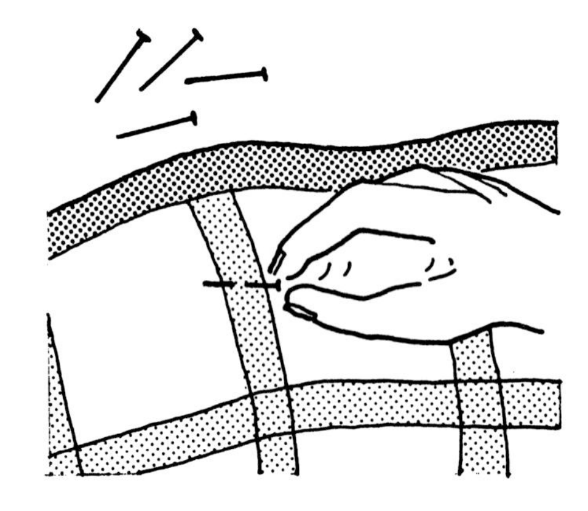

9. After the quilt is finished, check it carefully for pins. Remove all pins.

10. Do not use buttons on a quilt which is to be used by infants or young children. Buttons can be hazardous. Eyes for animals can be made easily from small circles of cloth, appliquéd to the duck or rabbit.

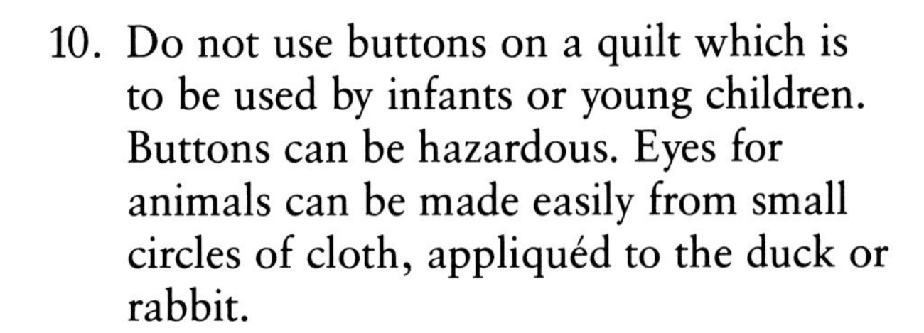

11. Do not worry if the quilt is not absolutely perfect. Some seams may not meet exactly; some edges may be slightly askew. The quilt does not have to be perfect to be special.

Give the quilt to a special baby!

1. Alphabet

The alphabet as a theme for children's quilts first appeared around the end of the nineteenth century. Its appearance coincided with the growth of public education, and its development paralleled the establishment of children's readers and primers.

Because the theme was never standardized, each alphabet quilt has a unique organization. Some of the best versions combine plain schoolbook lettering with a wide range of images and patterns.

The alphabet quilt of this project uses bold, rather old-fashioned blue letters as a border. The images are carefully chosen so that each letter corresponds to at least one picture. At the same time, there is an ambiguity about the images, and double readings are possible. In some cases, there is an extra level of organization in which certain squares relate to their neighbors. A hammer is located next to a group of nails, a hand reaches for an ice-cream cone, and an owl sits on a branch under a crescent moon.

The colors are not bright. The picture blocks use maroons, greens, reds, blues, and browns on light calico squares, randomly distributed. The backgrounds for the letters are also pale calicoes, but they are more organized: light red blocks alternate with very light green ones around the border. The quietness of the colors allows the images—the profiles of the pictures and shapes of the letters—to dominate the arrangement. The colors also recall those used in early textbooks—McGuffey readers with their brown and sepia tones.

The quilt is tacked rather than quilted. Blue yarn at the intersections of the squares superimposes a pattern over the jumble of images and gives depth to the surface of the "page." The tacking also adds a kind of no-nonsense utilitarian quality to the quilt.

Instructions

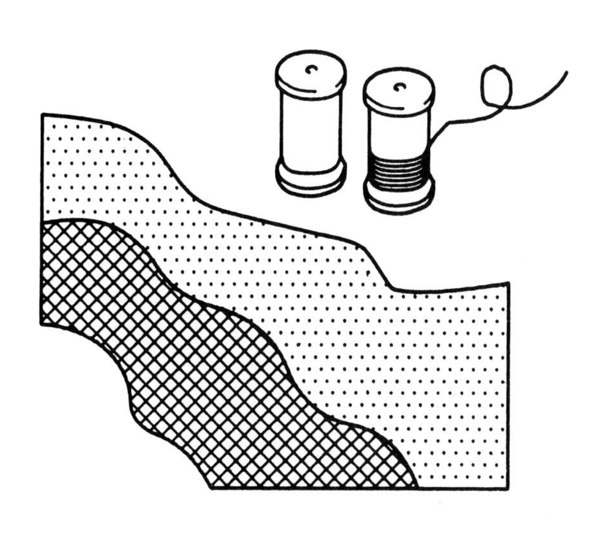

1. Materials:

   2 yards green print (backing and underline strips)
   ¾ yard blue print (letters)
   ½ yard light red print (letter background squares)
   ½ yard very light green print (letter background squares)
   1 yard of mixed light prints (background squares)
   ¾ yard of mixed dark prints (pictures)
   Cotton batting
   White thread
   Heavy blue thread or yarn for tacking

2. Pin patterns to fabric. Cut carefully.

   Cut a long edge strip, 2″ wide and 16′ long, from the green material.

   Cut two underline strips, 1″ wide, 25½″ long, from the green material.

   Cut two underline strips, 1″ wide, 40½″ long, from the green material.

3. Pin the picture elements to the background squares. Hand stitch along seam lines. Clip as required at curves and corners. Note that some of the pictures are made of two or more parts.

   The picture elements have no particular color assignments, and neither do their background squares.

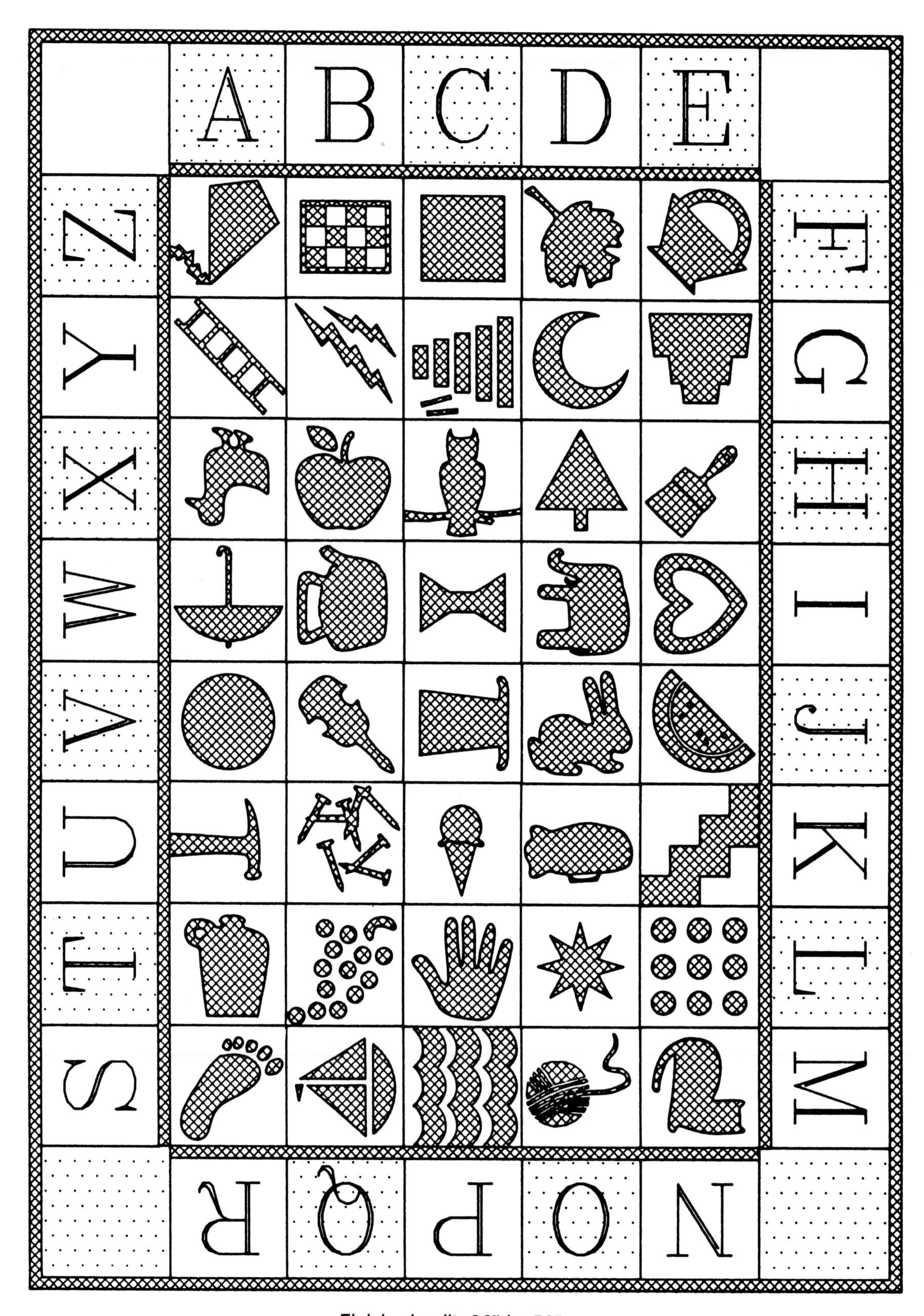

Finished quilt, 36″ by 52″

4. Pin the letters to their background squares. The letters are dark blue, but the background squares alternate between a light red print and a light green print. "A" and "F" start on the light red. "N" and "S" start on the light green.

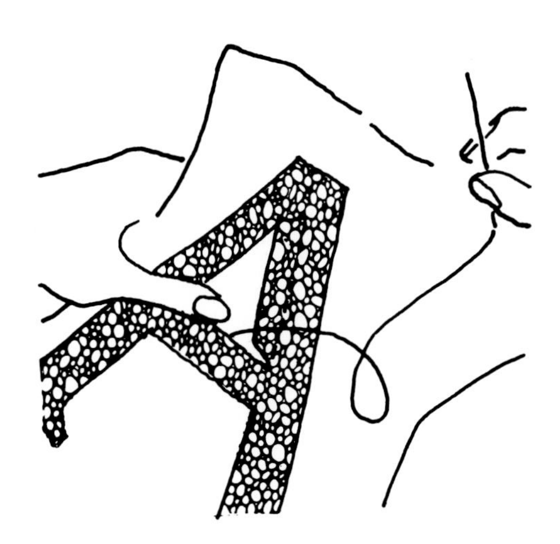

5. With a machine, sew together the rows of picture blocks. Assemble the rows, matching seams carefully.

6. Sew the letter blocks together.

   A-E is the first row.

   F-M is the second row.

   N-R is the third row.

   S-Z is the fourth row.

   Sew the four green underline strips to the rows of letter blocks.

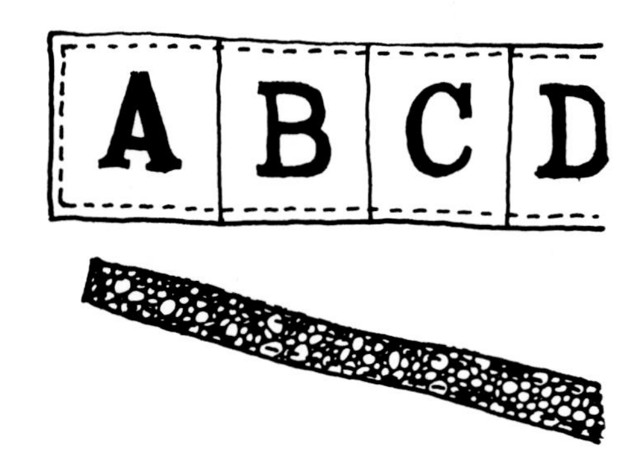

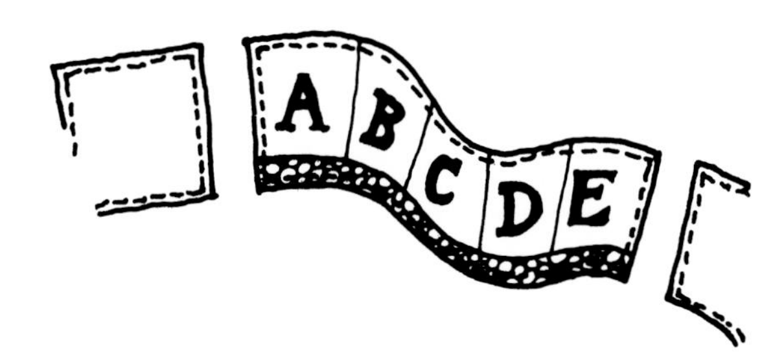

7. Sew the two light green corner squares to the ends of the A-E strip.

   Sew the two light red corner squares to the ends of the N-R strip.

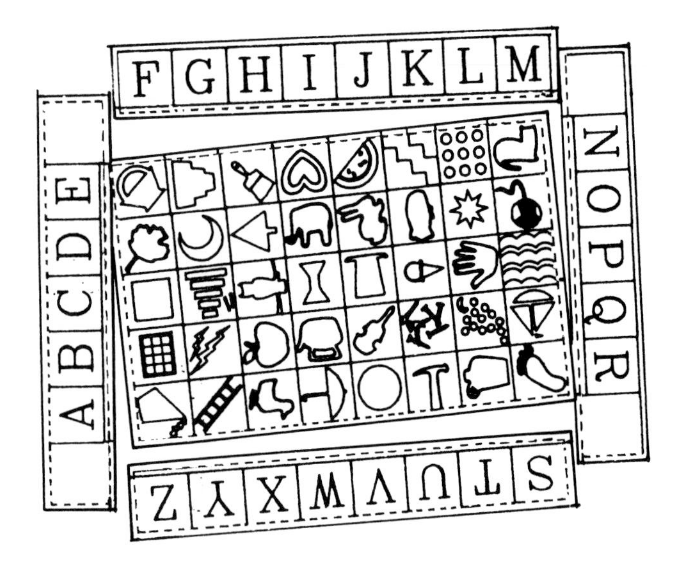

8. Complete the quilt top by sewing the letter borders to the picture block assembly.

9. Lay the quilt backing, face down, on a large table or work area. Lay the batting on top of it. Lay the quilt top, face up, on the batting. Pin through all three layers. Machine stitch along the edge of the quilt top. Trim close to the seam.

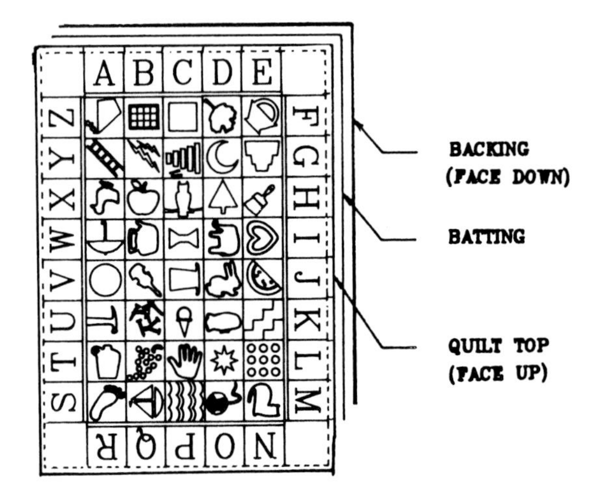

10. Press the seam allowances of the edge strip under. Hand stitch the strip around the quilt assembly.

11. Quilt stitch along both sides of the underline strips. Tack the rest of the quilt at the corners of the picture blocks.

Pattern Pieces

Shown one-half actual size

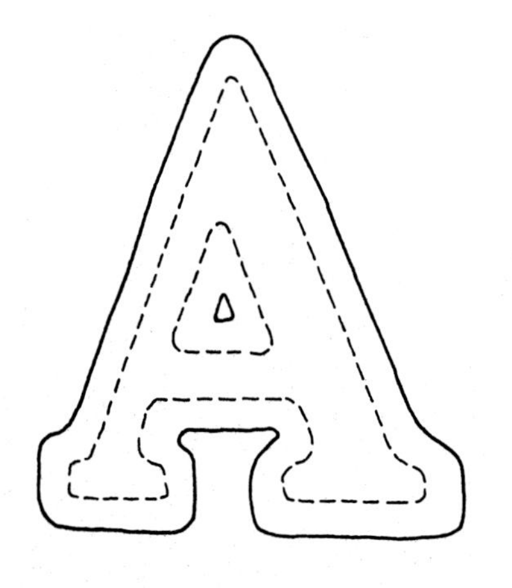
A

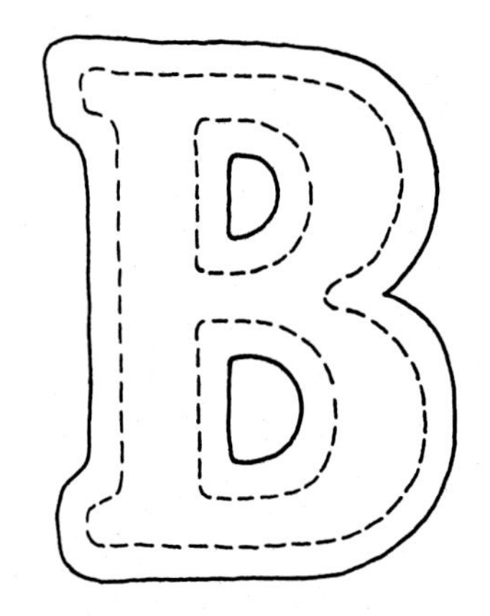
B

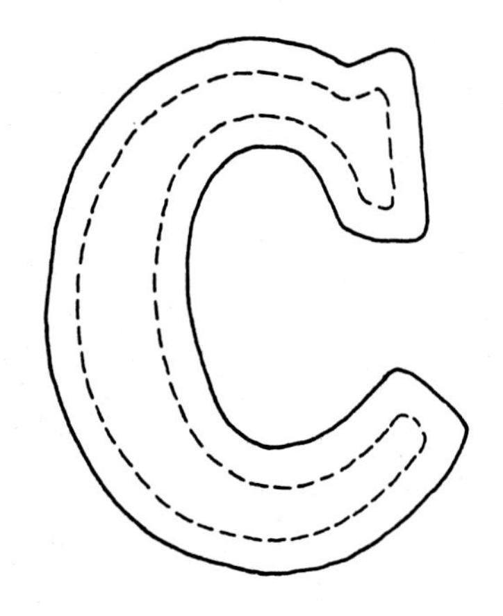
C

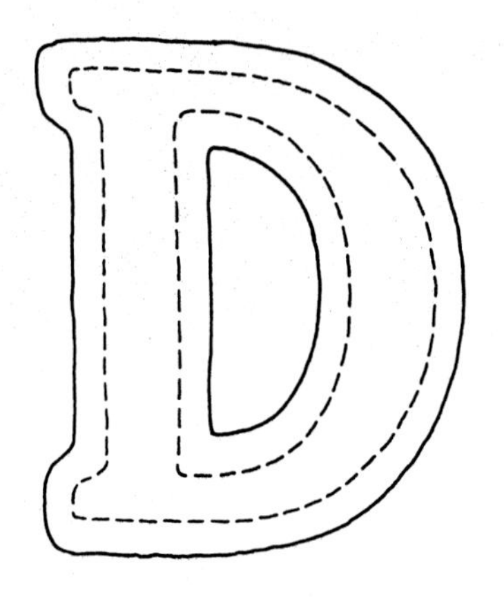
D

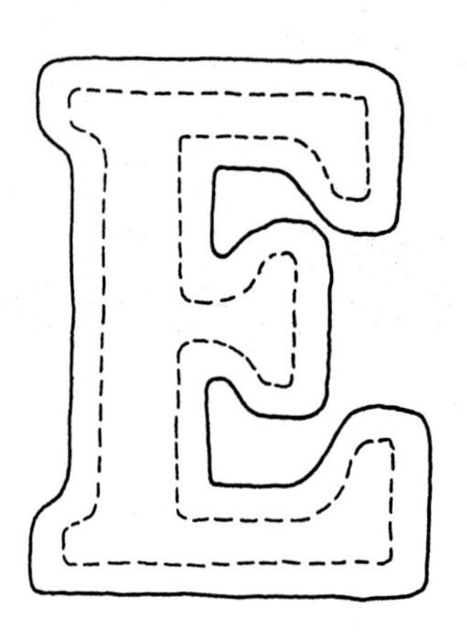
E

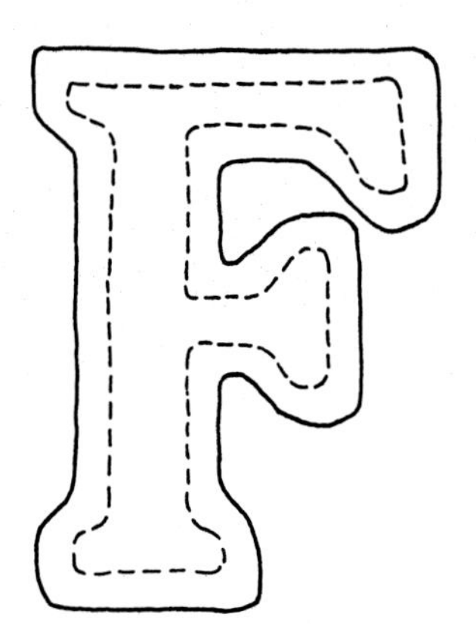
F

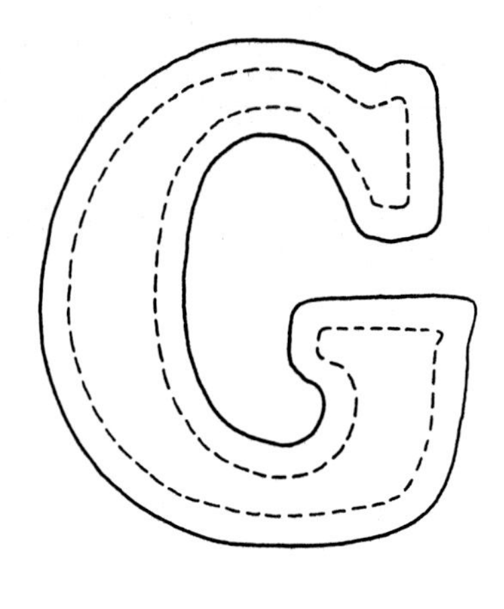
G

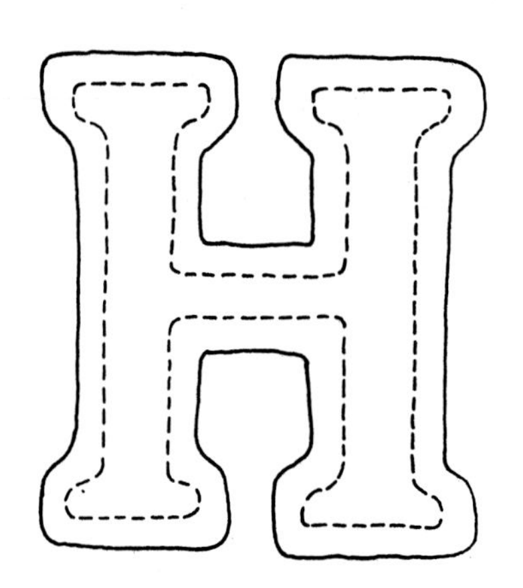
H

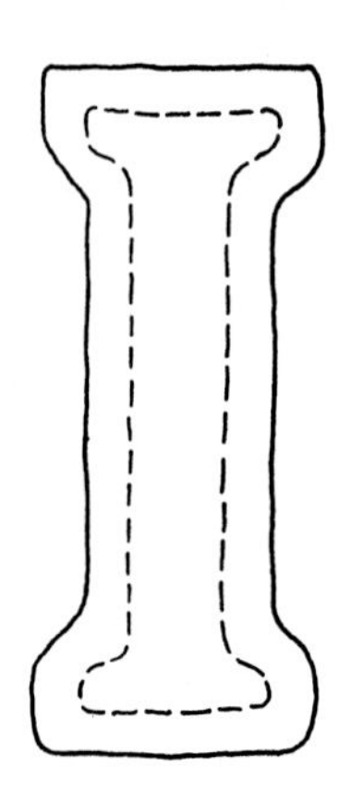
I

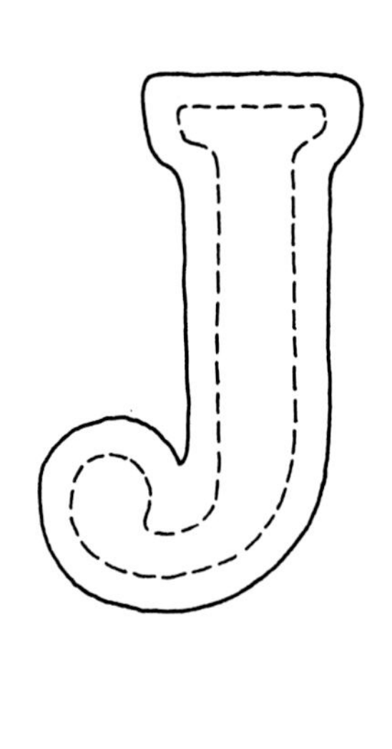
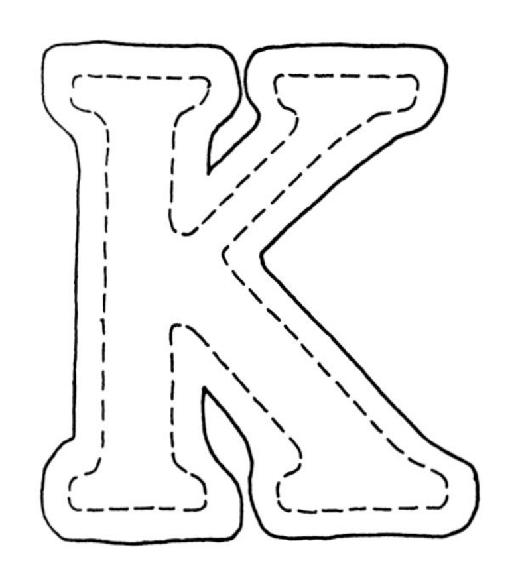
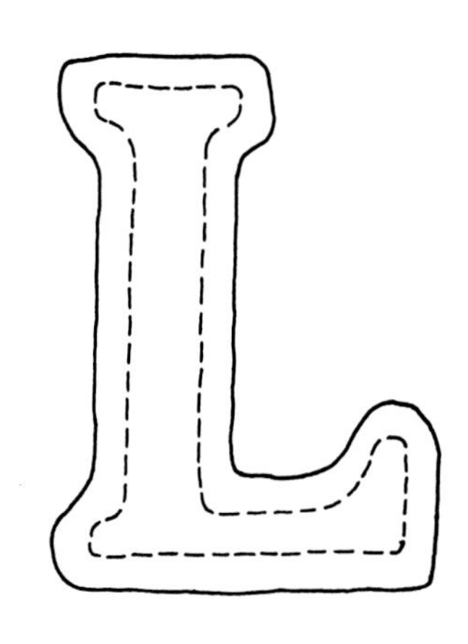
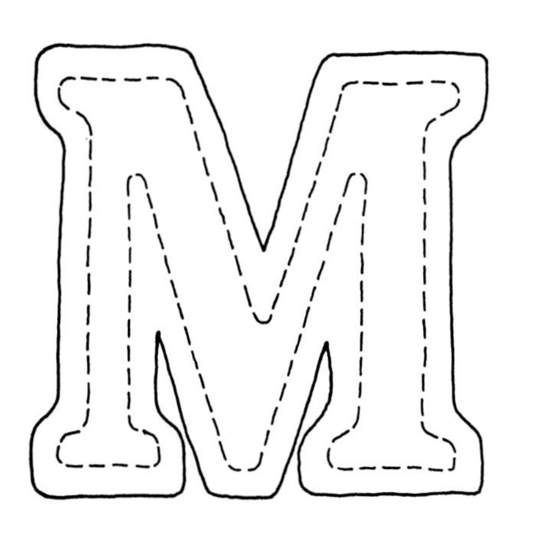
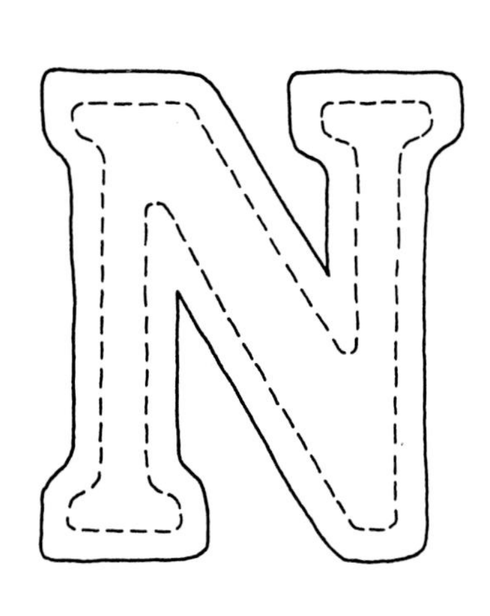
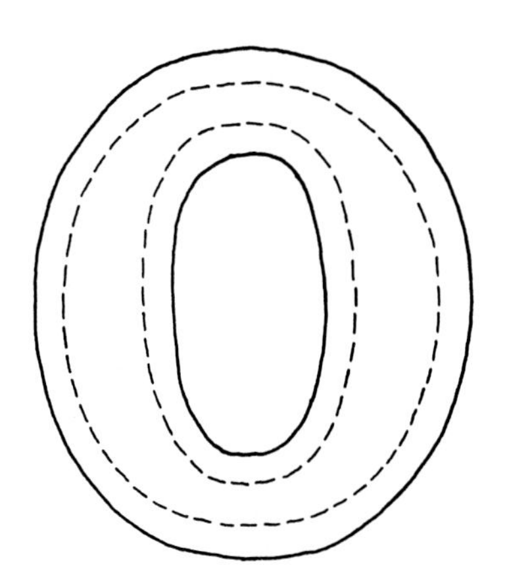
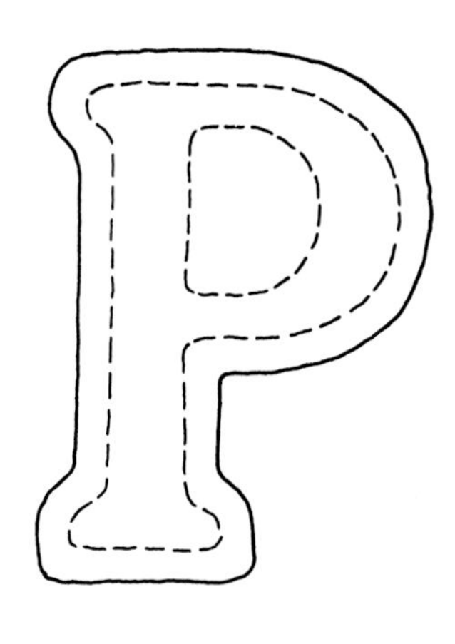
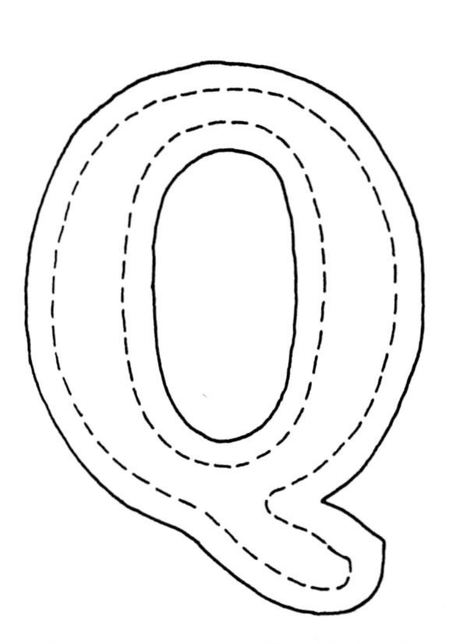
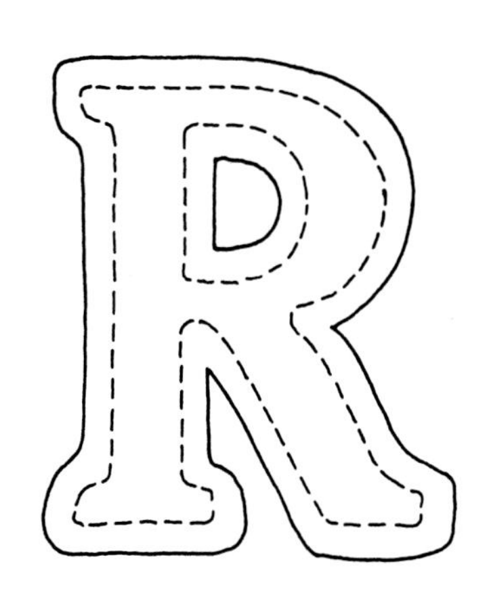

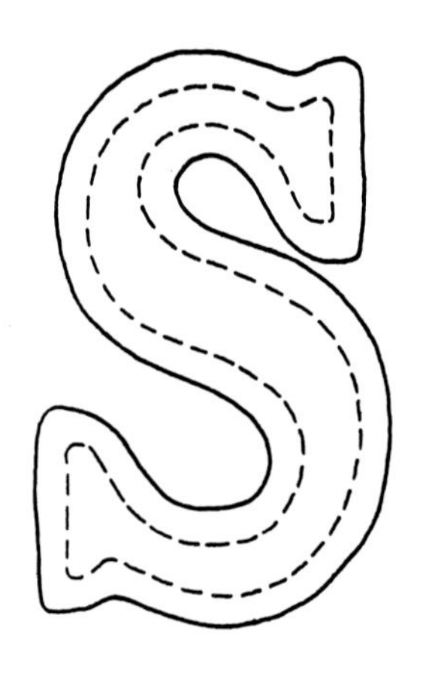
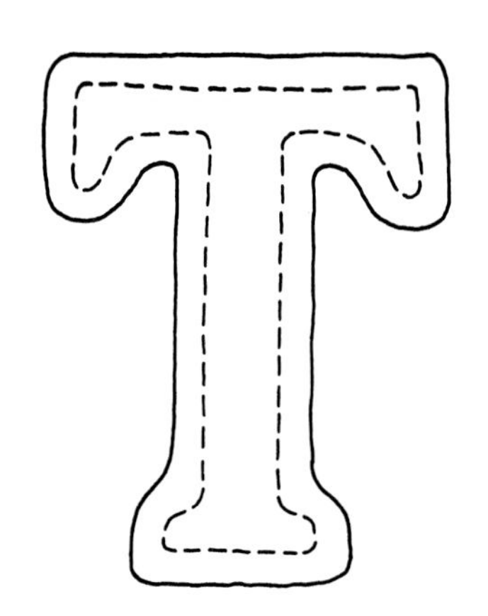
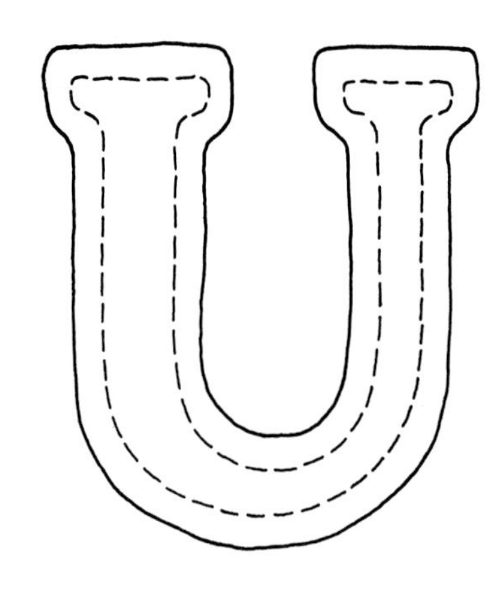
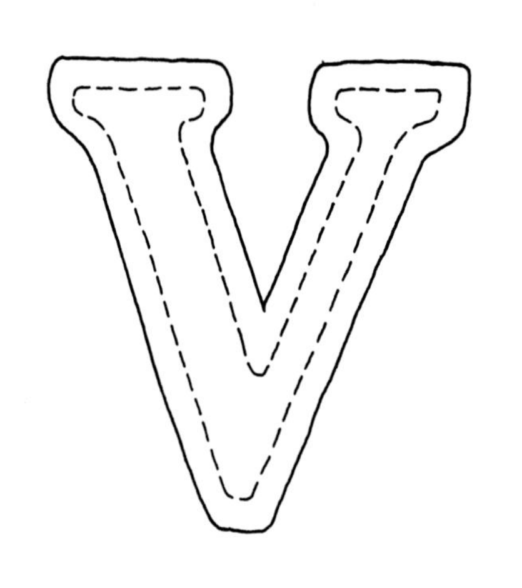
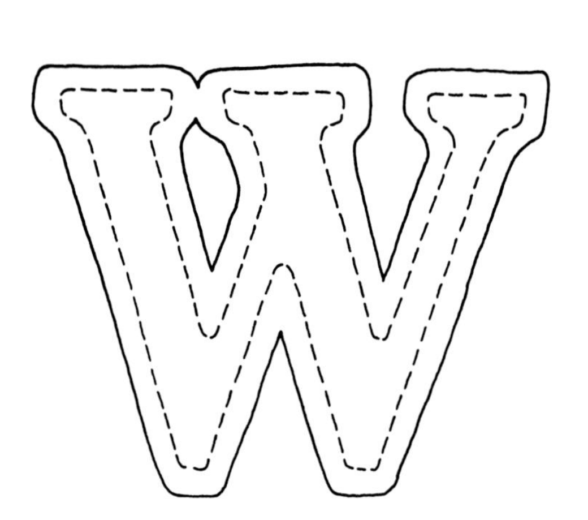
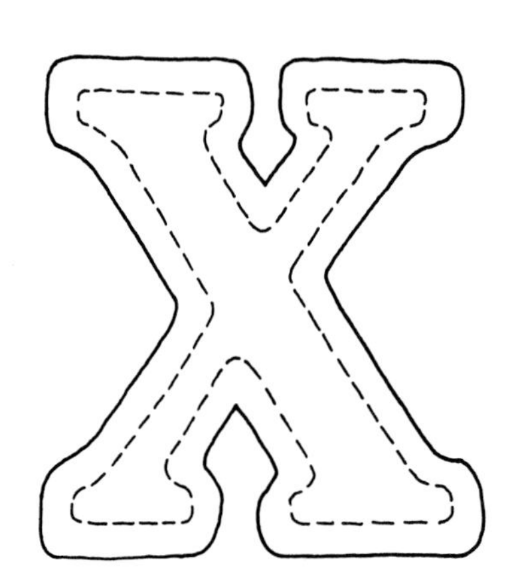
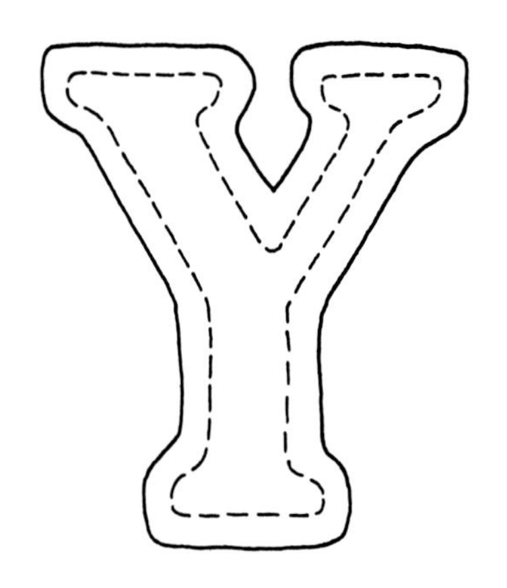
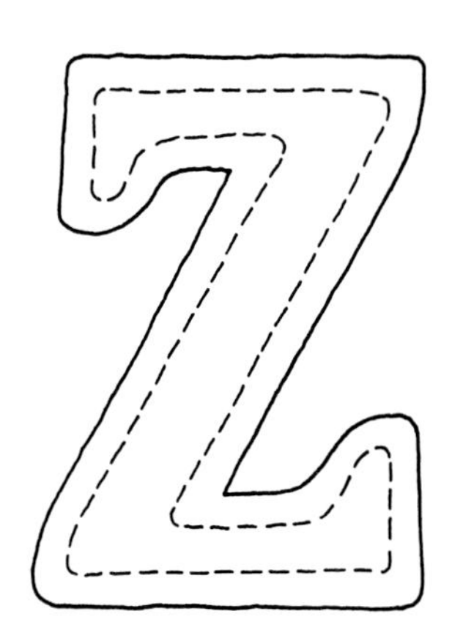
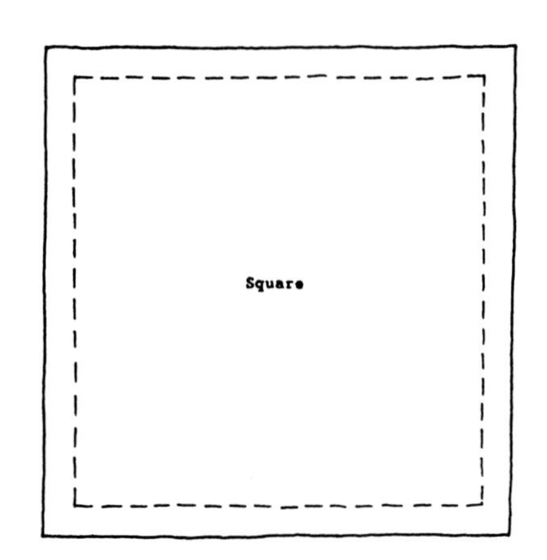
Square

Lightning
Basket
Top hat
Lightning
Zeppelin
Moon
Teakettle
Heart
Owl
Kite
Bow tie

Ladder
Rabbit
Boat pennant
Boat sail
Boat sail
Ice cream
Boat
Waves, cut 3
Ice-cream cone
Yarn
Star
Zigzag
Grape stem
Duck
Grapes, cut 13

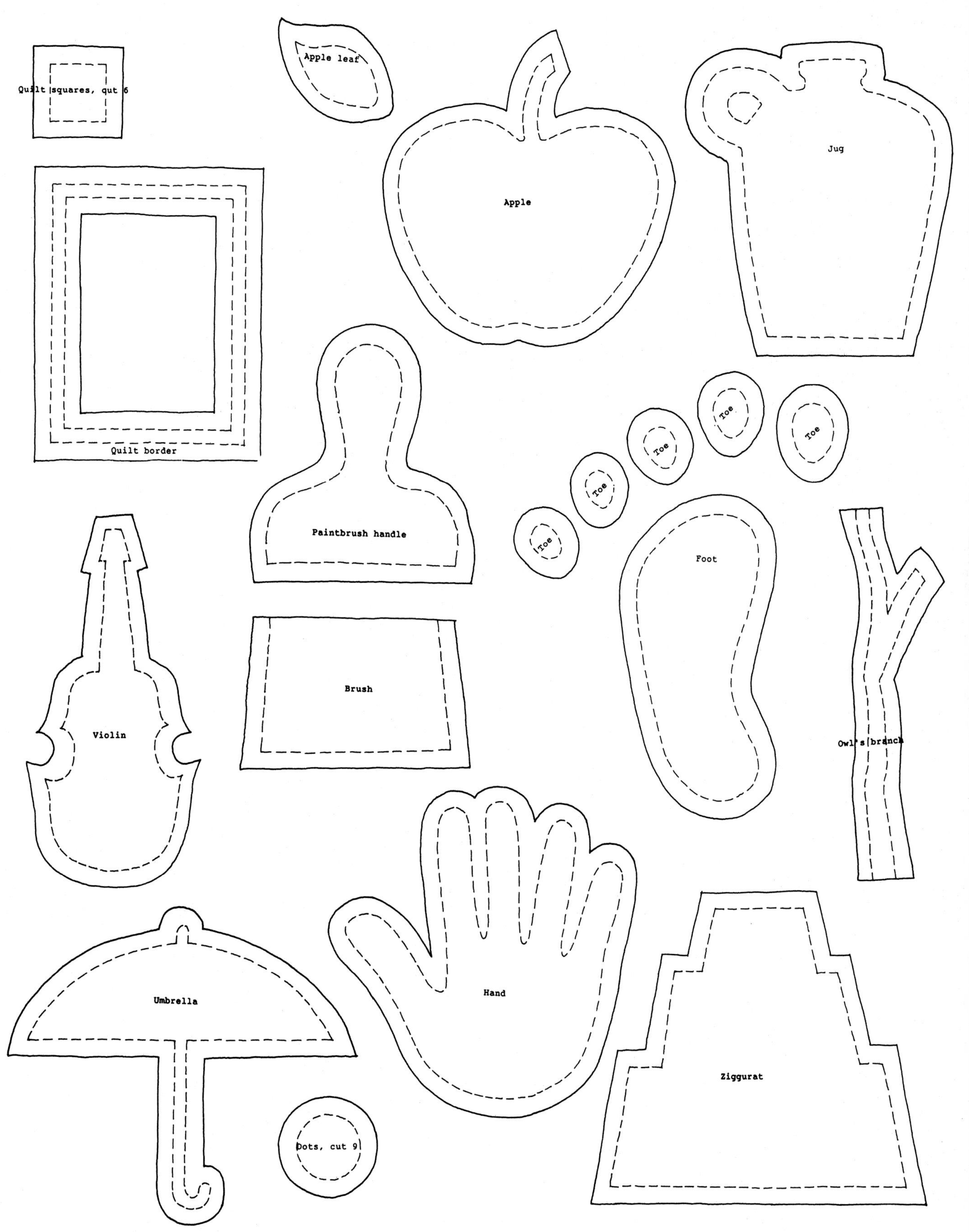
Quilt squares, cut 6
Apple leaf
Apple
Jug
Quilt border
Paintbrush handle
Toe
Toe
Toe
Toe
Toe
Toe
Foot
Violin
Brush
Owl's branch
Umbrella
Hand
Ziggurat
Dots, cut 9

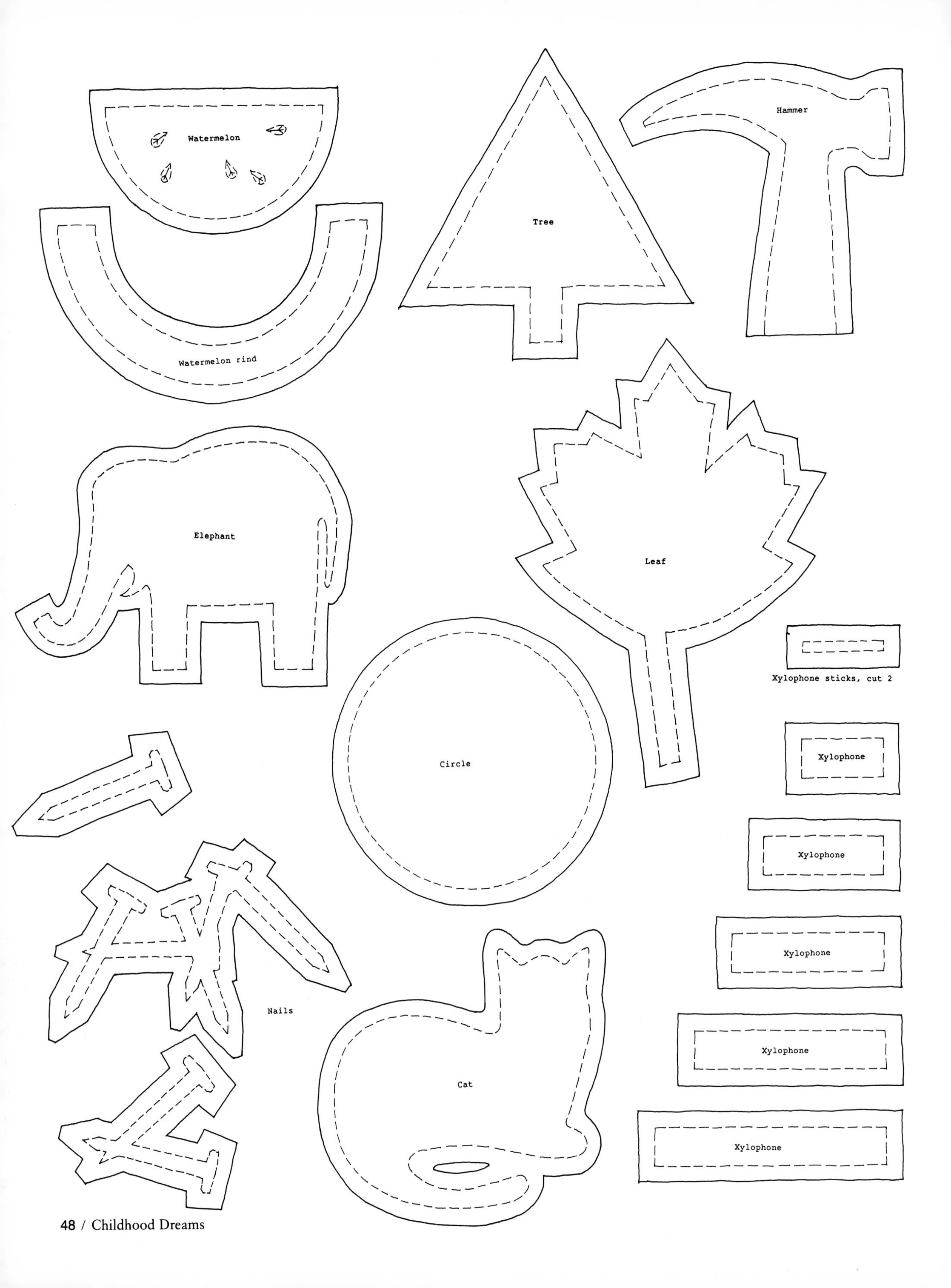
Watermelon
Tree
Hammer
Watermelon rind
Elephant
Leaf
Xylophone sticks, cut 2
Circle
Xylophone
Xylophone
Xylophone
Nails
Xylophone
Cat
Xylophone

2. Rabbits and Carrots

Rabbits have a time-honored spot in the nursery, and children's stories are filled with them. There is Peter Rabbit, the Velveteen Rabbit, Br'er Rabbit, Bugs Bunny, and the bunnies in *Goodnight Moon*. All these rabbits are somewhat mischievous, very clever, and usually set off against parents or other adults, with whom they are reconciled by story's end.

Rabbits have very distinctive profiles. The ears and the tails contribute to the strong graphic image. In contrast, carrots have simple shapes and vibrant coloring.

This quilt locates dark blue appliquéd rabbits in a carrot patch. The rabbits face each other across green lattice strips. The organization of the rabbits acknowledges the rectangular shape of the quilt, but it does not distinguish between "top" and "bottom" or "left" and "right."

The rabbits are partly camouflaged in their field; their blue matches the print of the background squares. The carrots, bunched three to a square, are border elements. They unfold around the rabbits, thereby locating them in the patch. This organization is a classic device. It resembles that seen in some Egyptian paintings, where palm trees unfold around lotus-filled pools. The same device is found on early maps, where city walls unwrap to reveal the city within.

Finished quilt, 36″ by 48″

Instructions

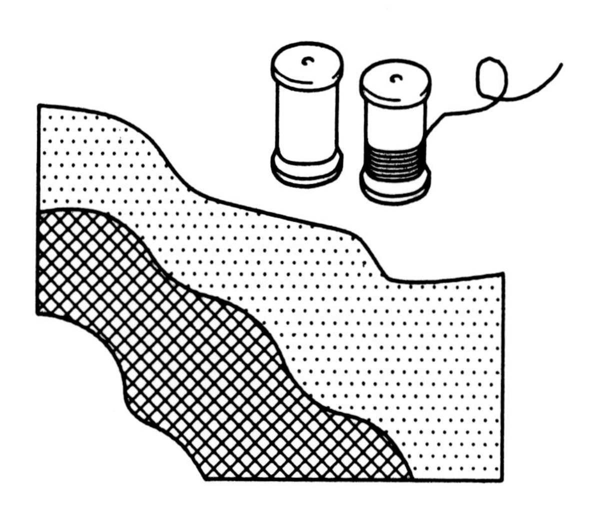

1. Materials:

   2½ yards blue print (rabbits and lattice strips)
   ½ yard green print (carrot tops and lattice strips)
   ½ yard orange print (carrots and lattice squares)
   1½ yards white and blue print (background squares)
   Cotton batting
   White, orange, green, and blue thread

2. Pin patterns to fabric. Cut carefully.

   Cut a long edge strip, 2″ wide and 14′ long, from the blue material.

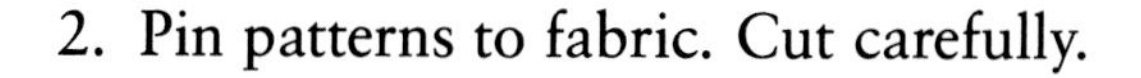

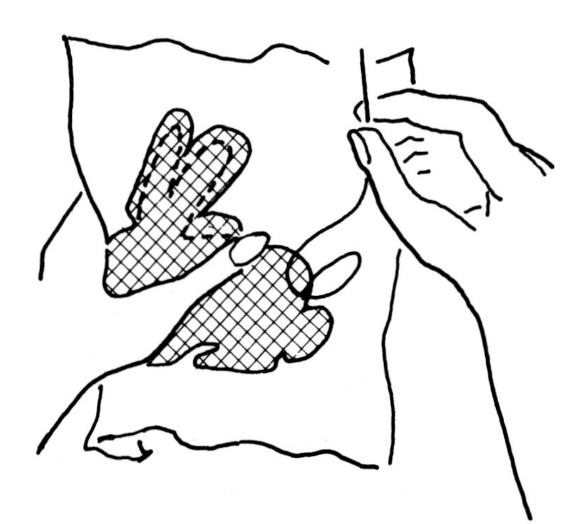

3. Pin rabbit to background square. Beginning next to the ears, hand stitch along seam line. Clip as required at curves and corners. Appliqué stitch the carrots and carrot tops to background squares. The carrot tops should be sewn first. The carrots will overlap the tops.

4. With a machine, sew together the rows of squares by alternating the appliqué squares with the lattice strips.

   Sew together the rows of strips, alternating the lattice strips with the lattice squares.

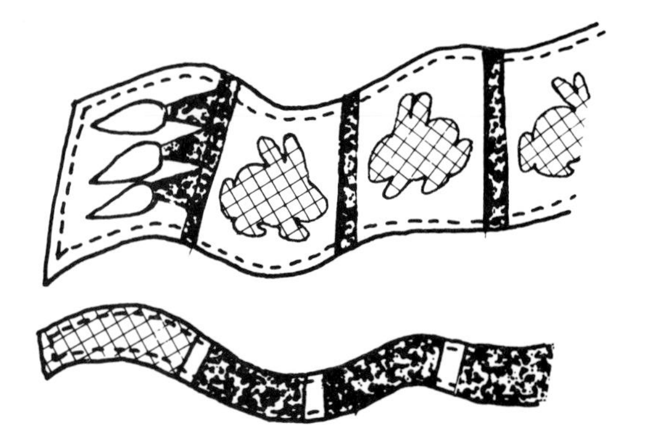

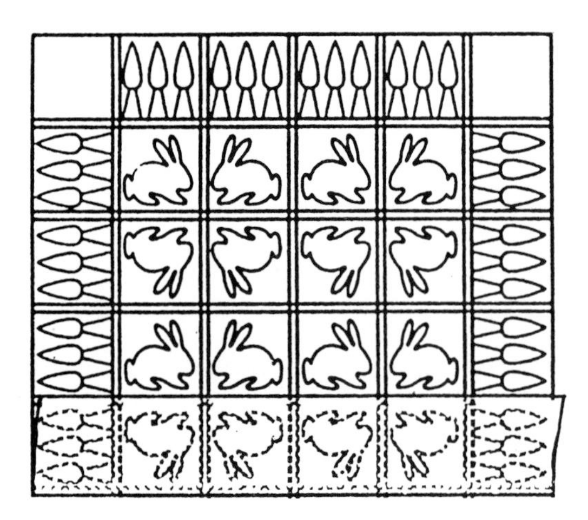

5. Assemble the quilt top by sewing together the rows of squares and strips, matching all seams carefully.

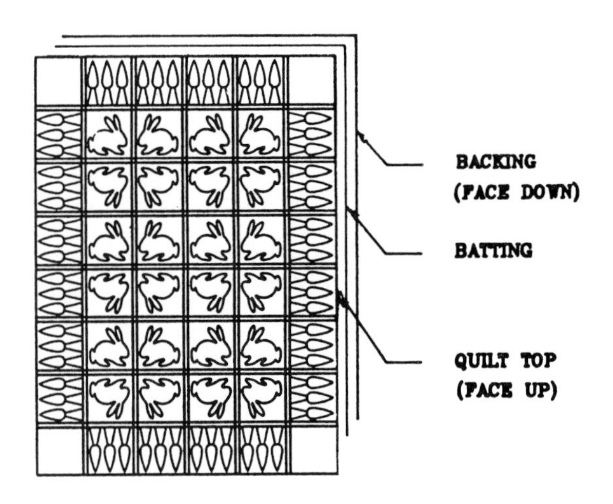

6. Lay the quilt backing face down on a large table or work area. Lay the batting on top of the backing. Lay the quilt top, face up, on the batting. Pin through all three layers. Machine stitch along the edge of the quilt top. Trim close to the seam.

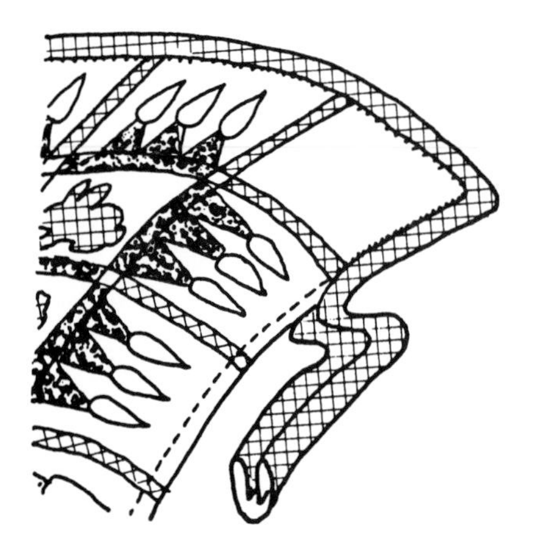

7. Press the seam allowances of the edge strip under. Hand stitch the strip around the quilt assembly.

8. For quilting, outline stitch around the rabbits and carrots, either by hand or with a machine.

Pattern Pieces

Shown one-half actual size

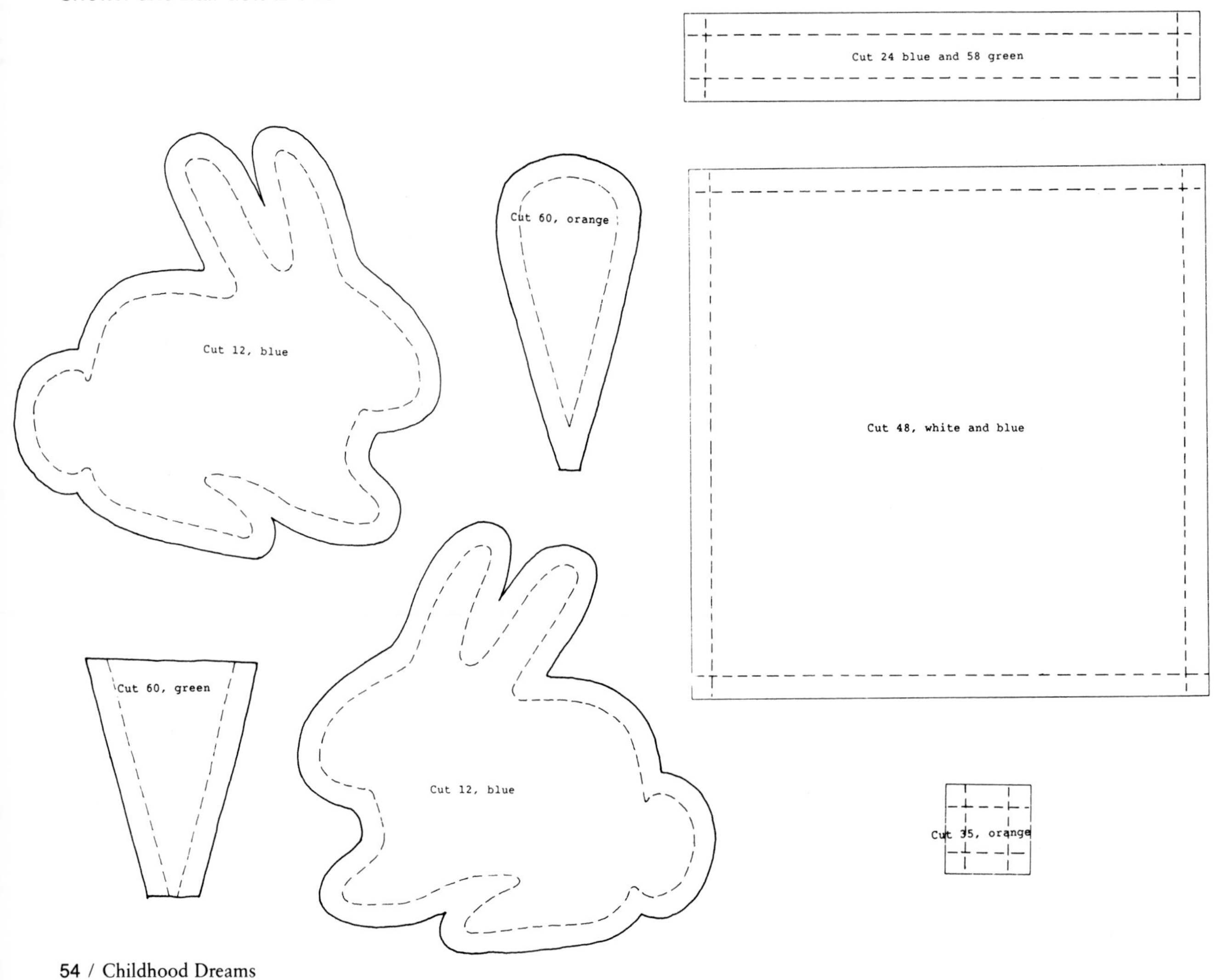

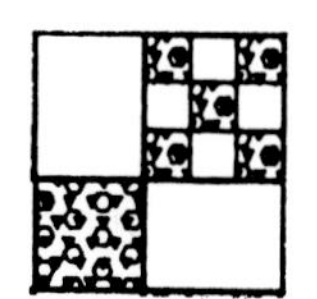

3. Nine-Patch

Old handmade quilts were additive. Each small piece was sewn to its neighbors to make a block, then the block units were joined to make the quilt top. The block was the critical unit, the molecule of the quilt, from which the properties and design of the overall spread could be envisioned.

Many patterns that were handmade, piece by piece, in earlier times can be sewn by machine today. The efficient technique for machine construction is typically quite different from the hand-sewing system. It can be a real challenge to adapt a moderately complicated pattern such as this nine-patch variation to a machine system.

The machine technique is not an additive process; it is a reductive one in which the overall quilt pattern is not revealed until near the end of the construction. The operational unit is the strip. Initially, the fabric is cut into strips of varying widths and lengths. The strips are sewn together and then cut into new strips. Subsequent operations sew the strips and then cut new ones until the entire quilt top is assembled. The whole procedure is a sort of abstract sequence, rather like a computer program.

The strip technique can be used for all sorts of regular patterns, including ones with triangular, rectangular, and square elements.

Instructions

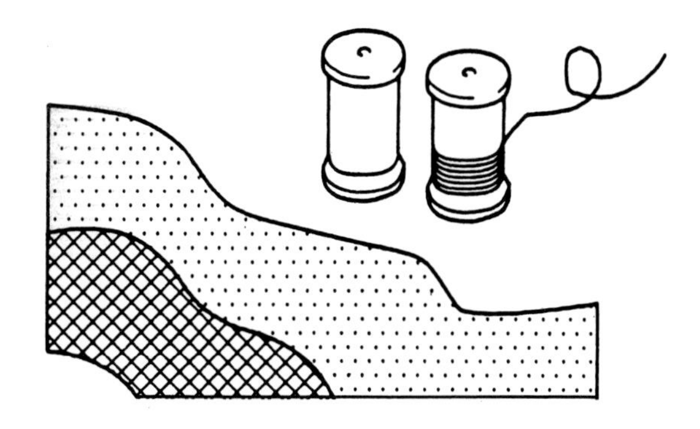

1. Materials:

   1½ yards cream cloth
   3 yards green print
   Cotton batting
   Cream and green thread
   Green string or yarn for tacking

2. Set aside 1½ yards of green cloth for quilt backing.

   Cut the cream cloth into strips:
   - 7 strips, 1¼″ wide, 30″ long
   - 8 strips, 2½″ wide, 15″ long
   - 7 strips 2¾″ wide, 30″ long
   - 8 strips 2¼″ wide, 30″ long

   Cut the remaining green cloth into strips:
   - 7 strips, 1¼″ wide, 15″ long
   - 8 strips, 2½″ wide, 30″ long
   - 8 strips, 2¼″ wide, 30″ long

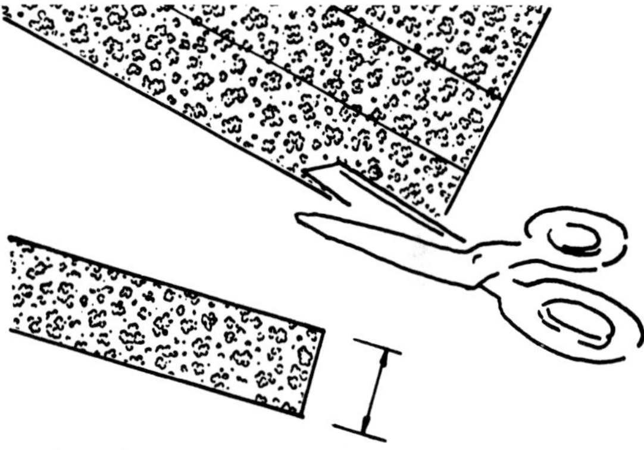

   Border strips:
   - 2 strips 2¼″ wide, 30¼″ long
   - 2 strips 2¼″ wide, 46¼″ long

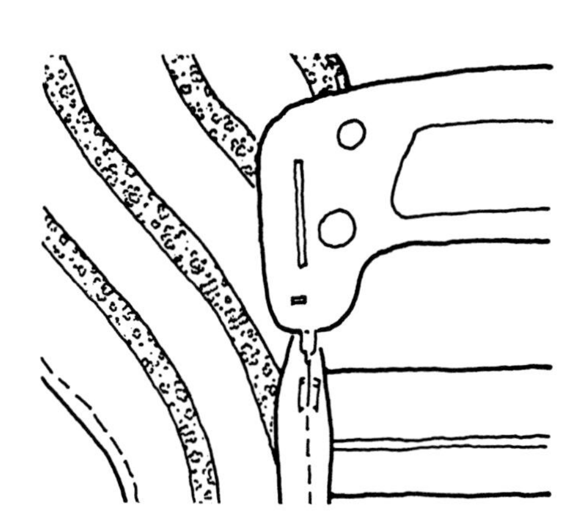

3. Sew the 2½″ wide, 15″ long cream strips to the 1¼″ wide, 15″ long green strips, alternating green and cream.

4. Trim the edges of the cloth just sewn if they are uneven. Measure and cut across the seams as shown. Cut 10 strips, 1¼″ wide.

   These are the "A" strips.

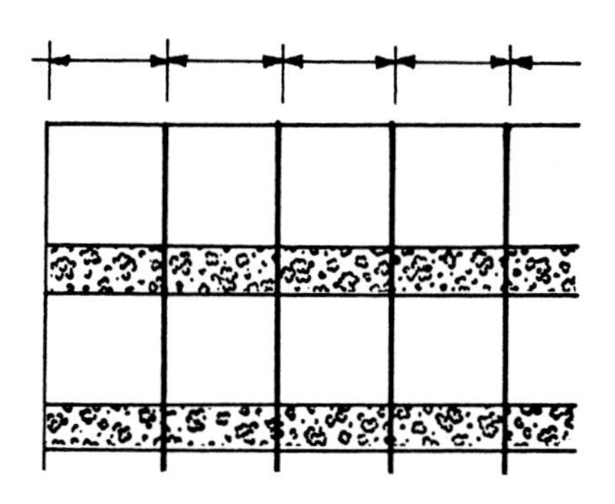

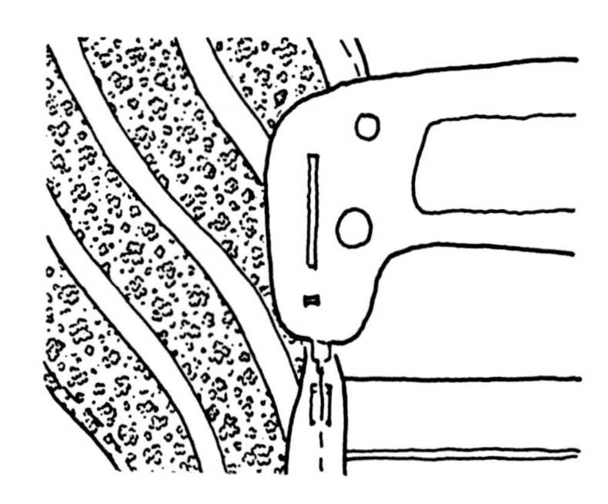

5. Sew the 2½″ wide, 30″ long green strips to the 1¼″ wide, 30″ long cream strips, alternating green and cream.

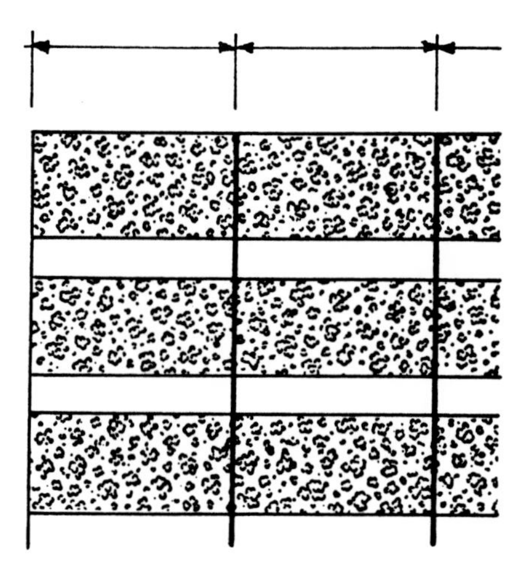

6. Trim the edges of the cloth just sewn if they are uneven. Measure and cut across the seams as shown. Cut 11 strips, 2½″ wide.

   These are the "B" strips.

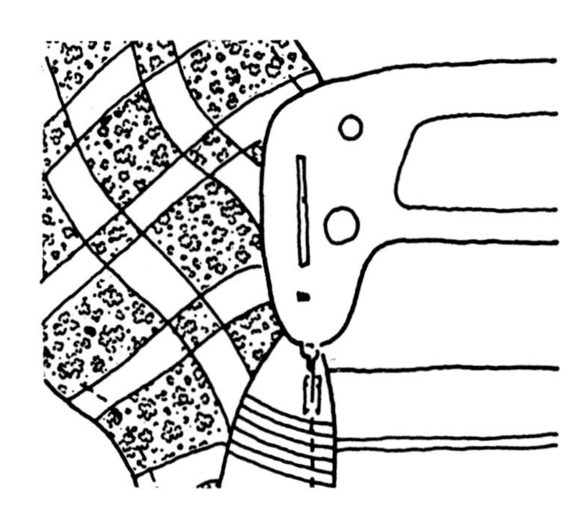

7. Sew the A and B strips together, carefully matching seams.

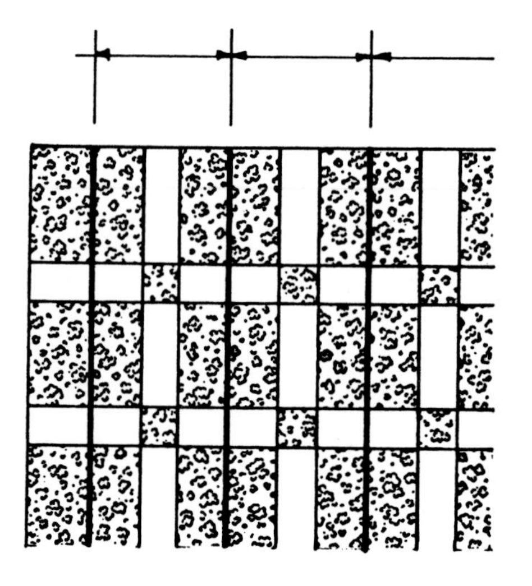

8. The cloth just sewn measures approximately 21″ by 30″. Trim the edges if they are uneven.

   Cut and discard 1¼″ strips from both long sides.

   Cut the remaining cloth into 7 strips, 2¾″ wide. Each strip should be centered on a thin cream line.

   These are the "C" strips.

Finished quilt, 33″ by 45″

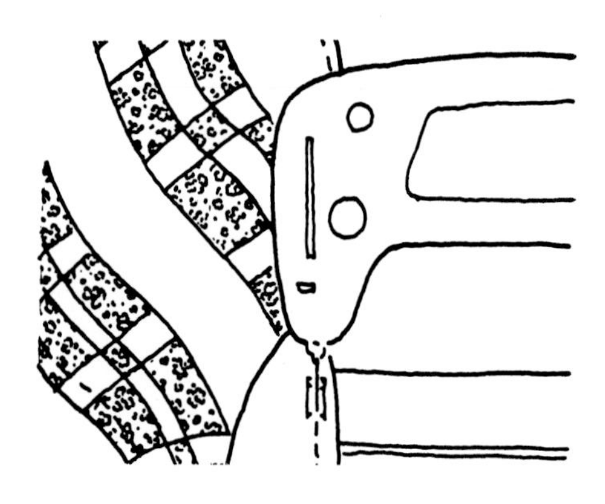

9. Sew the C strips to the 2¼″ wide, 30″ long cream strips.

10. The new cloth will be approximately 30″ by 30″. Trim the edges if they are uneven.

    Cut and discard 1¼″ from each long side.

    Cut the remaining cloth into 10 strips, each 2¾″ wide. Each strip should be centered on a nine-patch element as shown.

    These are the "D" strips.

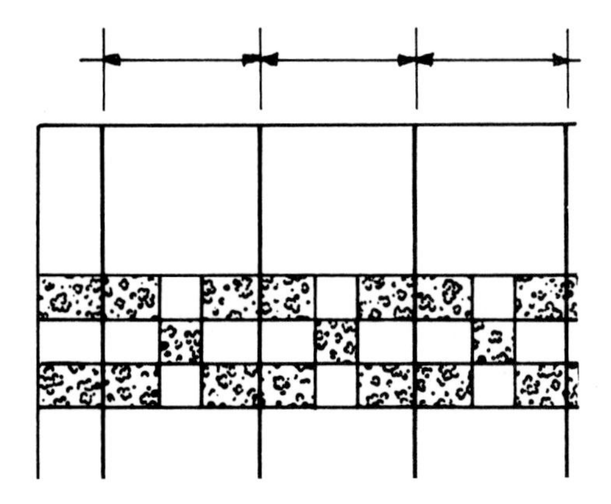

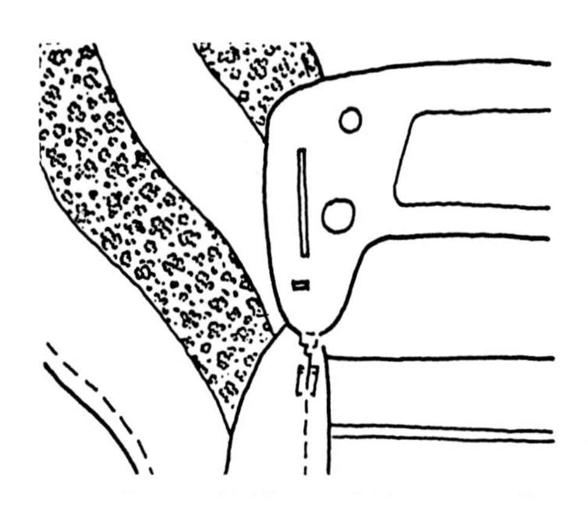

11. There are 8 green and 7 cream strips remaining. Sew them together, alternating colors.

12. Measure and cut across the cloth just sewn.

    Cut 11 strips, 2¼″ wide.

    These are the "E" strips.

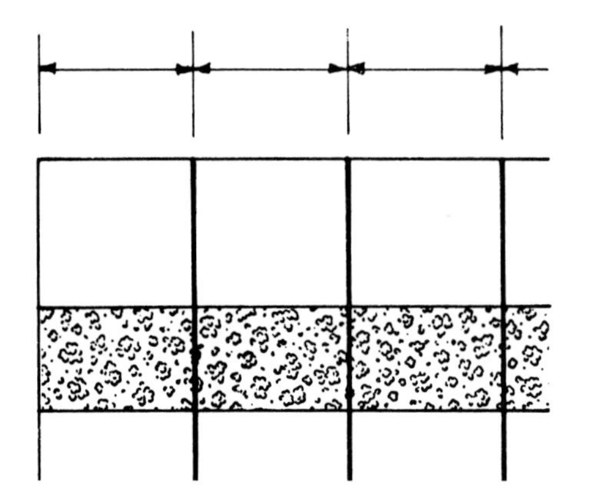

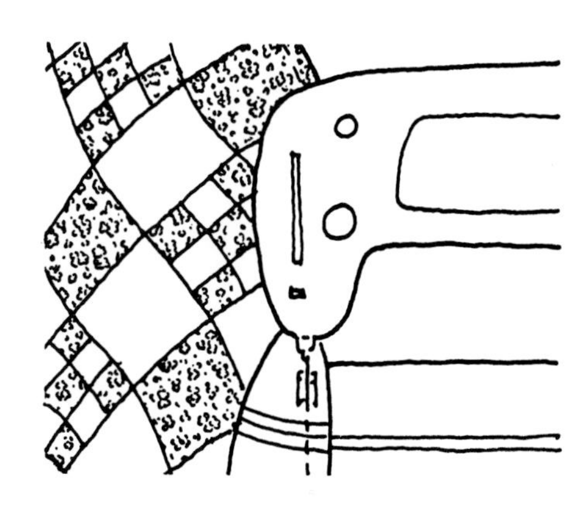

13. Sew the D strips and the E strips together, matching seams as shown.

    This is the quilt top, nearly finished.

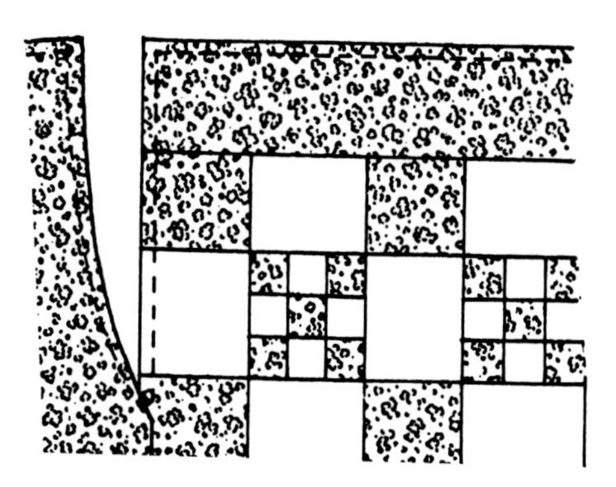

14. To complete the quilt top, sew the green border strip around it.

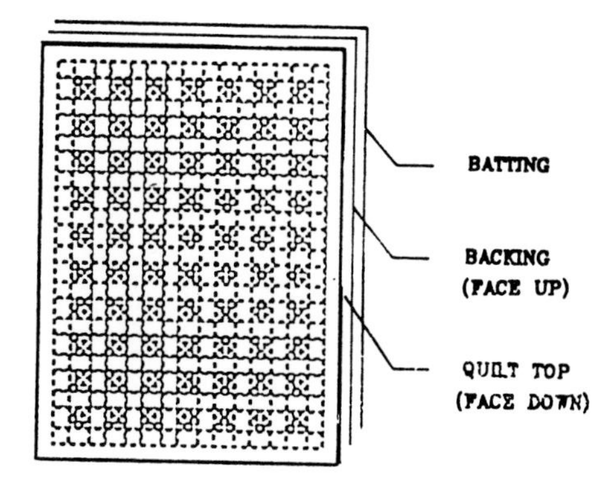

15. On a large table or work surface, lay the quilt batting down. Lay the backing material, face up, on top of the batting. Lay the quilt top, face down, on the backing. Pin around the edges.

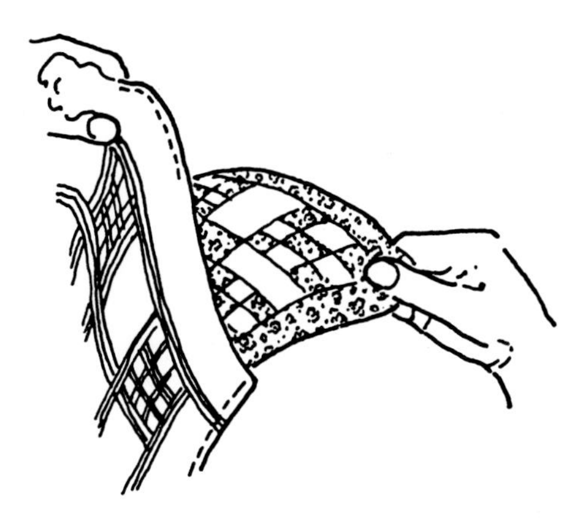

16. Sew around the edges, leaving an 8″ gap at the end. Trim the seams.

    Use the 8″ gap to turn the quilt right side out.

    Hand sew the 8″ gap closed.

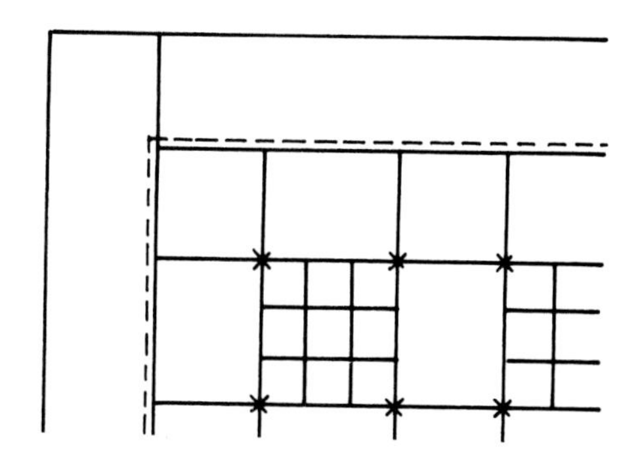

17. Sew through all layers of the quilt close to the edge of the border strip. Using the heavy green thread, tack the layers together at the corners of the nine-patches.

Finished quilt, 40″ by 50″

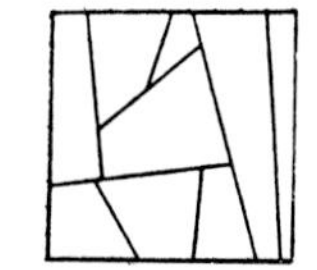

4. Crazy Blocks

Crazy quilts are hard to make. To begin with, they are usually carefully organized and their random appearance is an illusion. The successful ones are like collages, with careful balances of light and shade, decoration and background, size and scale, pattern and texture. It is an interesting coincidence that some of the most sophisticated crazy quilts come from the late nineteenth and early twentieth centuries, when artists were experimenting with planes, surfaces, distortions, and perception. It is as if the quilting women were exploring the same themes with needle and thread that the artists were addressing in their paintings and compositions.

Some quilts are hybrids, combinations of crazy elements and plain ones. Some of the most interesting ones impose the rigor of a geometrical grid over a group of crazy blocks. The practical reason for this type of arrangement is that the crazy blocks are easier to assemble than an entire expanse of fabric. The design consequence is that there is a tension between the grid and the apparently random elements.

Crazy Blocks is a gridded crazy quilt, or a "contained" crazy. The rotated squares alternate with plain wine-red elements, and the whole field is set off with dark blue borders.

For simplicity this quilt uses a single crazy block with nine colors. The blocks appear to be different because the colors are not repeated in the same position from block to block. As is often the case, the craziness is not confusion but complexity. Once the system is understood, the design is clear.

In this quilt the plain dark solids become background elements, while the brightly colored fragments dominate. Ornamental quilt stitching in colored threads around the fragments completes the design.

Instructions

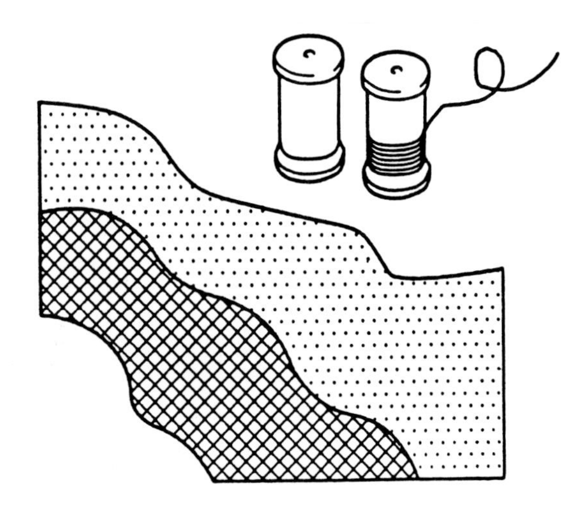

1. Materials:

   2½ yards solid navy blue cloth (backing, borders, and crazy elements)
   1 yard solid maroon cloth (plain squares and crazy elements)
   ¼ yard each of ten solid colors: pale yellow, gold, orange, red, light green, light blue, blue-gray, purple, green, and forest green
   Cotton batting
   Colored thread

2. Set aside 1½ yards of navy blue cloth for backing.

   Cut maroon squares and triangles using pattern pieces. Cut navy blue border pieces:
   2 pieces 5½″ wide, 40″ long
   2 pieces 5½″ wide, 30½″ long

   Cut long edge strip from navy blue, 2″ wide and 14′ long.

   Stack six colors of cloth. Pin pattern pieces 1 to 9 to the stack.

   Cut carefully.

   Stack the remaining six colors of cloth, pin pattern pieces 1 to 9 and cut carefully.

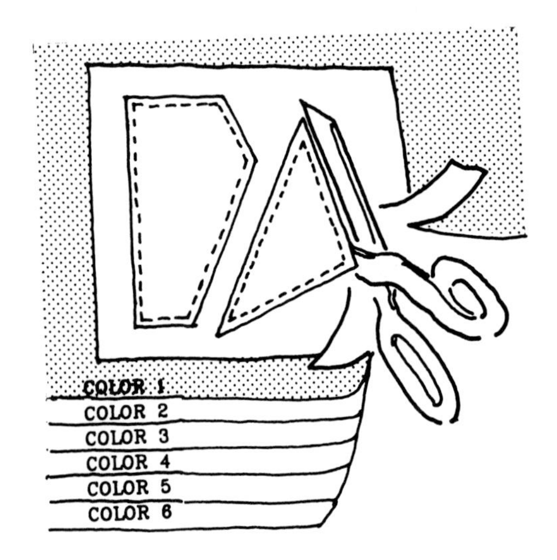

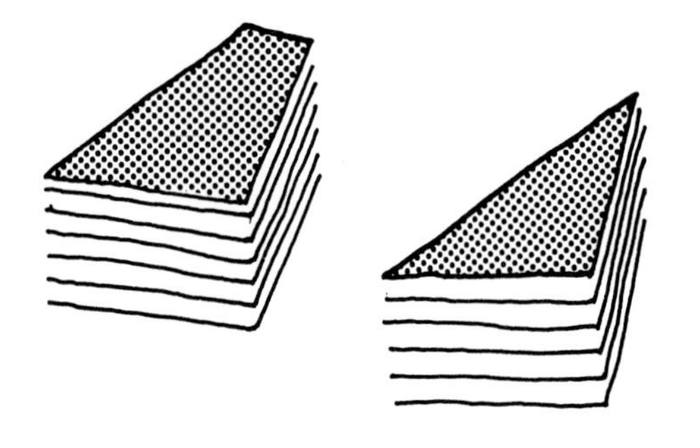

3. Lay the first batch of pattern pieces over the second group. There will be nine stacks, each with twelve colors of materials.

SUSAN GALLAGHER
Pieced Fabric

HENRI MATISSE
Cut Paper

4. Organize the colors into a "crazy" arrangement by taking the top color of the first stack and moving it to the bottom of the stack. Then take the top two colors of the second stack and move them to the bottom of that stack. Take the top three colors from the third stack, etc., and repeat for each stack until all nine stacks are done.

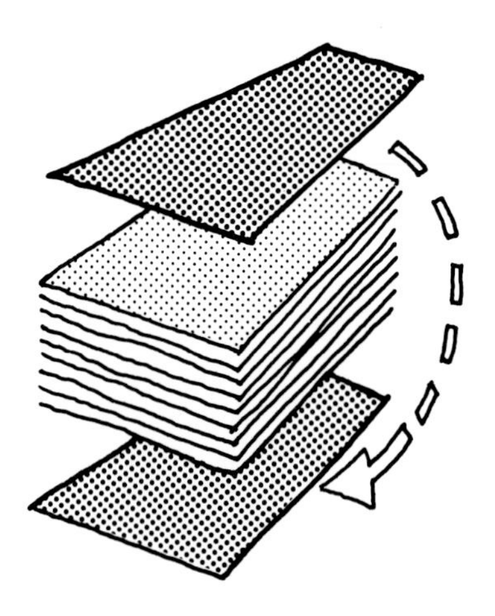

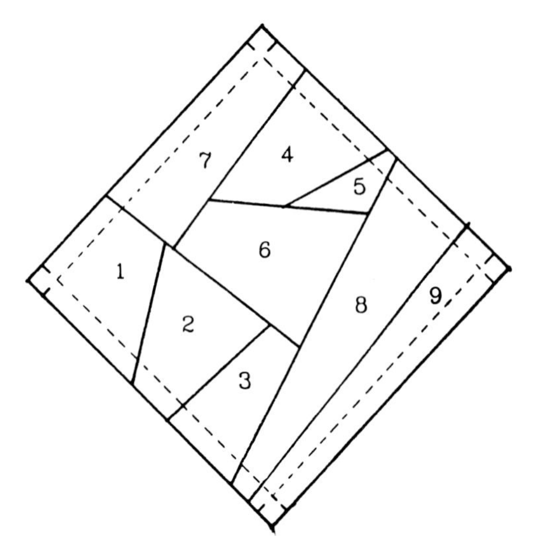

5. Now sew the crazy blocks, using the top colors of the stacks for each of the nine pattern pieces. Each finished block will have a different arrangement and combination of colors.

6. Sew the crazy blocks into strips. Each strip will start with a maroon triangle, and then a crazy block. The shortest strips will end immediately with another maroon triangle. The longer strips will have an alternating sequence of maroon squares and crazy blocks before ending with a maroon triangle.

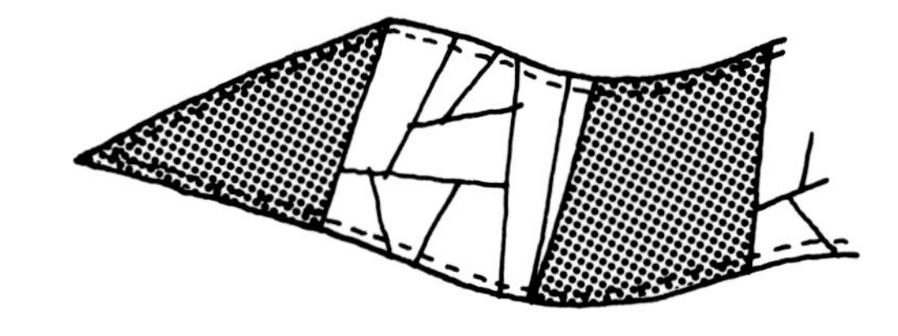

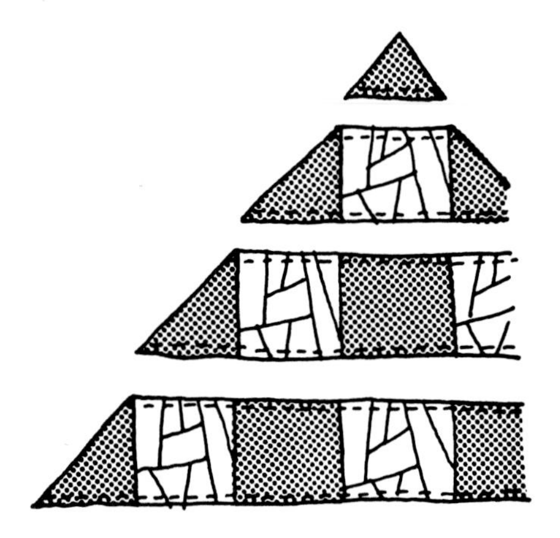

7. Assemble the quilt top by sewing together the rows of squares and crazy blocks, matching all seams carefully.

8. To finish the quilt top, join the 30½″ navy blue pieces with the maroon corner blocks to form the top and bottom border strips. Join these newly created strips and the 40″ side strips to the quilt top.

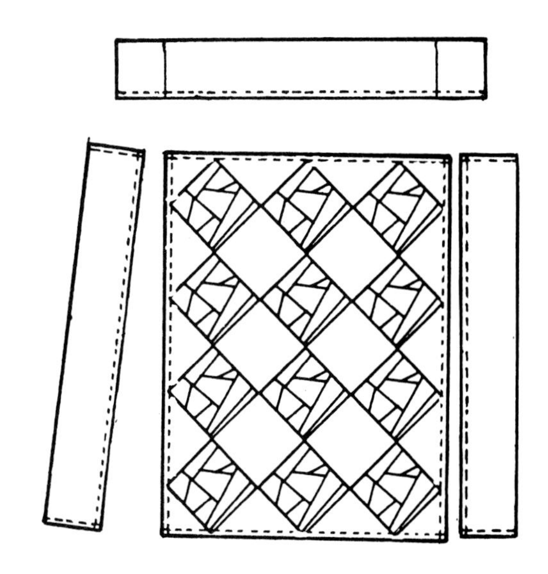

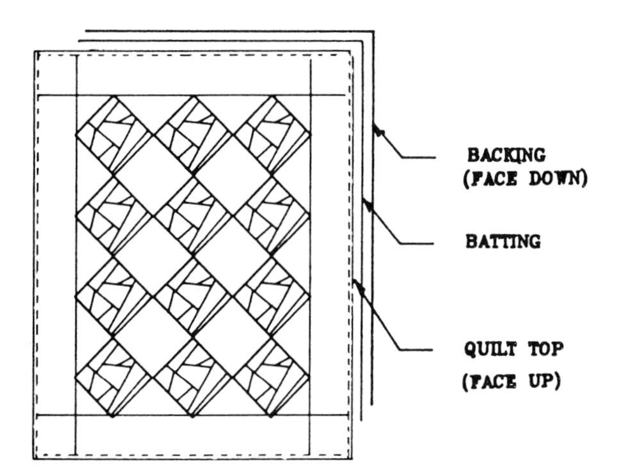

9. Lay the quilt backing, face down, on a large table or work area. Lay the batting on top of the backing. Lay the quilt top, face up, on the batting. Pin through all three layers. Machine stitch along the edge of the quilt top. Trim close to the seam.

10. Press the seam allowances of the edge strip under. Hand stitch the strip around the quilt assembly.

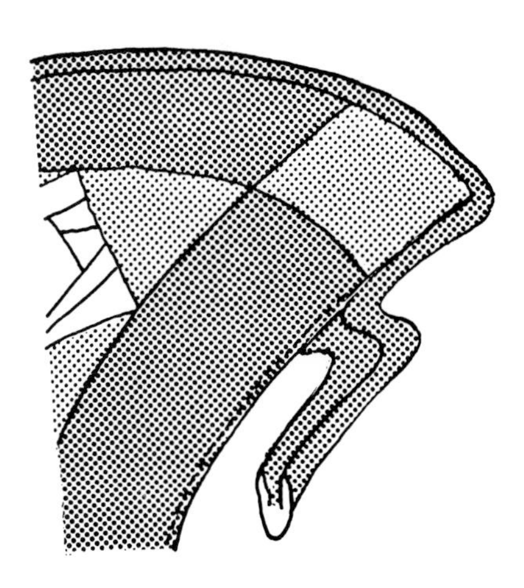

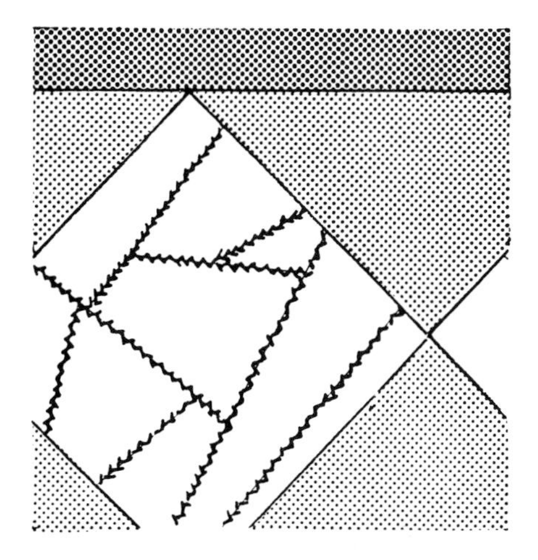

11. For quilting, use a feather stitch or other decorative stitch along the individual elements in each crazy block. Use brightly colored thread.

Pattern Pieces

Shown one-half actual size

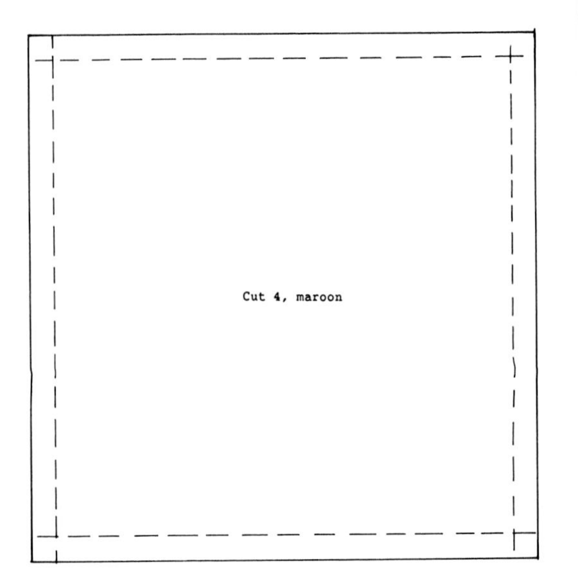

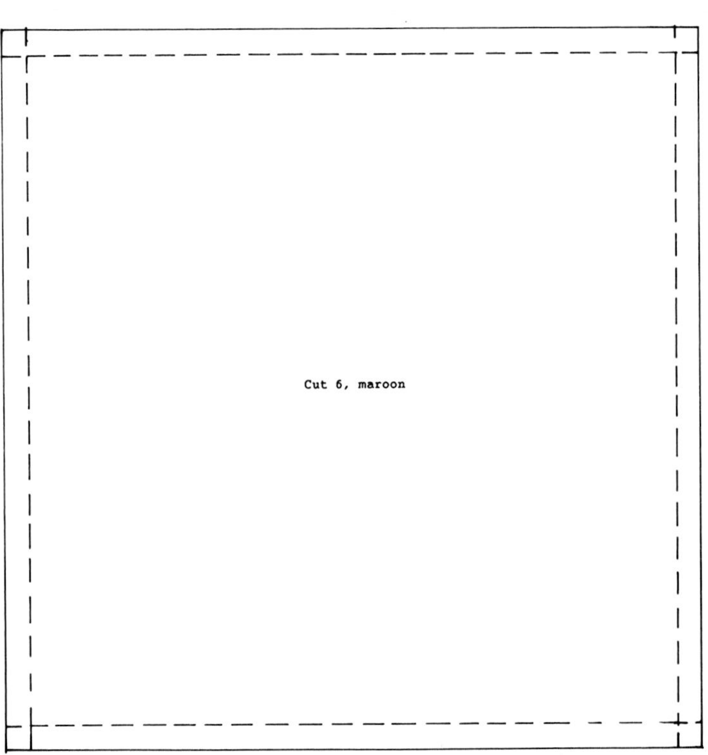

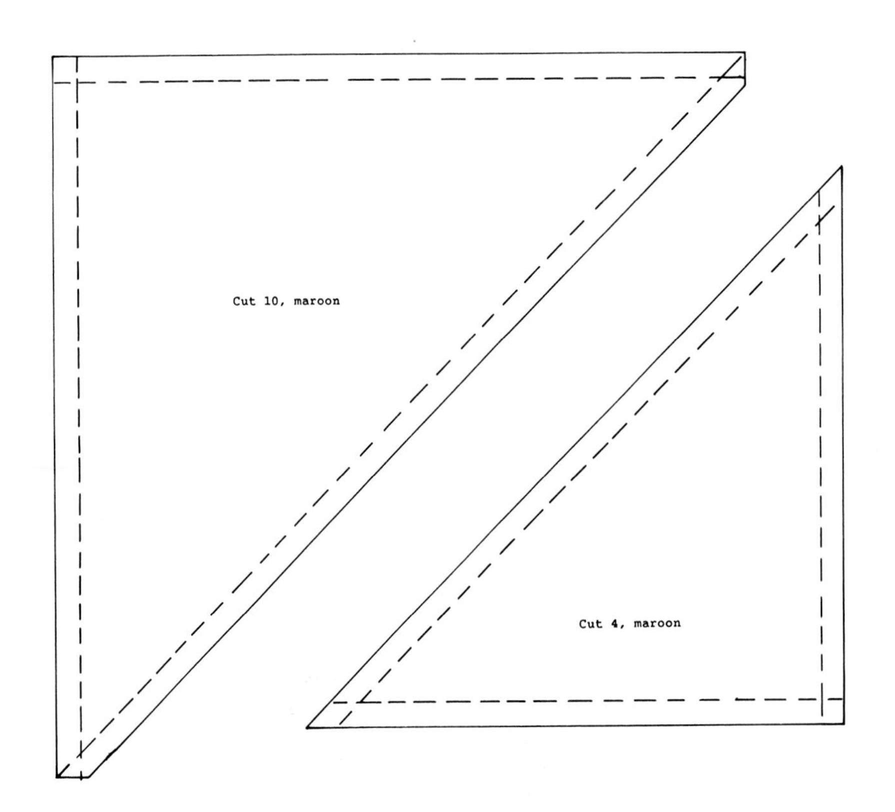

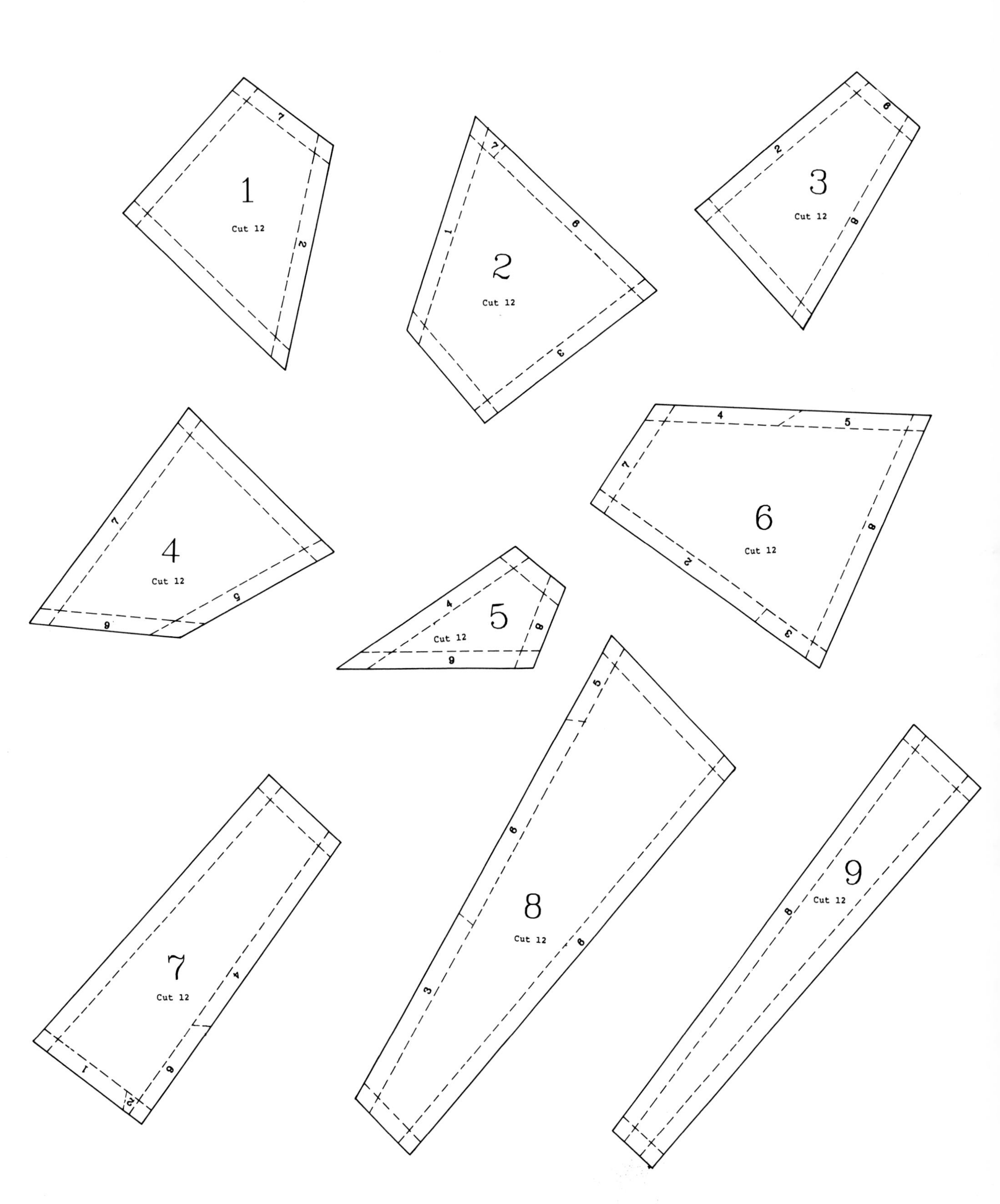
1
Cut 12
2
Cut 12
3
Cut 12
4
Cut 12
5
Cut 12
6
Cut 12
7
Cut 12
8
Cut 12
9
Cut 12

Finished quilt, 36″ by 48″

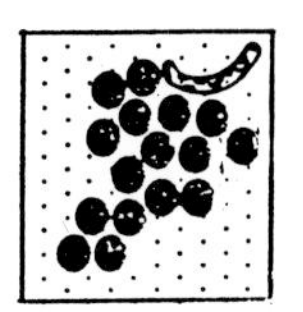

5. Grapevines

Curving vines, ornamented with fruits or flowers, are a traditional quilt motif. They are often used to create a border pattern, like a great wreath framing some scene or display. On these quilts the vines are beautiful. They curve gracefully and the leaves respond to the curves. The flowers or fruits hang like jewels on the ring of vines and leaves.

This quilt honors the vine. The motif is not a secondary element in a larger design. The entire composition uses only three types of blocks. The leaf block is used along the edges, the grape block is found just inside the leaves, and the vine block is used at the center and corners.

Each grape block has a single cluster of grapes, diagonally oriented across the square. The grapes themselves are lightly stuffed and randomly arranged within the cluster. They are done in an assortment of dark blue calico prints. The prints, with their tiny colored shapes, add sparkle and richness to the grapes.

The leaf blocks feature slightly curved vines, with broad leaves fitting into the gentle arcs.

The vine blocks are used to complete the corners, to allow the greenery to make a ring. Corner blocks are often a very difficult proposition, because the block must "face" two different directions. Here, the vine elements are designed to fill the corners in a graceful and satisfying way.

The background for all the blocks is a pale green print, which contrasts with the superimposed white grid. The lattice, made of a heavy white cotton piqué, makes a trellis for all the grapevines.

Instructions

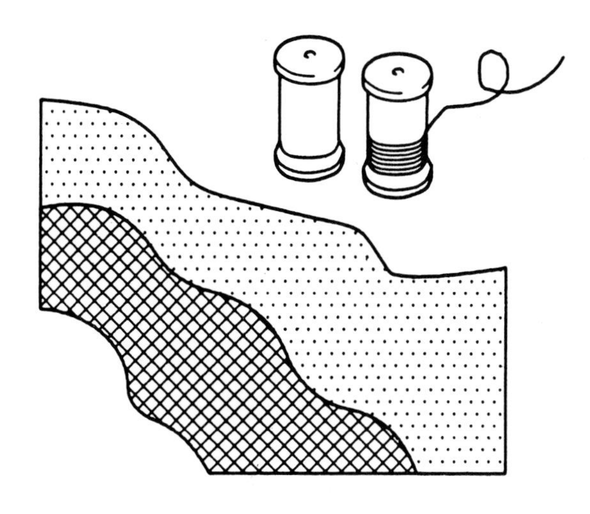

1. Materials:

   2½ yards green print (leaves, vines, and backing)
   ¼ yard mixed blue prints (grapes)
   ½ yard white cotton piqué (lattice strips)
   1½ yards light green print (background squares)
   Cotton batting
   White, green, and blue thread

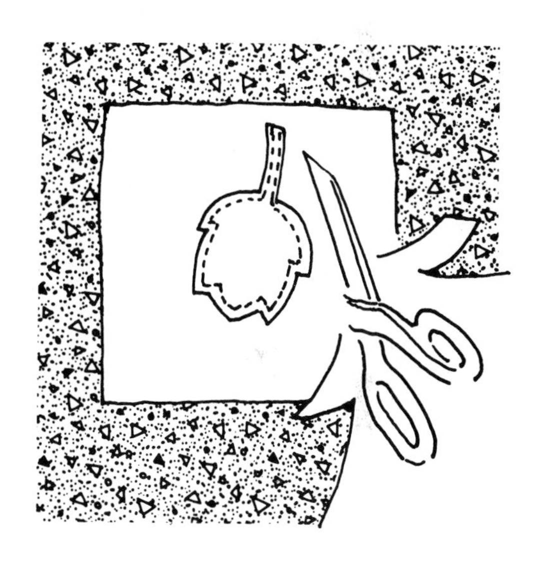

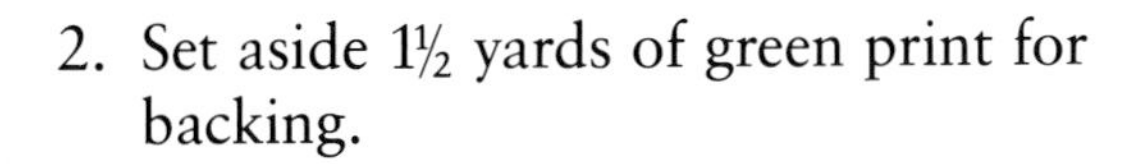

2. Set aside 1½ yards of green print for backing.

   Pin patterns to fabric. Cut carefully.

   Cut a long edge strip, 2″ wide and 14′ long, from the green material.

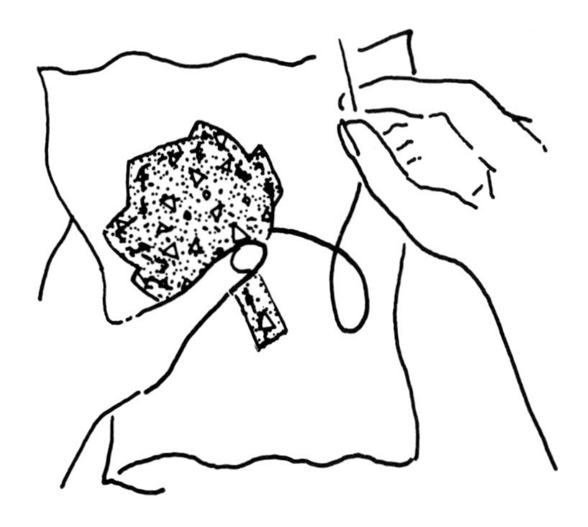

3. Pin leaf to background square. Beginning at end of stem, hand stitch along seam line. Clip as required at curves and corners.

   Pin arced vine element to background square, making sure that the beginning and the end of the vine piece meet the edges of the background squares at the centers. The vine will overlap the leaf stem. Hand stitch along seam lines.

4. Pin curved vine element to background square. The vine should begin and end at the centers of the square edges. Hand stitch along seam lines.

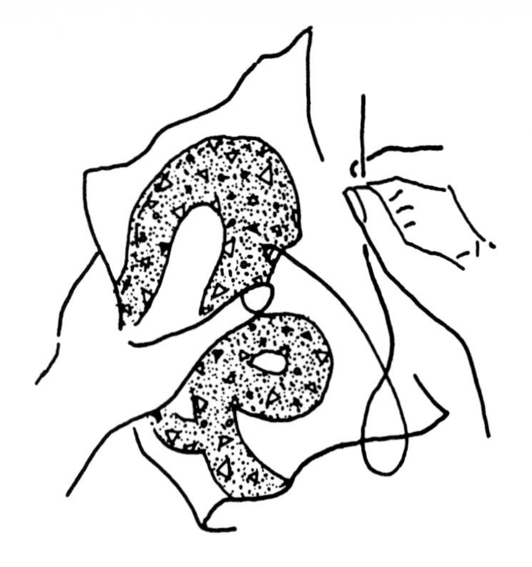

5. Arrange grapes in a cluster formation on background squares. The cluster should have a diagonal orientation, from one corner to its opposite. Using a pencil or dull instrument, insert a bit of stuffing into each partly sewn grape before completing the seam. Sew the grape stem at the corner of the background square, at the top of the bunch.

6. With a machine, sew together the rows of squares by alternating the appliqué squares with the lattice strips.

   Sew together the rows of strips, alternating the lattice strips with the lattice squares.

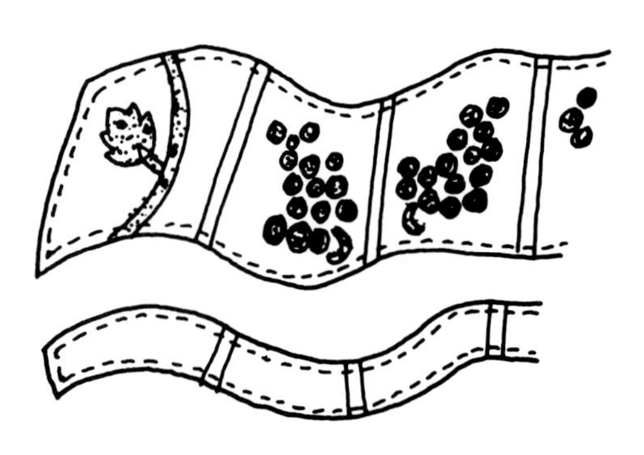

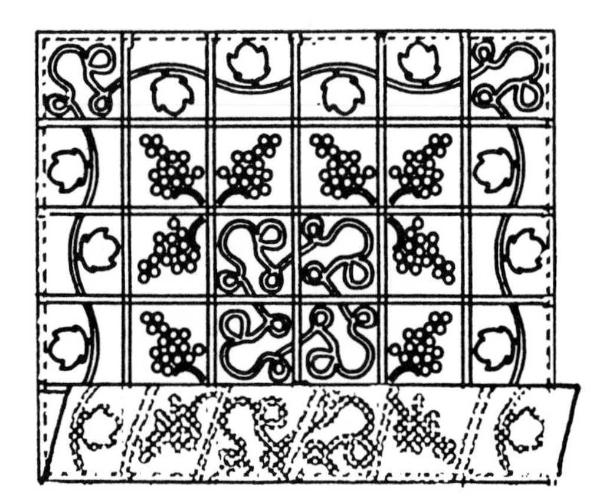

7. Assemble the quilt top by sewing together the rows of squares and strips, matching all seams carefully.

8. Lay the quilt backing face down on a large table or work area. Lay the batting on top of the backing. Lay the quilt top, face up, on the batting. Pin through all three layers. Machine stitch along the edge of the quilt top. Trim close to the seam.

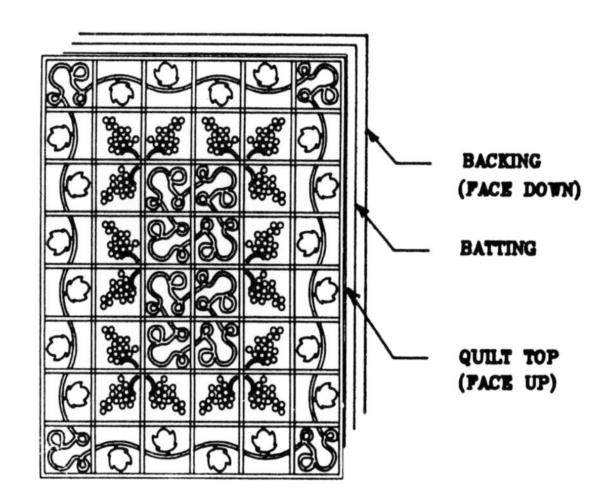

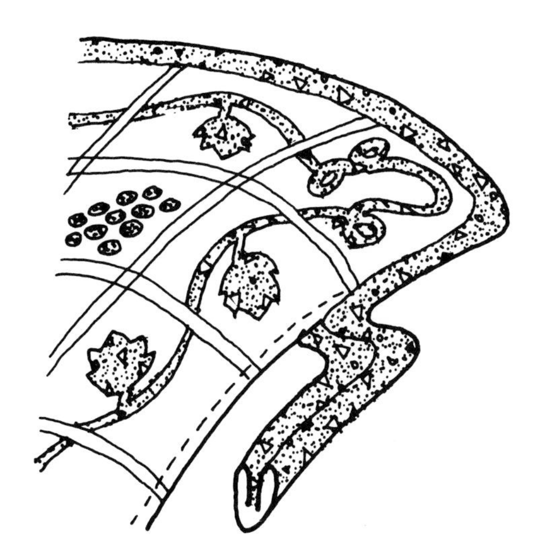

9. Press the seam allowances of the edge strip under. Hand stitch the strip around the quilt assembly.

10. For quilting, outline stitch around the lattice strips, either by hand or with a machine.

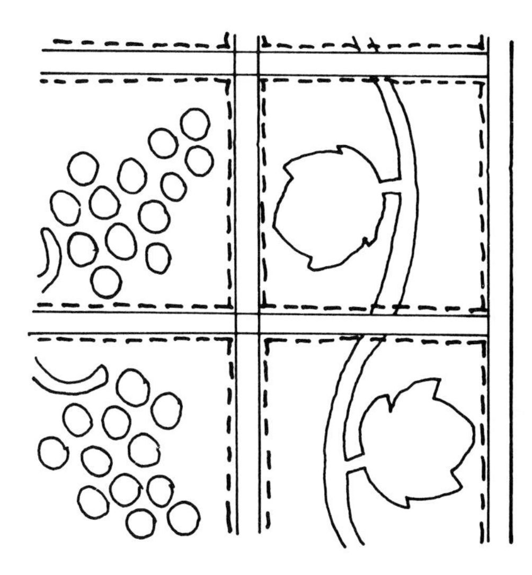

Pattern Pieces

Shown actual size

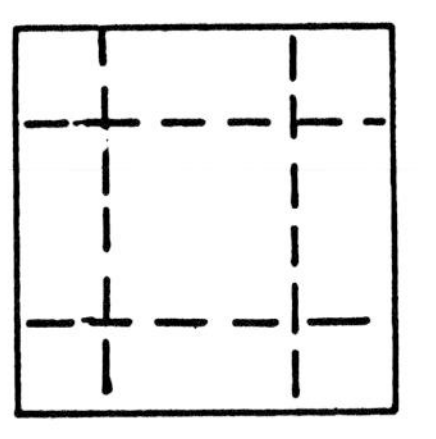

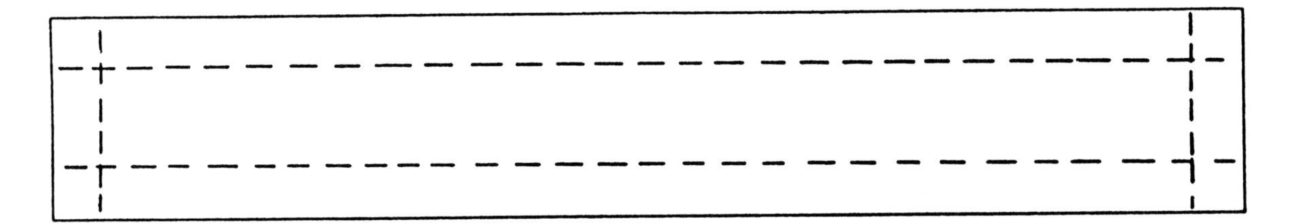

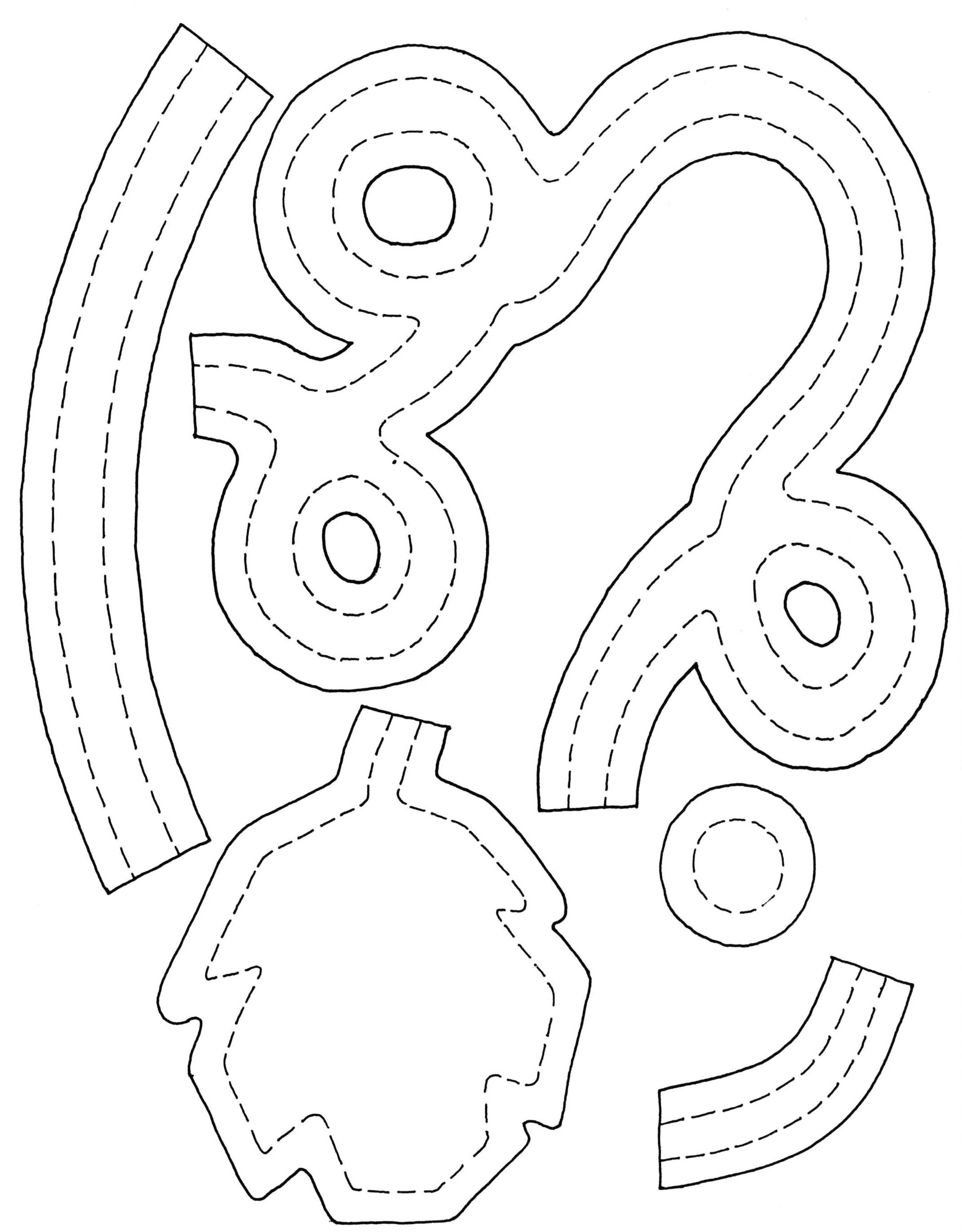

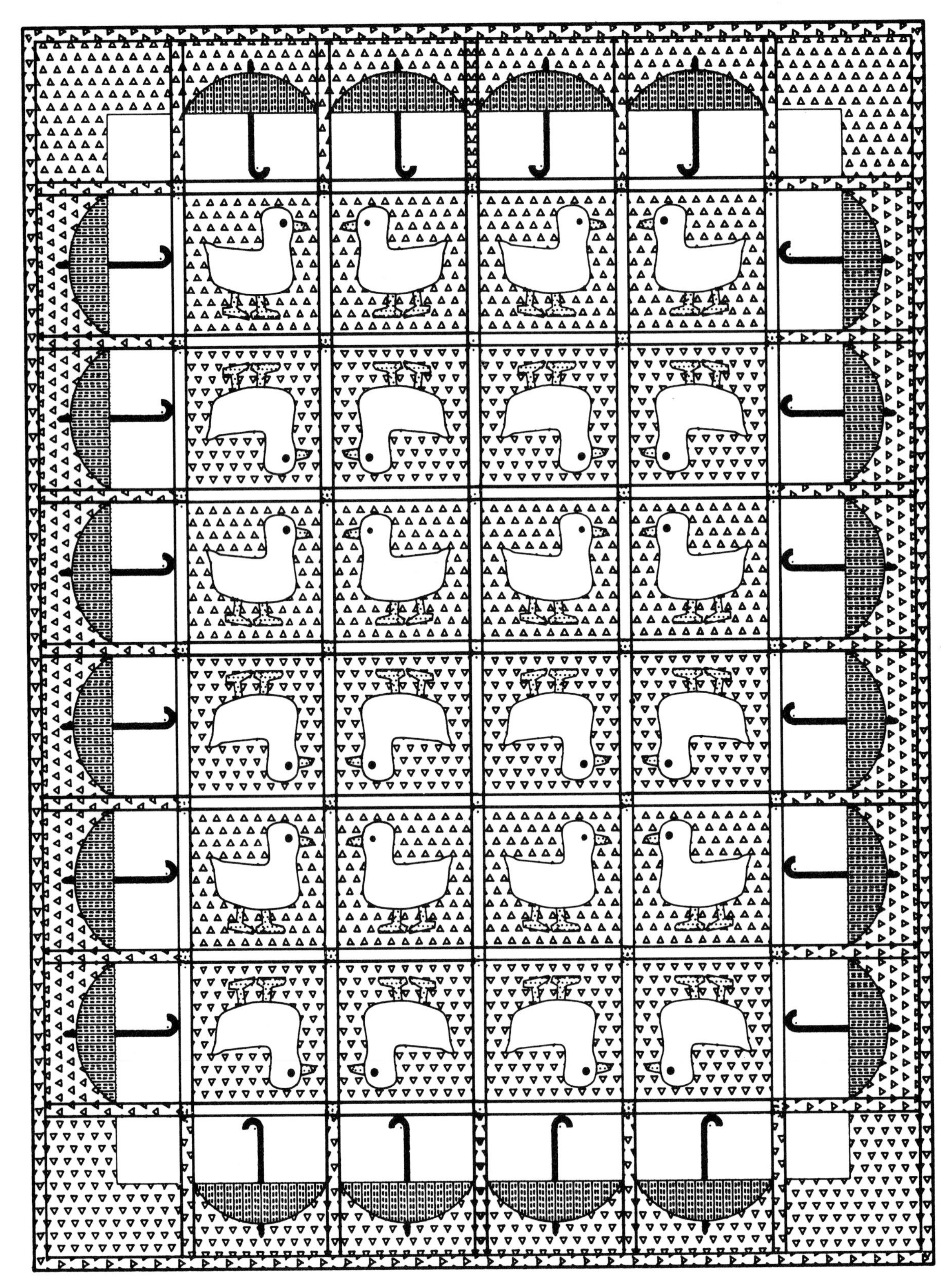

Finished quilt, 36" by 48"

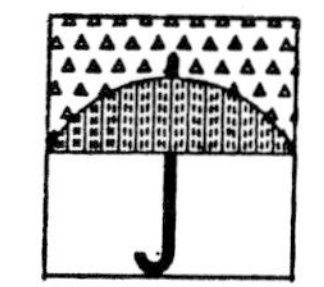

6. Ducks and Umbrellas

Ducks and geese are common characters in children's books. Usually they are depicted as silly, foolish creatures, sometimes because they are playing in the rain, other times because they are chatting with foxes. These characterizations are moralizing ones; their aim is to discourage children from splashing in puddles or from talking to strangers.

On this quilt, ducks are paired with umbrellas and the two figures generate the design. There are two different types of pictorial blocks. One type shows pale ducks in a rainy blue field. The ducks are done in reverse appliqué. Direct appliqué techniques would not work in this case because the pale cloth of the bodies (a "feathery" yellow print on white fabric) is too light to be used on top of the blue background. The bills and feet are made from a bright yellow print. The bills are done in reverse appliqué in order to maintain a continuity of line with the bodies. The feet, which are usually described as gangly and clumsy, are done in direct appliqué. The switch in technique from body to feet emphasizes the awkwardness of the feet.

The umbrella blocks show umbrellas in their classic form. Wide open, broad and black, with dark rain above and light yellow below, they make a protective edge around the quilt. The umbrellas are not completely black. They are a calico print, splashed with small dots that correspond to those in the blue print. This correspondence gives them a kind of rainy sparkle. It is also important to note that the umbrellas do not quite meet—and in the gaps between them, rain pours down.

Instructions

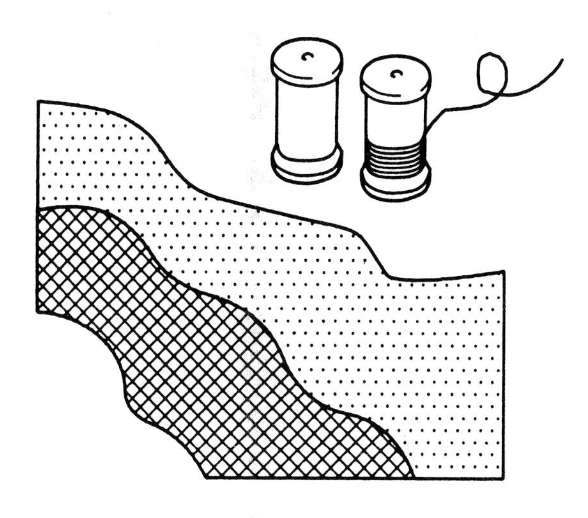

1. Materials:

   3 yards medium blue print (backing and duck squares)
   ¼ yard black print (umbrellas)
   1 yard white and yellow print (duck squares and lattice strips)
   ¼ yard yellow print (duck bills and feet)
   ¼ yard solid black (umbrella handles and lattice squares)
   Cotton batting
   White and blue thread

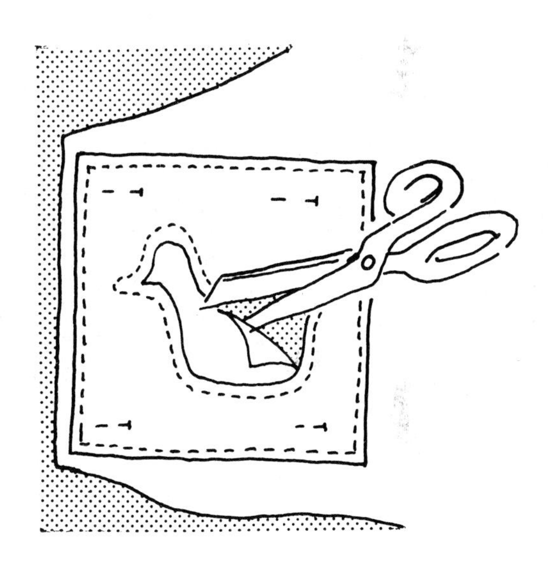

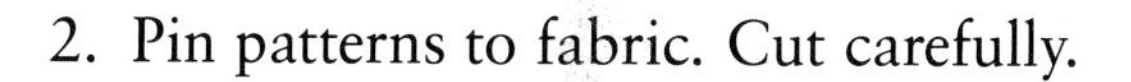

2. Pin patterns to fabric. Cut carefully.

   Cut a long edge strip, 2″ wide and 14′ long, from the medium blue material.

3. Pin duck square over duck background, pinning beak cloth in proper location. Hand stitch along the seam line. At the duck belly, fold the seam allowances for the duck feet under and tuck the tops of the feet over the belly edge. Sew across the tops of the feet. Clip curves and corners as necessary.

   Finish square by sewing across duck bill and around duck feet.

4. Sew the blue and white elements of the umbrella squares together. Sew umbrella handles to the squares, then sew umbrellas over handles.

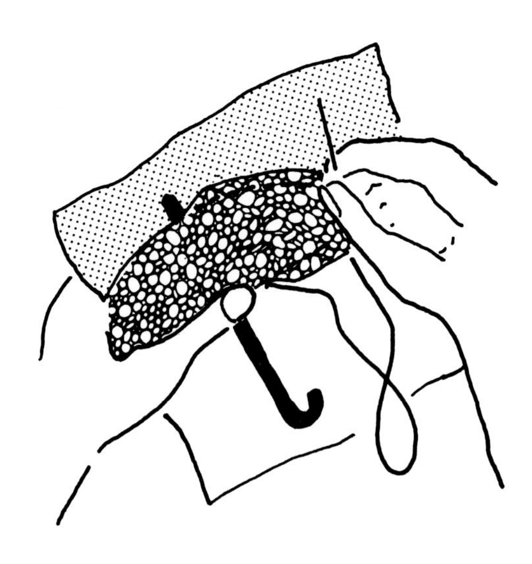

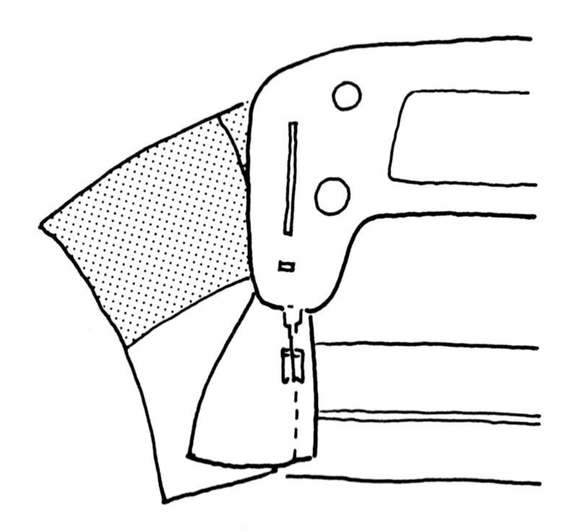

5. The corner squares are made of three small blue squares and a single white square.

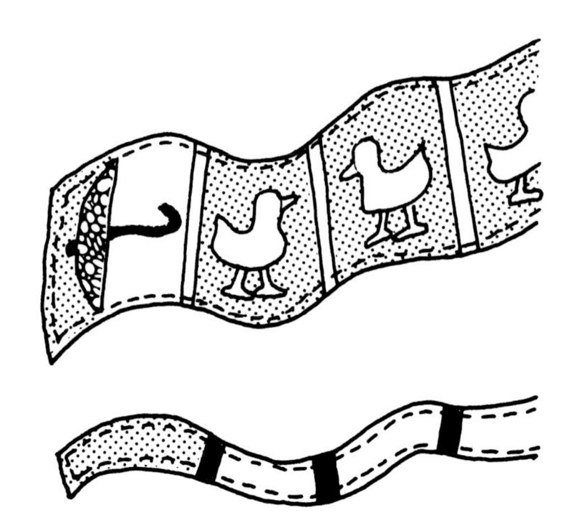

6. With a machine, sew together the rows of squares by alternating the appliqué squares with the lattice strips.

   Sew together the rows of strips, alternating the lattice strips with the lattice squares.

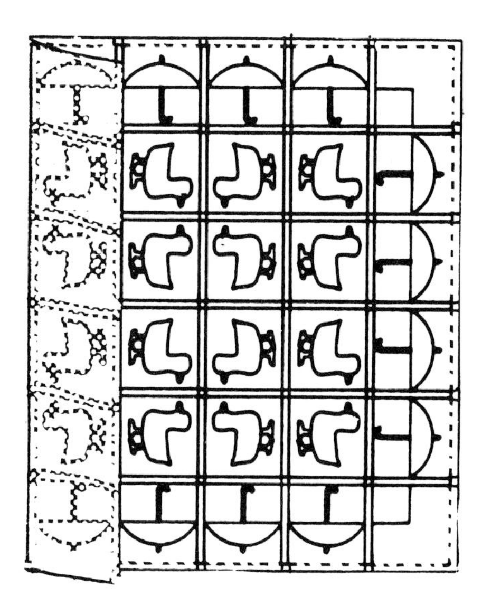

7. Assemble the quilt top by sewing together the rows of squares and strips, matching all seams carefully.

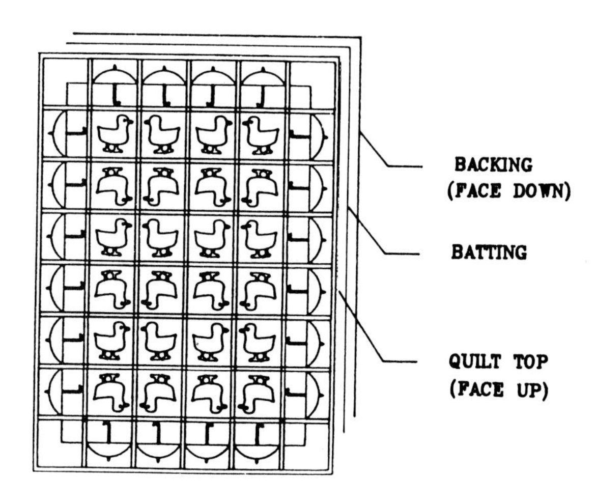

8. Lay the quilt backing face down on a large table or work area. Lay the batting on top of the backing. Lay the quilt top, face up, on the batting. Pin through all three layers. Machine stitch along the edge of the quilt top. Trim close to the seam.

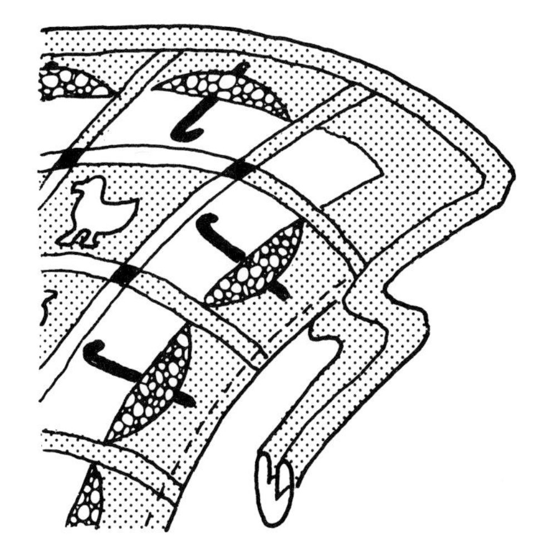

9. Press the seam allowances of the edge strip under. Hand stitch the strip around the quilt assembly.

10. For quilting, outline stitch inside along the tops of the umbrellas and on the inside of the ducks as shown.

Pattern Pieces

Shown one-half actual size

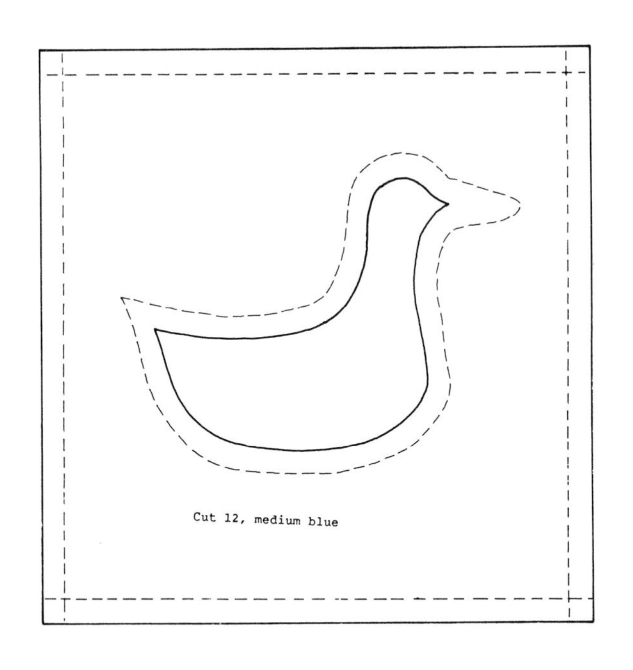

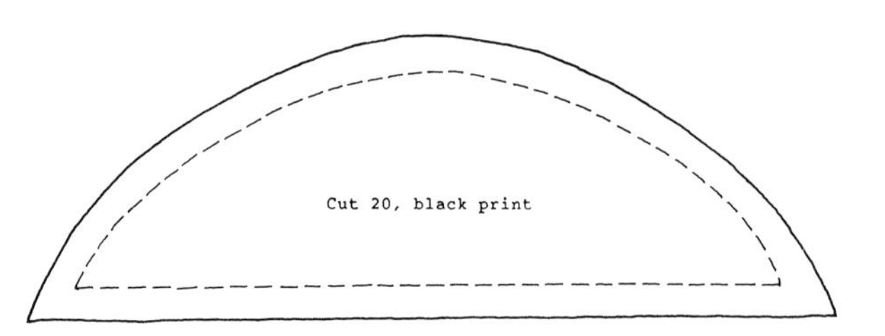

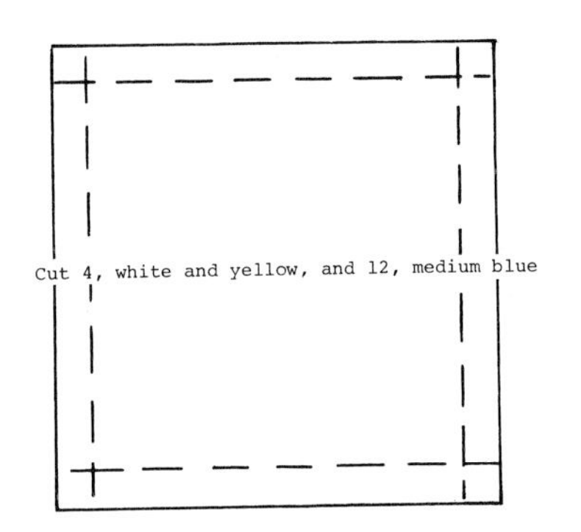

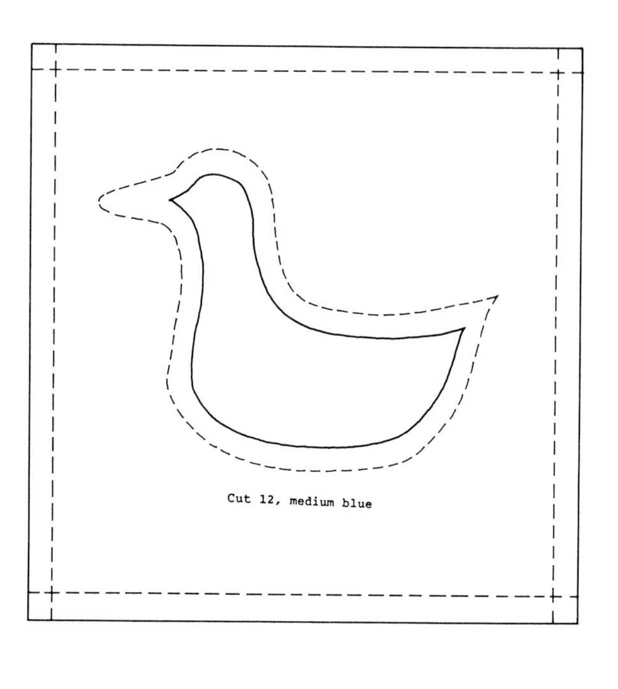
Cut 12, medium blue

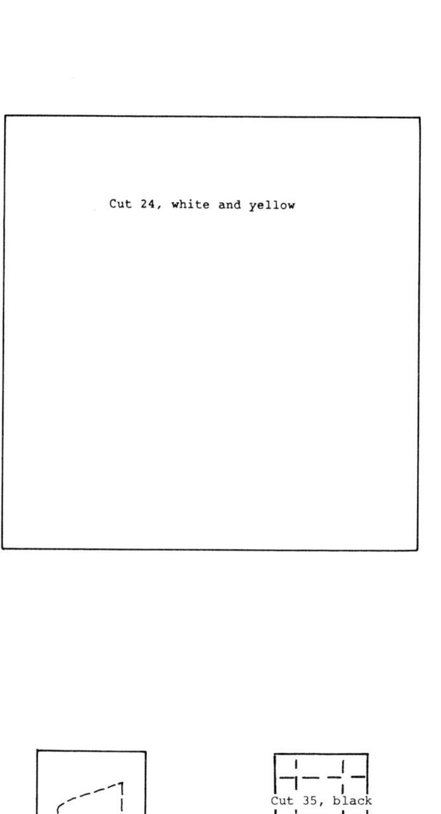
Cut 24, white and yellow

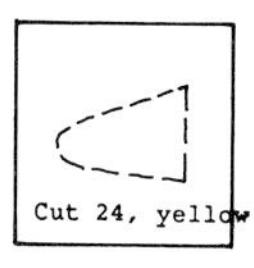
Cut 24, yellow

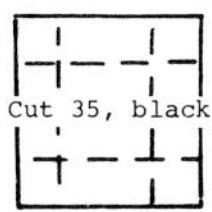
Cut 35, black

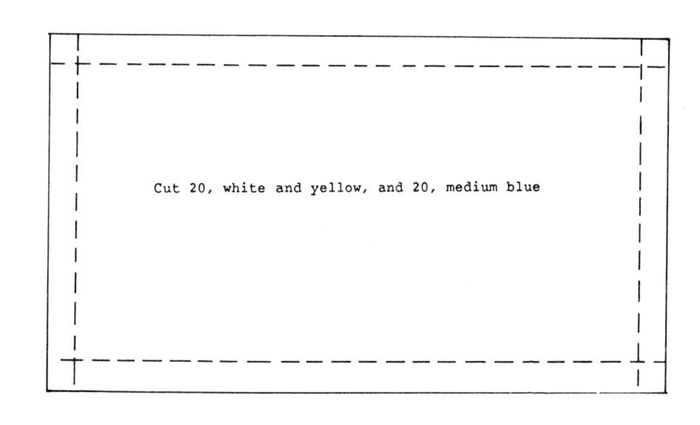
Cut 20, white and yellow, and 20, medium blue

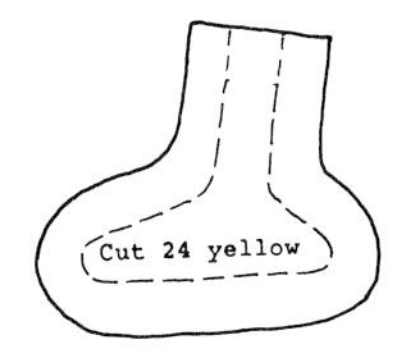
Cut 24 yellow

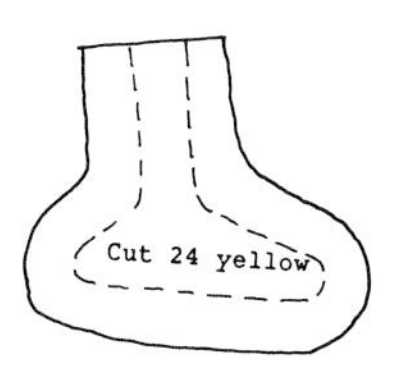
Cut 24 yellow

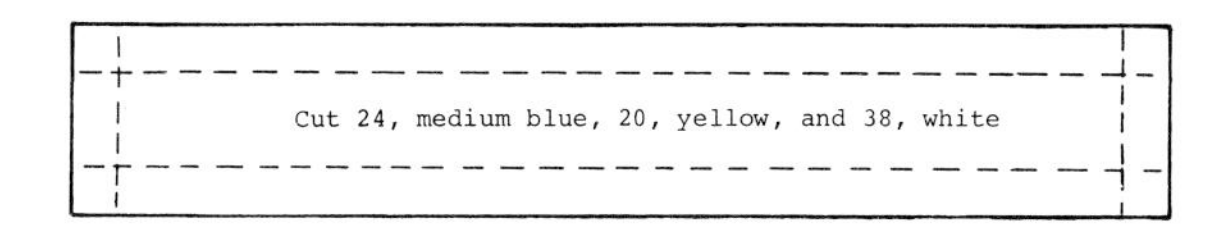
Cut 24, medium blue, 20, yellow, and 38, white

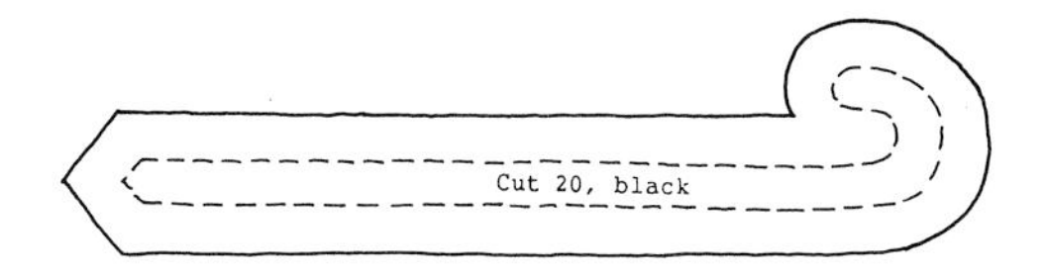
Cut 20, black

Finished quilt, 36″ by 48″

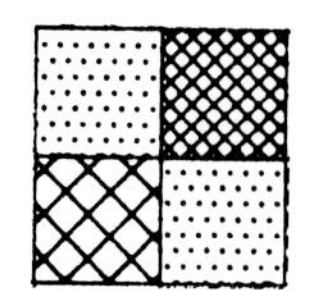

7. Leaves

The Leaves quilt has a two-color nine-patch square as its basic unit, but each square has a different pair of colors. Six colors weave through the quilt in the long direction, while eight different colors cross its width. In each direction the tones start with the greens and pale yellows that represent summer colors. These are followed by the oranges and golds that are part of autumn's palette. The final shades in each direction are the scarlets and dark browns that show up at the end of the season.

The use of tiny elements—there are 432 "leaves"—helps to make a "forest." The arrangement of colors, while it has a dominant direction from green to brown, has a secondary organization in which the early shades mingle with the later ones. This interweaving and grading of tones contributes to a sort of fluttering effect, as if the forest were stirred by wind.

The Leaves quilt was inspired by Amish traditions. Admirers of Amish quilts are always struck by their simplicity of form and richness of color. The stripped-down design, the bareness of the pattern, are essential to this quality. Without fussy forms and complicated prints, the colors attain a vibrancy and intensity that are lacking in certain more complex quilts.

Another interesting fact about Amish work is that it so often contains very dark tones. Dark browns, purples, navy blues, and even black appear in Amish quilts for both adults and children. This use is in distinct contrast to the prevailing opinions of the times, which favored lighter, more "cheerful" shades in works intended for children.

Instructions

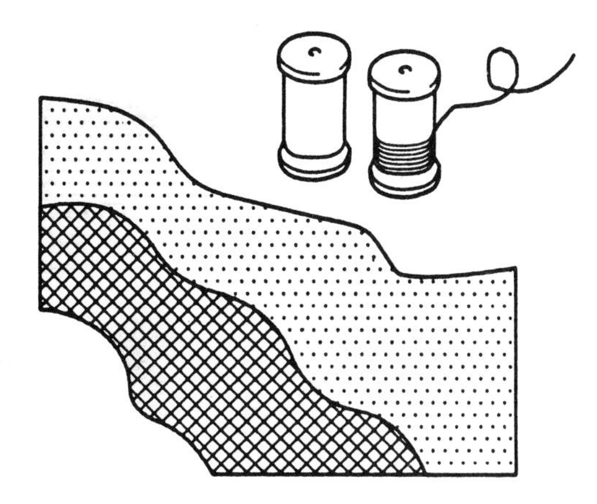

1. Materials:

   ¼ yard each of the following solid colors: pale yellow, spring green, emerald green, tan, orange, orange-red, scarlet, brown, forest green, yellow, gold, maroon, light brown, and dark purple

   1½ yards of backing material

   Cotton batting

   Quilting thread in the above colors

2. Cut 2½″ squares from all the fabrics. Either use the pattern piece or cut 2½″ wide measured strips, and cut again to make the squares.

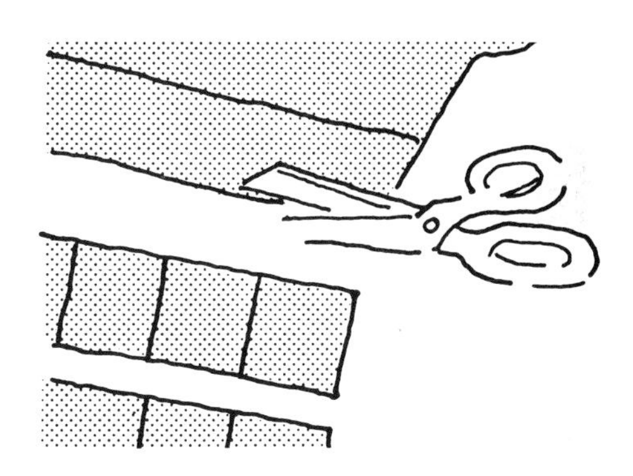

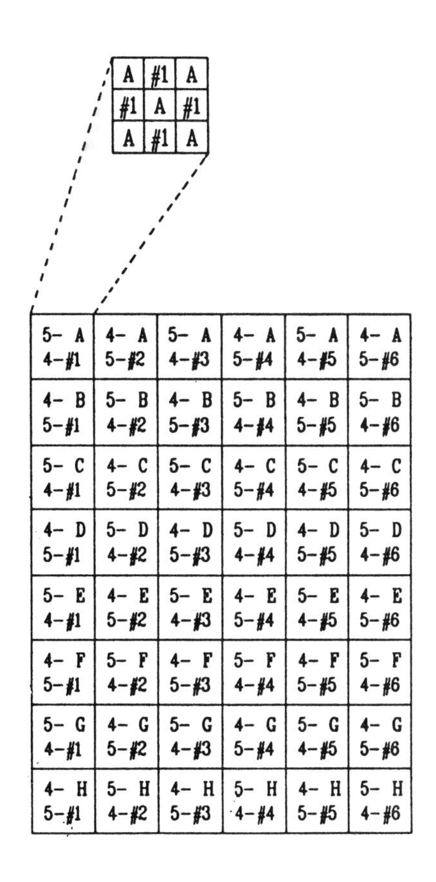

A	#1	A
#1	A	#1
A	#1	A

5- A 4-#1	4- A 5-#2	5- A 4-#3	4- A 5-#4	5- A 4-#5	4- A 5-#6
4- B 5-#1	5- B 4-#2	4- B 5-#3	5- B 4-#4	4- B 5-#5	5- B 4-#6
5- C 4-#1	4- C 5-#2	5- C 4-#3	4- C 5-#4	5- C 4-#5	4- C 5-#6
4- D 5-#1	5- D 4-#2	4- D 5-#3	5- D 4-#4	4- D 5-#5	5- D 4-#6
5- E 4-#1	4- E 5-#2	5- E 4-#3	4- E 5-#4	5- E 4-#5	4- E 5-#6
4- F 5-#1	5- F 4-#2	4- F 5-#3	5- F 4-#4	4- F 5-#5	5- F 4-#6
5- G 4-#1	4- G 5-#2	5- G 4-#3	4- G 5-#4	5- G 4-#5	4- G 5-#6
4- H 5-#1	5- H 4-#2	4- H 5-#3	5- H 4-#4	4- H 5-#5	5- H 4-#6

3. The best way to make this quilt is to sew the small squares together to make a series of nine-square blocks. Each block is different from all the others; no two have the same pair of colors.

   The chart shows how the nine small squares are sewn together, and it also identifies the number and color of small squares that make up each block.

   Rows of colors:
   - A is pale yellow
   - B is spring green
   - C is emerald green
   - D is tan
   - E is orange
   - F is orange-red
   - G is scarlet
   - H is brown

   Columns of colors:
   - 1 is forest green
   - 2 is yellow
   - 3 is gold
   - 4 is maroon
   - 5 is light brown
   - 6 is dark purple

4. On a large table or work surface, lay out the 5 squares and 4 squares that will make up each block. This is an important step, as it is very easy to get confused and sew the wrong squares together.

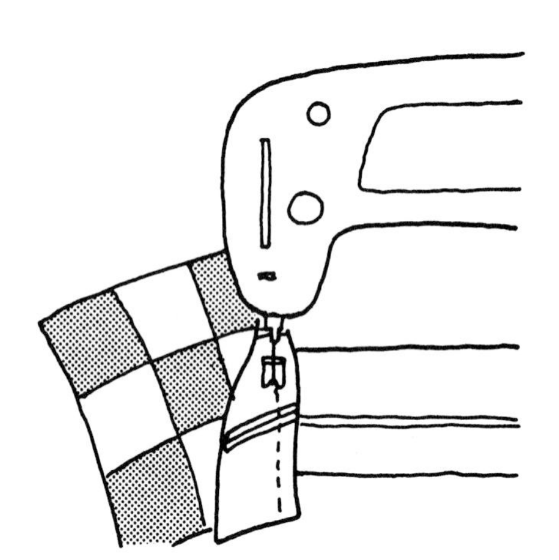

5. Sew the nine-square blocks together using the stacks of small squares from the table. Return each finished block to its place on the table.

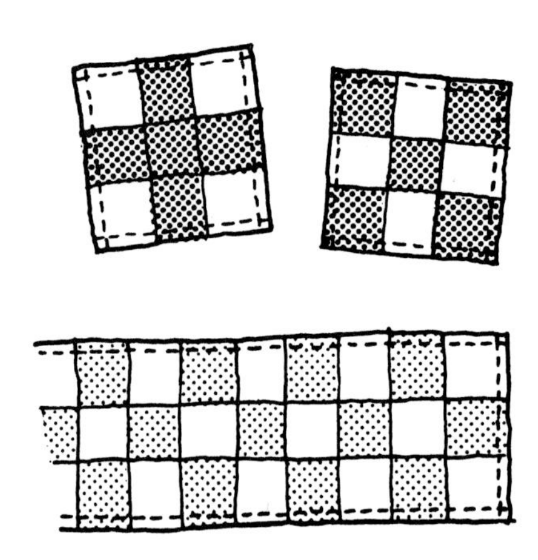

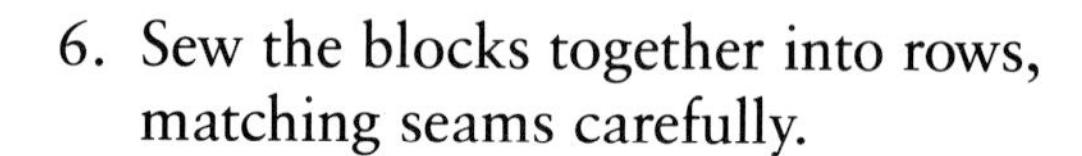

6. Sew the blocks together into rows, matching seams carefully.

   Assemble the rows to make the quilt top.

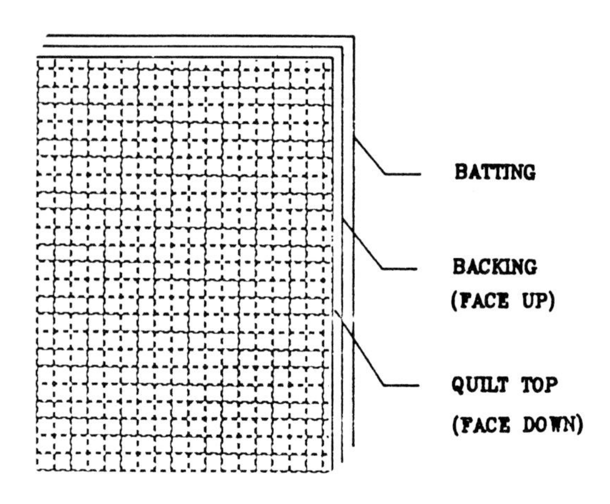

7. Lay the quilt batting on the table or work surface. Lay the backing material, face up, on the batting. Lay the quilt top, face down, on the backing. Pin through all three layers. Sew around the edge, leaving 8″ unsewn at the end. Trim close to seam.

8. Turn the quilt right side out by pulling it through the 8″ gap.

   Sew the gap closed by hand.

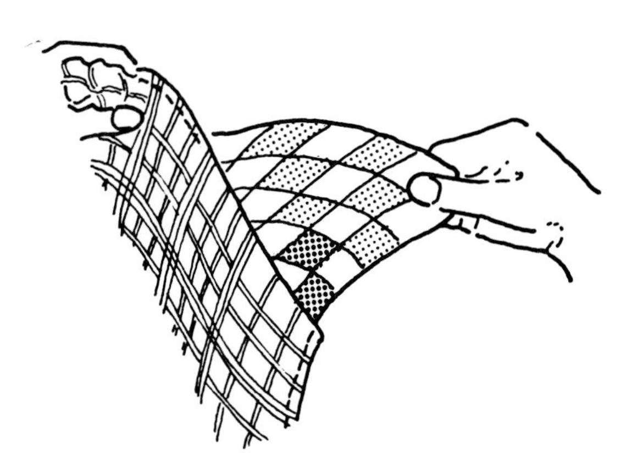

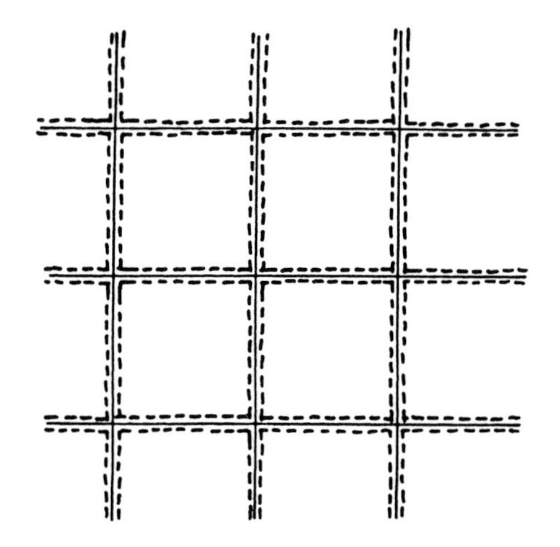

9. For quilting the three layers together, sew around each small square close to its edges. Use thread that matches the square color.

Pattern Piece

Shown actual size

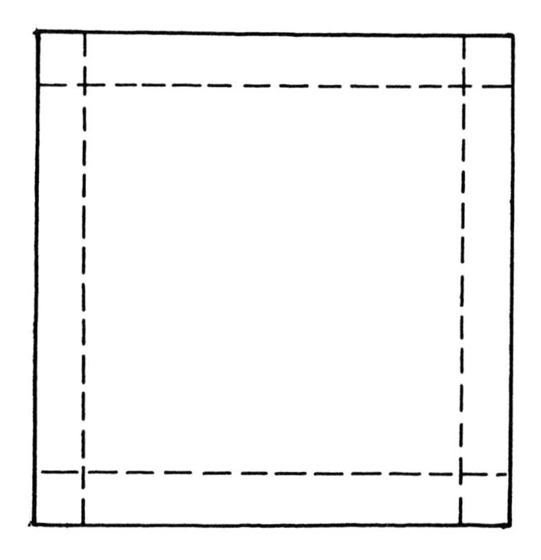

Cut 27 of colors A, B, C, D, E, F, G, H
36 of colors 1, 2, 3, 4, 5, 6

8. Hearts and Hands

Hands and hearts are archetypal human symbols. They make an early appearance in cave paintings from prehistoric times. They continue to appear in painting and sculpture from a range of ages and cultures. Hands express both individuality and community along with care, protection, and creation. Hearts are potent images too. Even before their biological functions were understood, they were singled out as special organs and associated with love, generosity, and friendship.

A crib quilt seems a particularly appropriate place to join the two images, since infants need the protection and care that the two emblems signify.

This quilt uses a palette of reds and blues. The dark blue hands are appliquéd onto light red squares, while the hearts are done in reverse appliqué—bright red on light blue. A medium blue tone, used in the lattice strips, mediates between the two intense colors.

The use of reverse appliqué for the heart squares creates an interesting layering effect at the border, an effect in which the border can be understood in two different ways. The corner squares—light blue, but without the applied red—suggest that the border is a continuous frame around the field, but the red appliqué pieces deny it. They suggest that the field is the result of an intersection, a place where two zones cross.

Finished quilt, 36" by 48"

Instructions

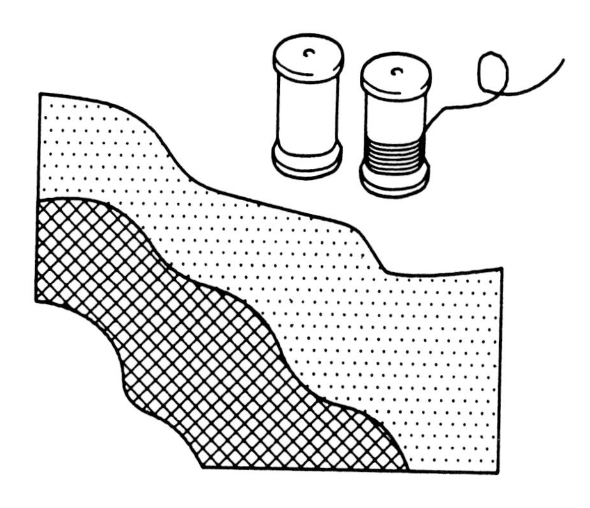

1. Materials:

   2 yards medium blue print (backing and lattice strips)
   ¾ yard red print (hearts and lattice squares)
   ¾ yard light red print (hand background)
   ¾ yard light blue print (heart background)
   ¾ yard dark blue print (hands)
   Cotton batting
   White thread

2. Pin patterns to fabric. Cut carefully.

   Cut a long edge strip, 2″ wide and 14′ long, from the medium blue material.

3. Pin heart square over heart background. Hand stitch along the seam line. Clip as required at curves and corners.

   Appliqué hands to hand background squares, beginning next to the thumbs. Clip as required between fingers and along curves.

4. With a machine, sew together the rows of squares by alternating the appliqué squares with the lattice strips.

   Sew together the rows of strips, alternating the lattice strips with the lattice squares.

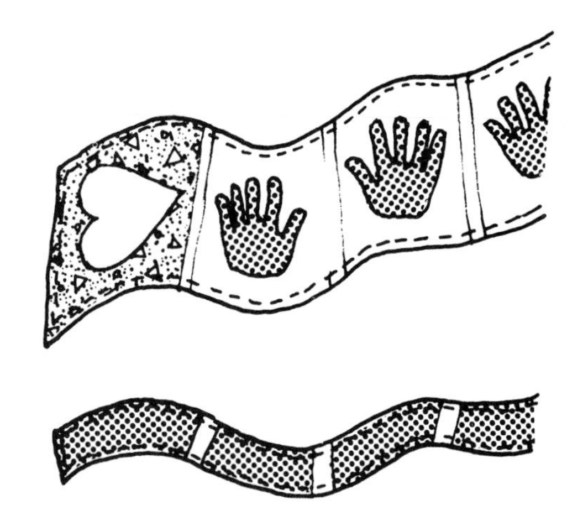

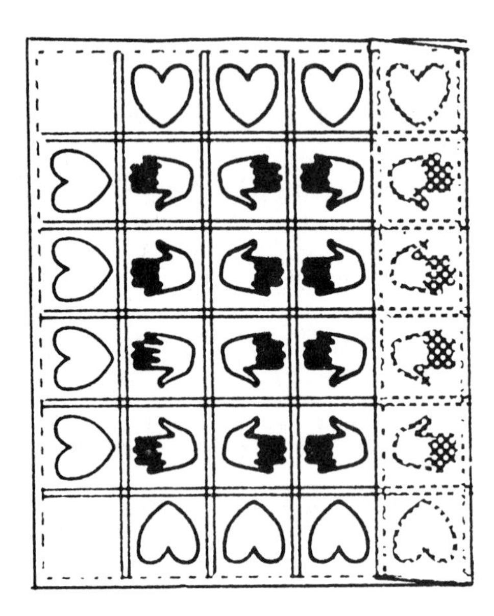

5. Assemble the quilt top by sewing together the rows of squares and strips, matching all seams carefully.

6. Lay the quilt backing face down on a large table or work area. Lay the batting on top of the backing. Lay the quilt top, face up, on the batting. Pin through all three layers. Machine stitch along the edge of the quilt top. Trim close to the seam.

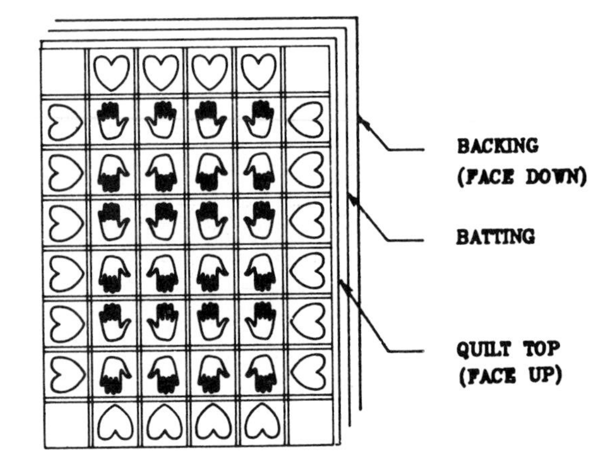

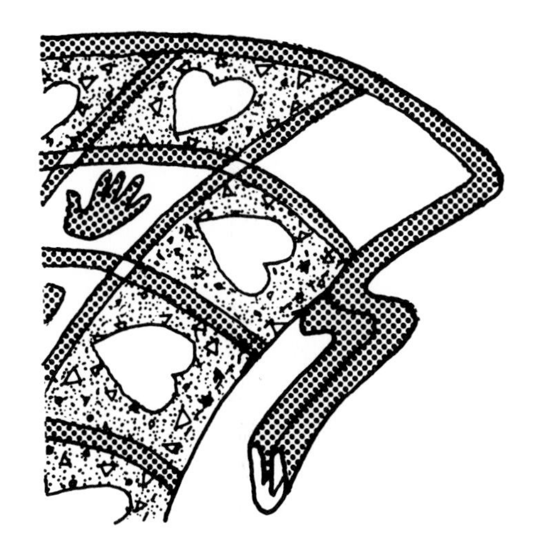

7. Press the seam allowances of the edge strip under. Hand stitch the strip around the quilt assembly.

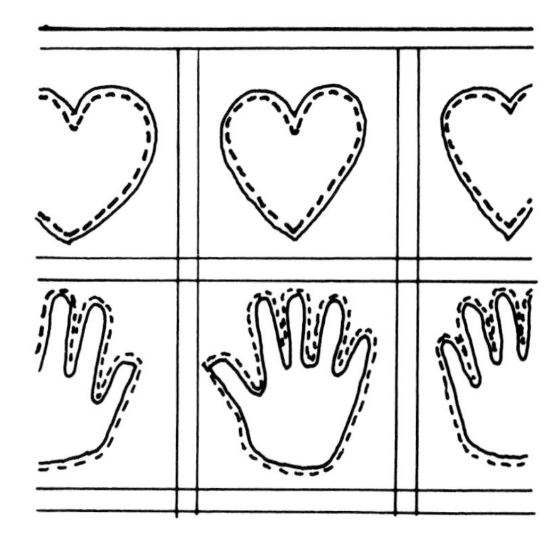

8. For quilting, outline stitch inside the hearts and outside the hands, either by hand or by machine.

Pattern Pieces

Shown one-half actual size

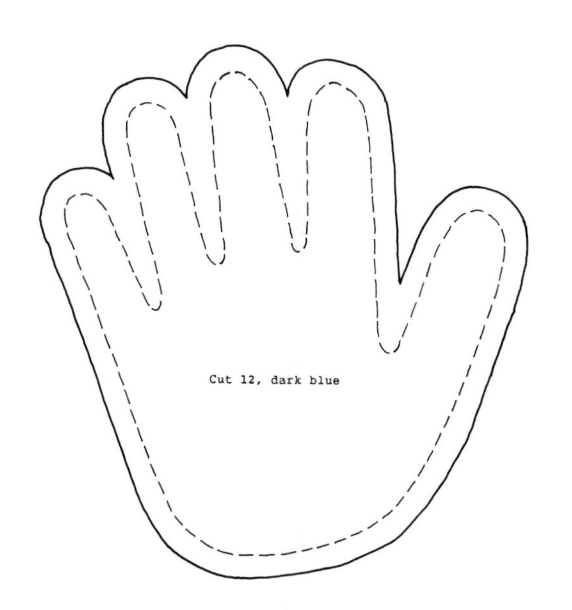

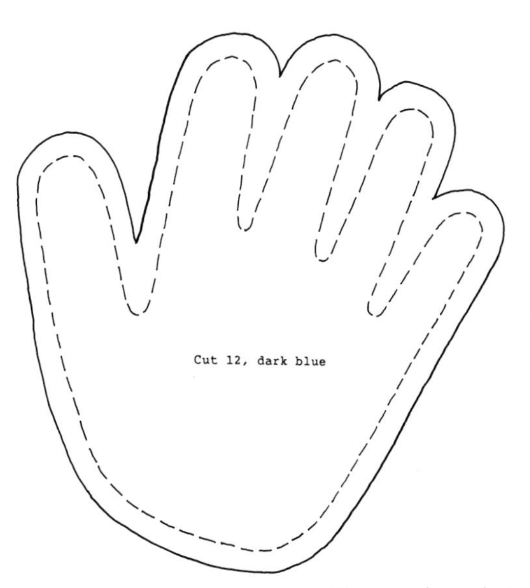

Cut 20, red

Cut 24 light blue and 24 light red

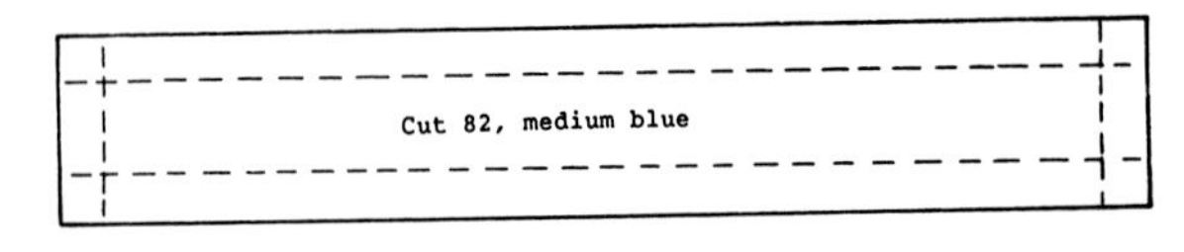
Cut 82, medium blue

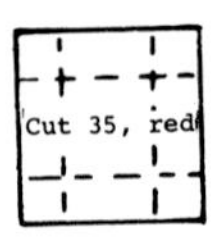
Cut 35, red

9. Crazy Quilt

This quilt was inspired by the behavior of light, and by the phenomena of reflection, refraction, and transparency. Light is critical to visual perception; it makes color, shape, and shadow.

The pattern is generated by a net of intersecting straight lines. They are randomly arranged, and the resulting shapes are irregular triangles, quadrilaterals, and other polygons. At the edges the intersecting lines of the net are transformed into a series of parallel lines, as if organized by a laser or prism. At the same time, the irregular shapes become a sequence of regular rectangles and squares.

The surface is colored with four closely related colors: a navy blue, a turquoise, a lavender, and a blue-green. In order to make distinct elements on a flat planar surface, four colors are exactly the right number. Three colors would be inadequate, and a fifth shade would be superfluous. In mathematics this situation is known as the "four-color map theorem." The rigor of the quilt derives from the severity of its geometry and from its strict limitation of colors. The fabrics are solid colors since prints would dilute the design by distracting from the elements and lines.

Like the colors, the quilting stitching reinforces the geometry of the design. Each polygonal shape is quilted along its perimeter (just inside the seam line) in a matching thread.

Instructions

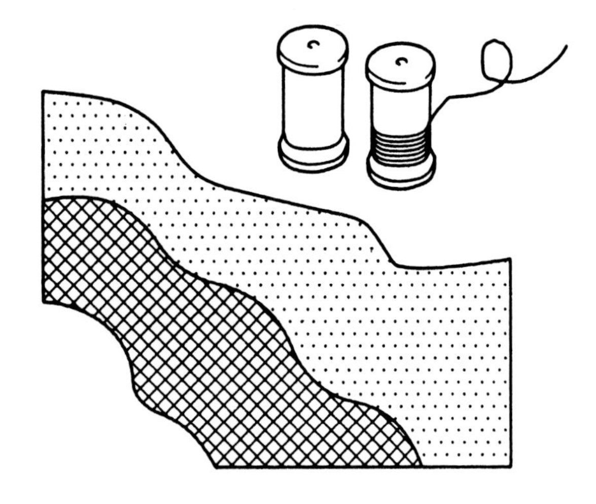

1. Materials:

   ¾ yard each of solid turquoise, green, and lavender
   2½ yards of solid navy blue
   Cotton batting
   Turquoise, green, lavender, and navy blue thread

2. The easiest way to assemble this quilt is to divide it into eight separate zones. Zones 1 through 4 make up the field of the quilt; zones 5 through 8 make up the border.

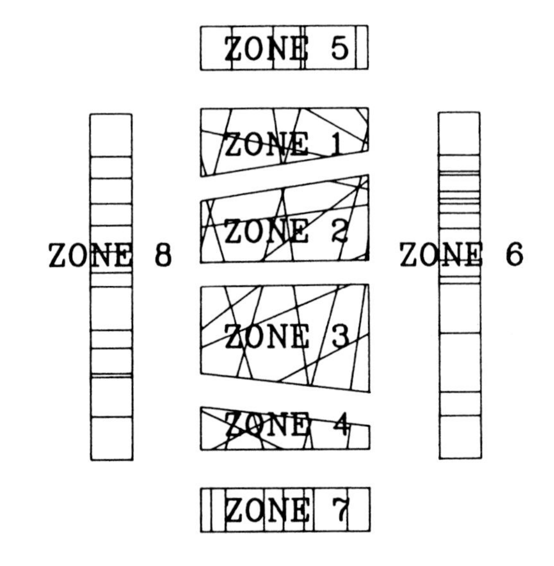

3. Set aside 1½ yards of navy blue for backing.

   All pattern pieces are marked with a circle indicating which color material is to be used. The solid circle represents navy blue; the dotted one, turquoise; the cross-hatched, green; and the empty one, lavender. Pin patterns to fabric and cut carefuly. Cut one element from every pattern piece unless noted otherwise.

   Cut a long edge strip, 2″ wide and 14′ long, from navy blue material.

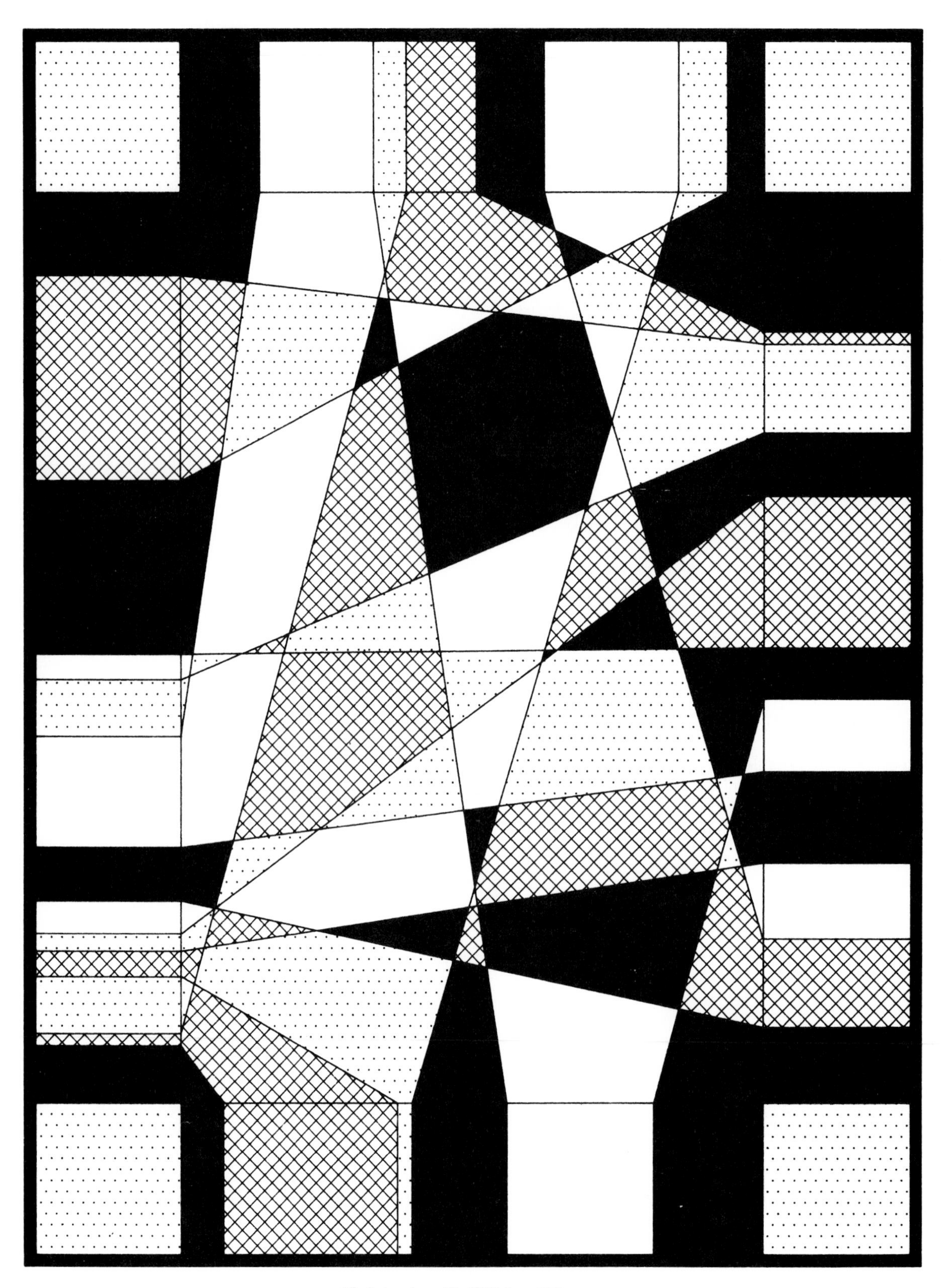

Finished quilt, 36″ by 48″

4. Each pattern piece has the numbers of adjoining pieces written along the edges.

   Sew the elements of each zone together. Zone 1 has elements 1 to 13 in it. Zone 2 has elements 14 to 37. Zone 3 has elements 38 to 55. Zone 4 has elements 56 to 69.

   Sew the four zones together, matching seams carefully.

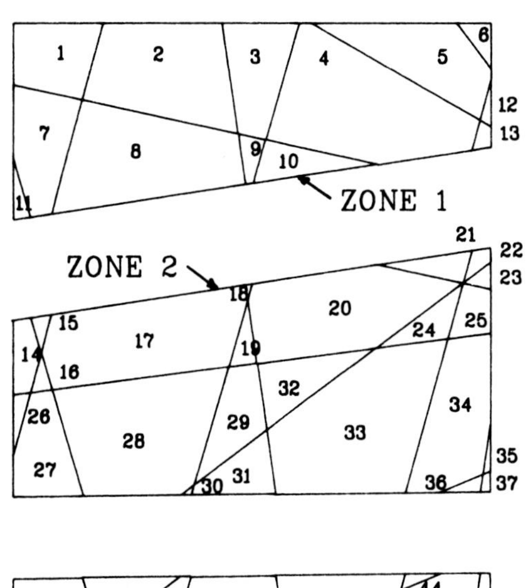

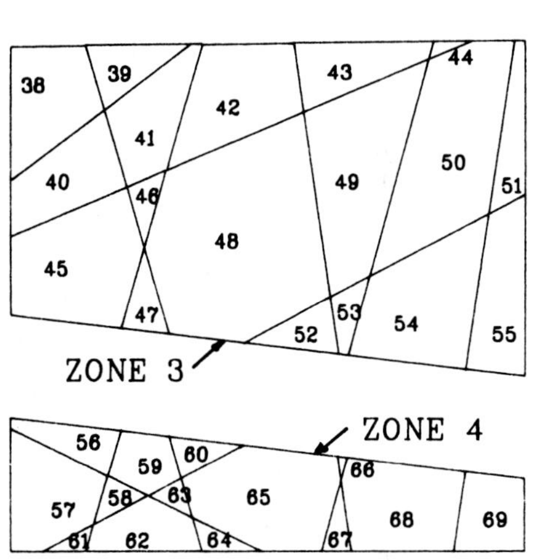

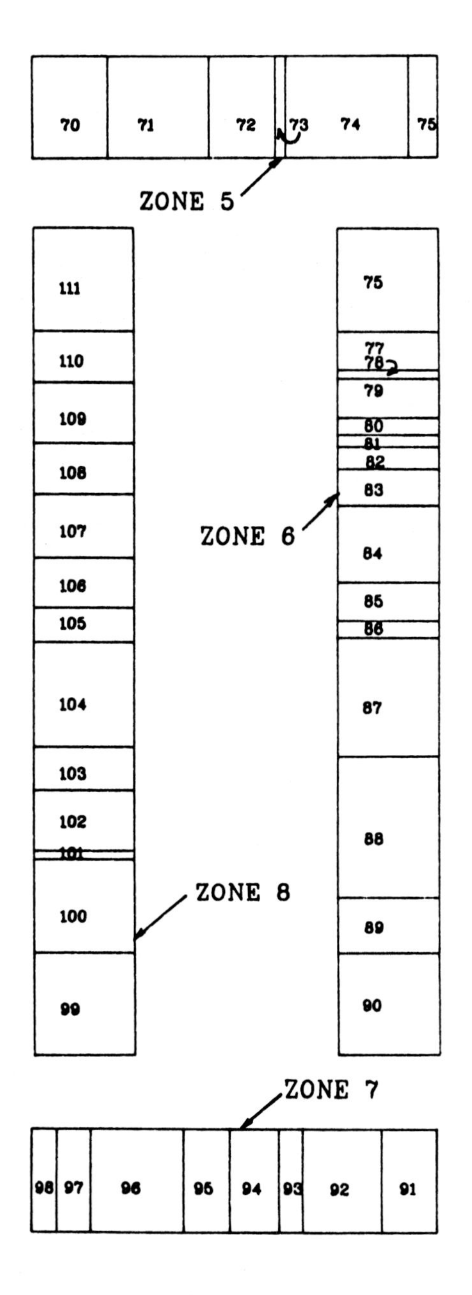

5. Sew the border zones together. Zone 5 has elements 70 to 75. Zone 6 begins and ends with corner squares 76 and 90, with elements 77 to 89 between. Zone 7 has elements 91 to 98. Zone 8 begins and ends with corner squares 99 and 111, with elements 100 to 110 between.

   Sew the border zones to the quilt zones already assembled, matching seams carefully. Sew zones 5 and 7 first, then finish with zones 6 and 8.

6. Lay the quilt backing, face down, on a large table or work surface. Lay the batting on top of it. Lay the quilt top, right side up, on top of the batting. Pin through all three layers, smoothing them to eliminate wrinkles or bumps. Machine stitch along the edge of the quilt top. Trim close to the seam.

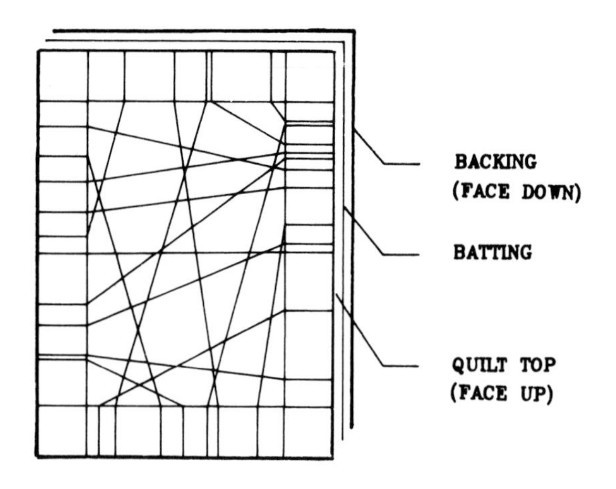

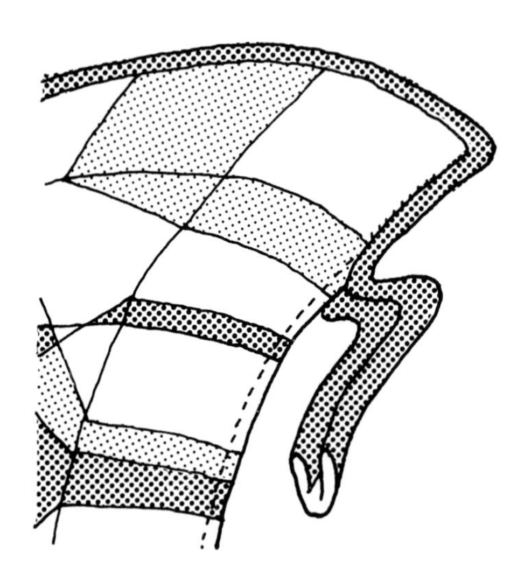

7. Press the seam allowances of the edge strip under. Hand stitch the strip around the quilt assembly.

8. For quilting the three layers together, sew around each quilt element just inside its seam lines. Use thread that matches the element.

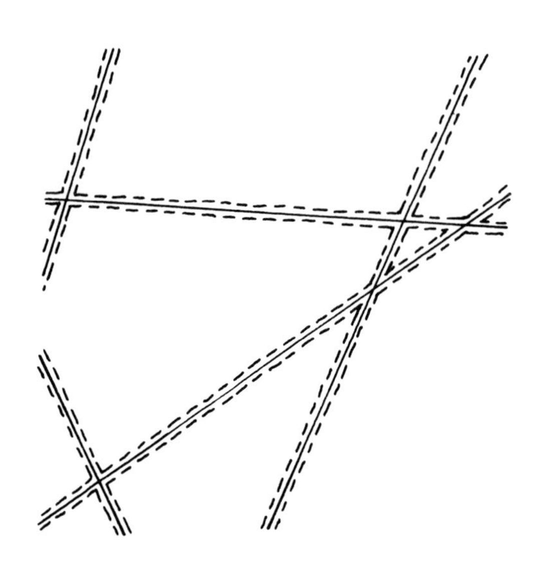

Pattern Pieces

Shown one-half actual size

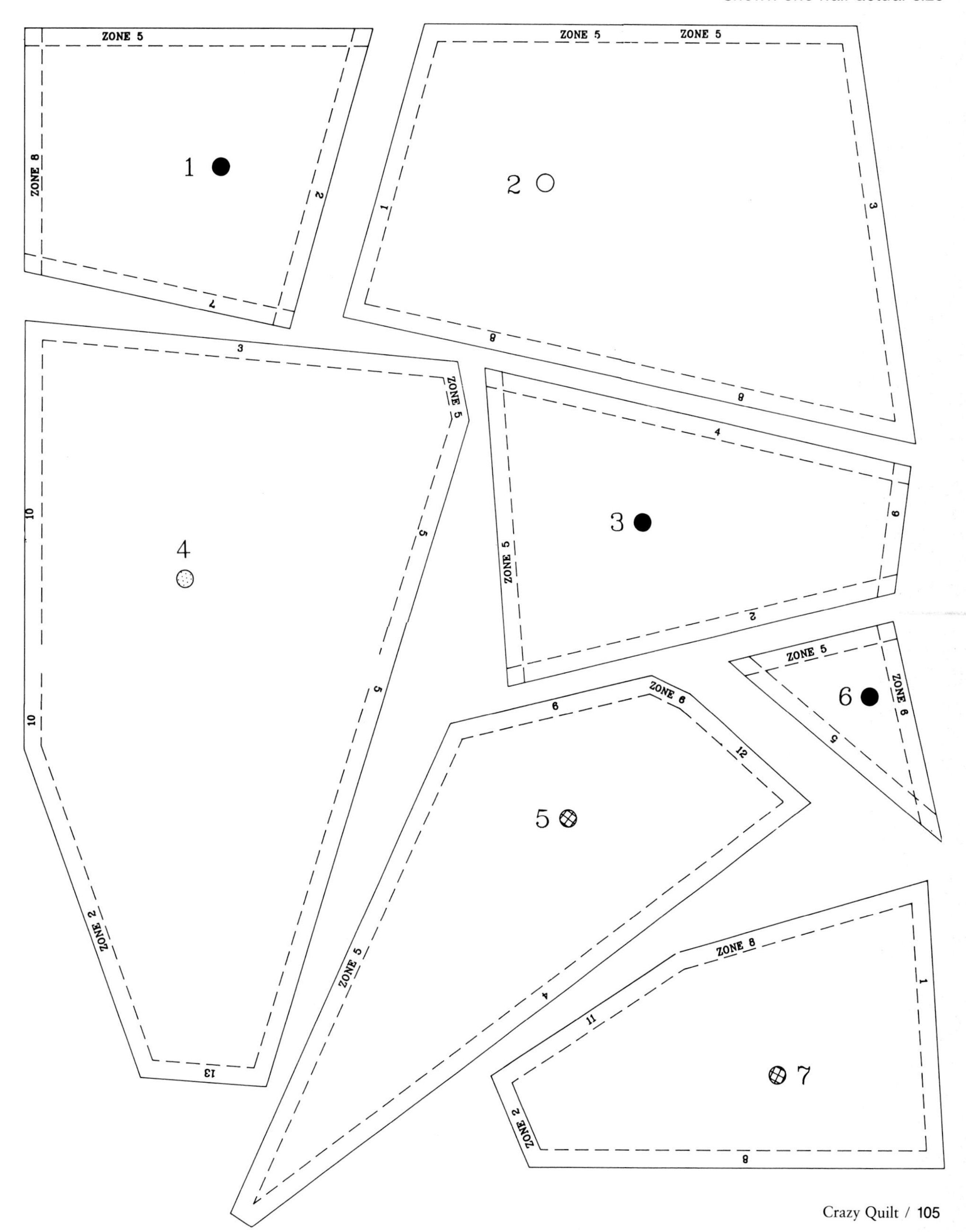

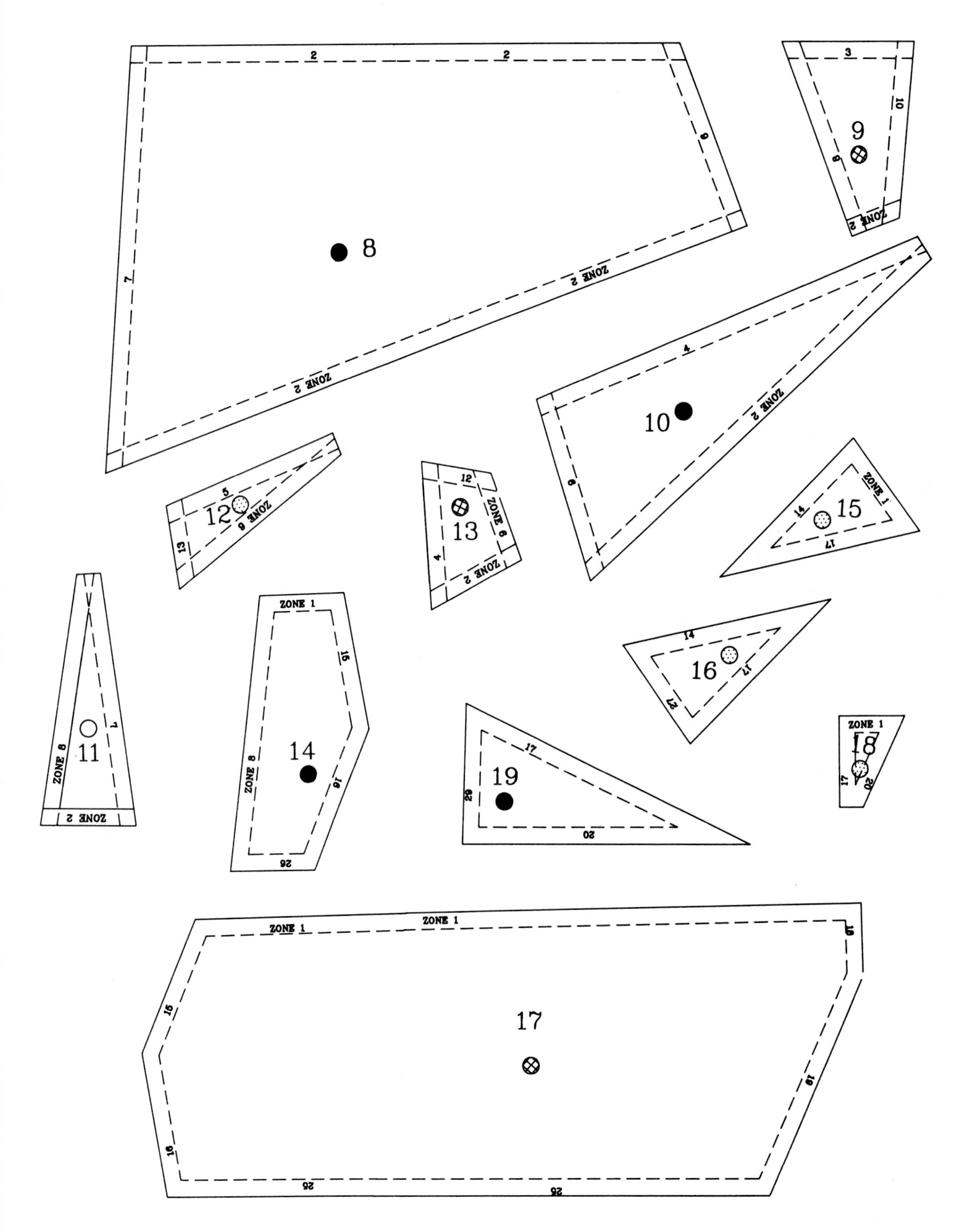

8
9
10
11
12
13
14
15
16
17
18
19
ZONE 1
ZONE 2
ZONE 6
ZONE 8

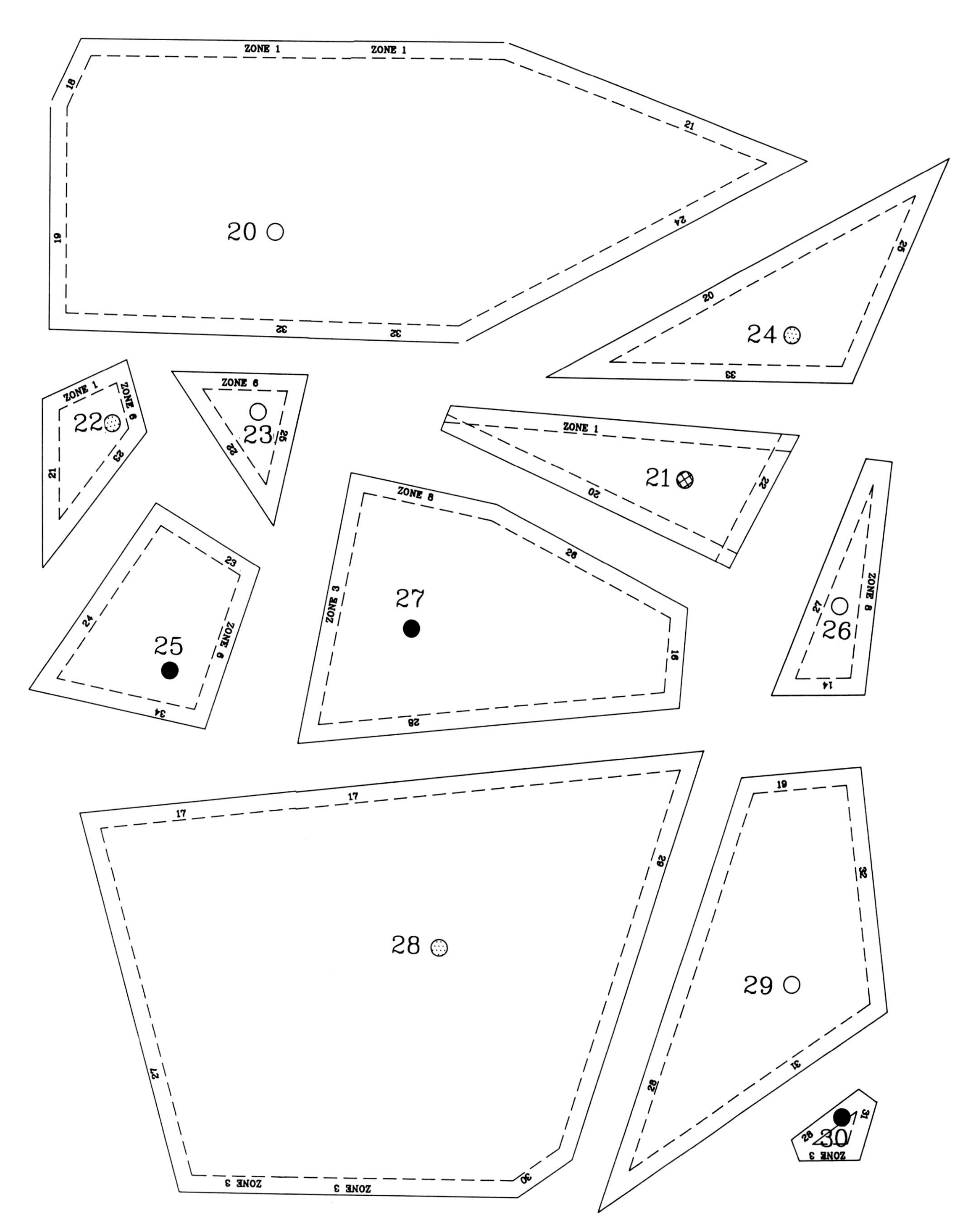
ZONE 1
ZONE 1
18
21
19
20
24
32
32
25
20
24
33
ZONE 1
ZONE 6
22
21
23
ZONE 6
23
22
25
ZONE 1
21
20
22
ZONE 6
26
27
ZONE 3
16
28
23
24
25
ZONE 6
34
ZONE 6
27
26
14
17
17
29
28
27
ZONE 3
ZONE 3
30
19
32
29
31
28
31
28
30
ZONE 3

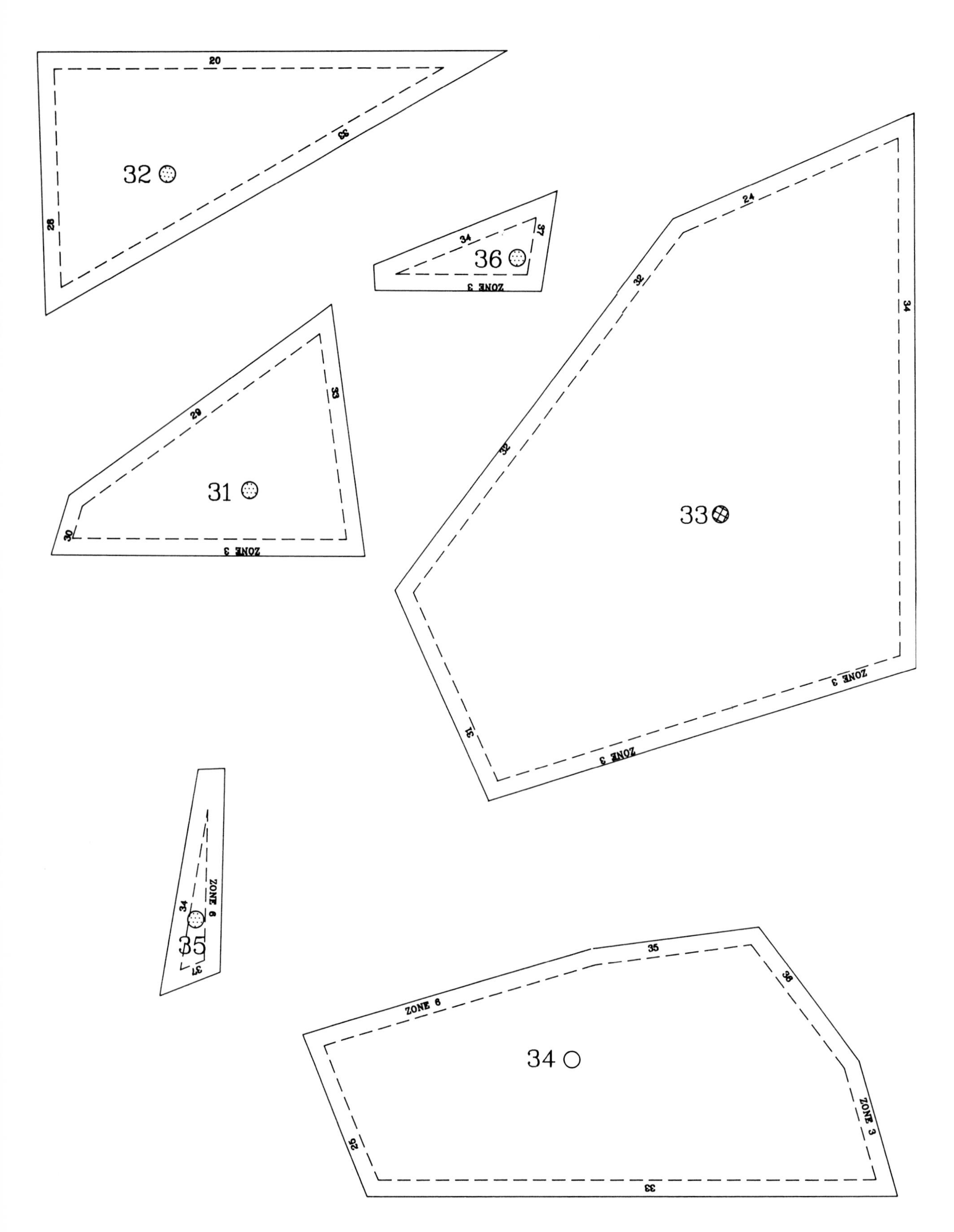
20
33
28
32
34
37
36
ZONE 3
24
32
34
29
33
31
30
ZONE 3
32
33
ZONE 3
31
ZONE 3
ZONE 6
34
35
37
35
36
ZONE 6
34
ZONE 3
25
33

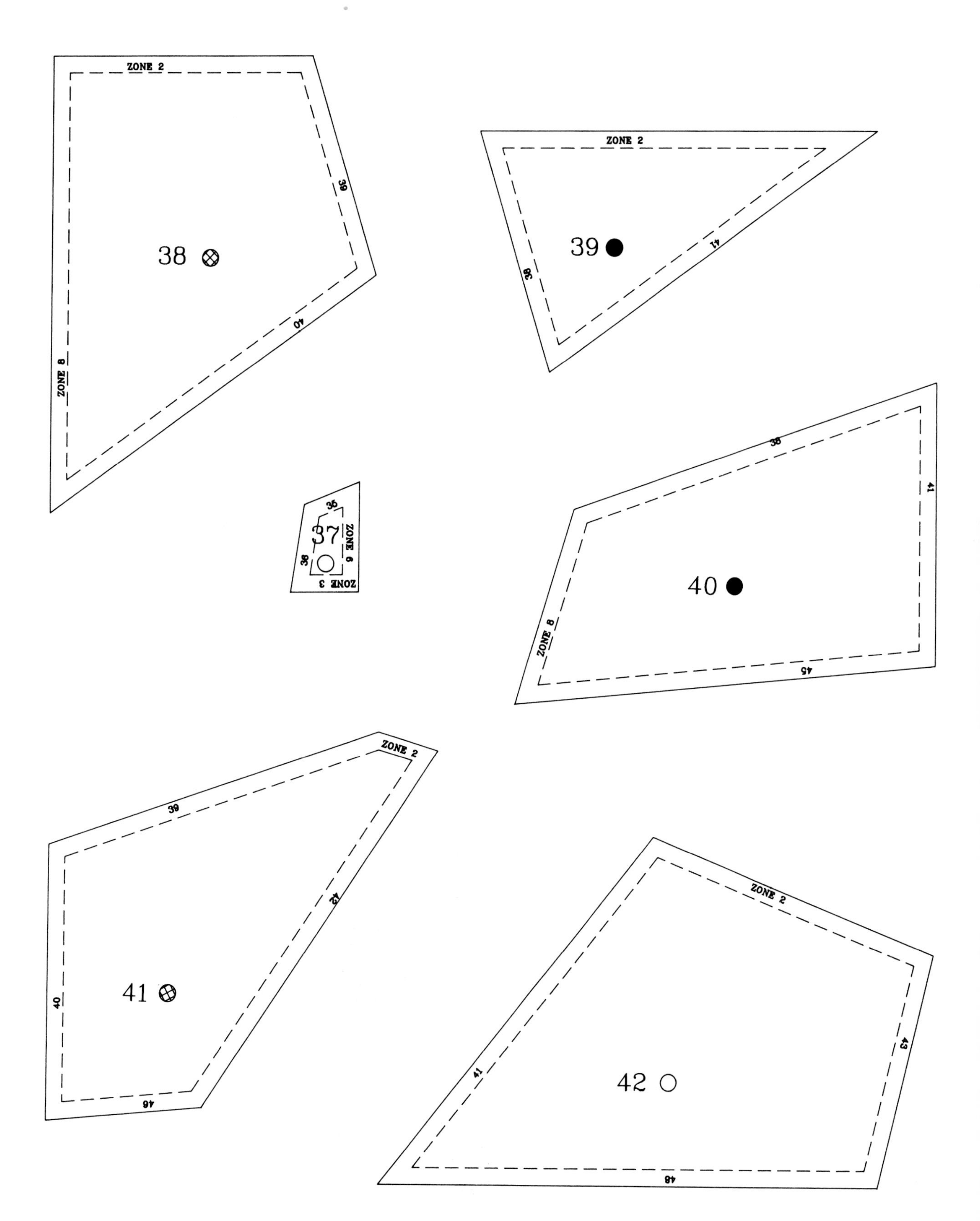
ZONE 2
39
38
40
ZONE 8
ZONE 2
39
38
41
36
37
ZONE 6
38
ZONE 3
38
41
40
ZONE 8
45
ZONE 2
39
42
41
40
46
ZONE 2
43
41
42
48

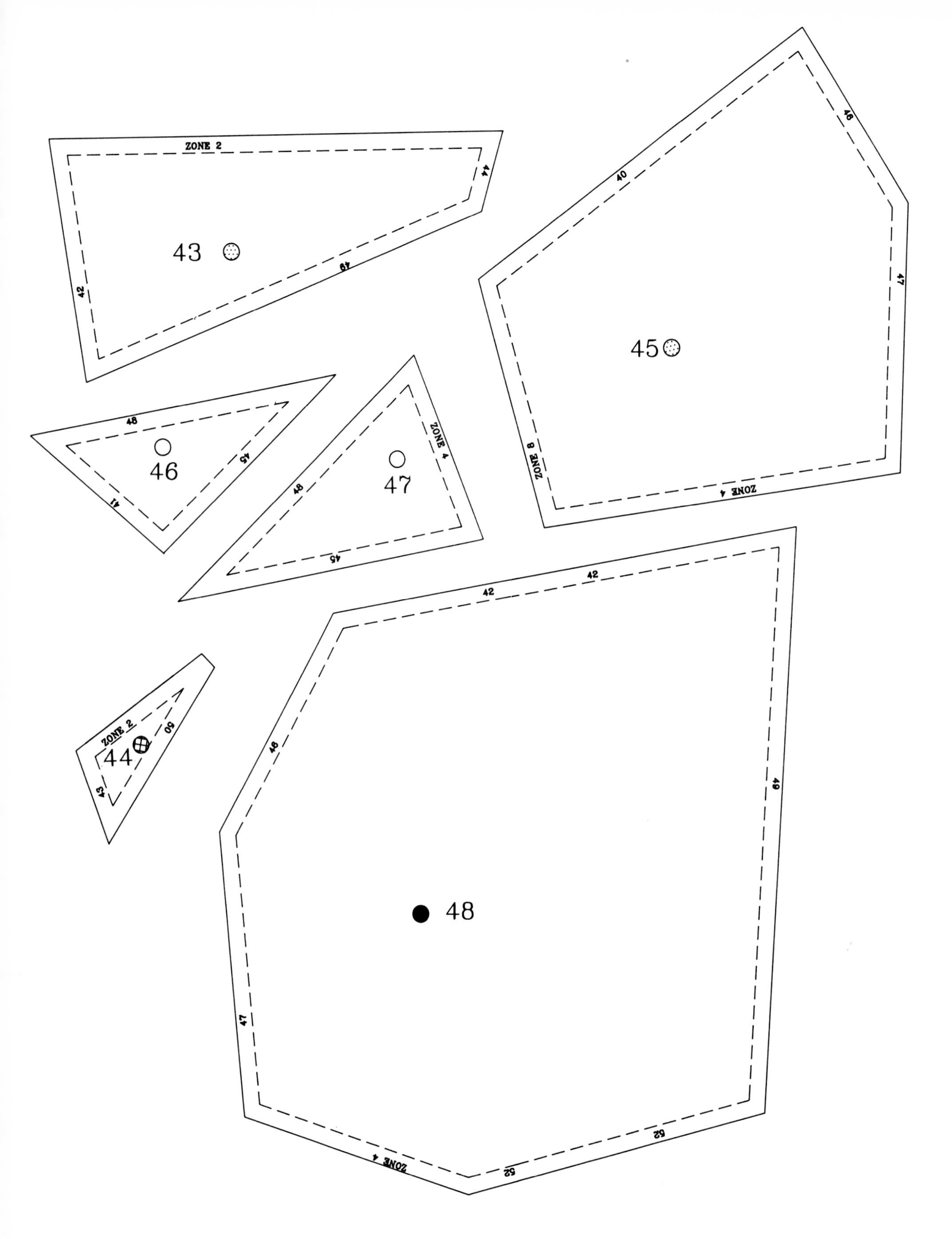
ZONE 2
44
43
49
42
40
46
47
45
ZONE 8
ZONE 4
48
45
46
41
ZONE 4
47
48
45
42
42
ZONE 2
44
60
43
46
49
48
47
52
ZONE 4
52

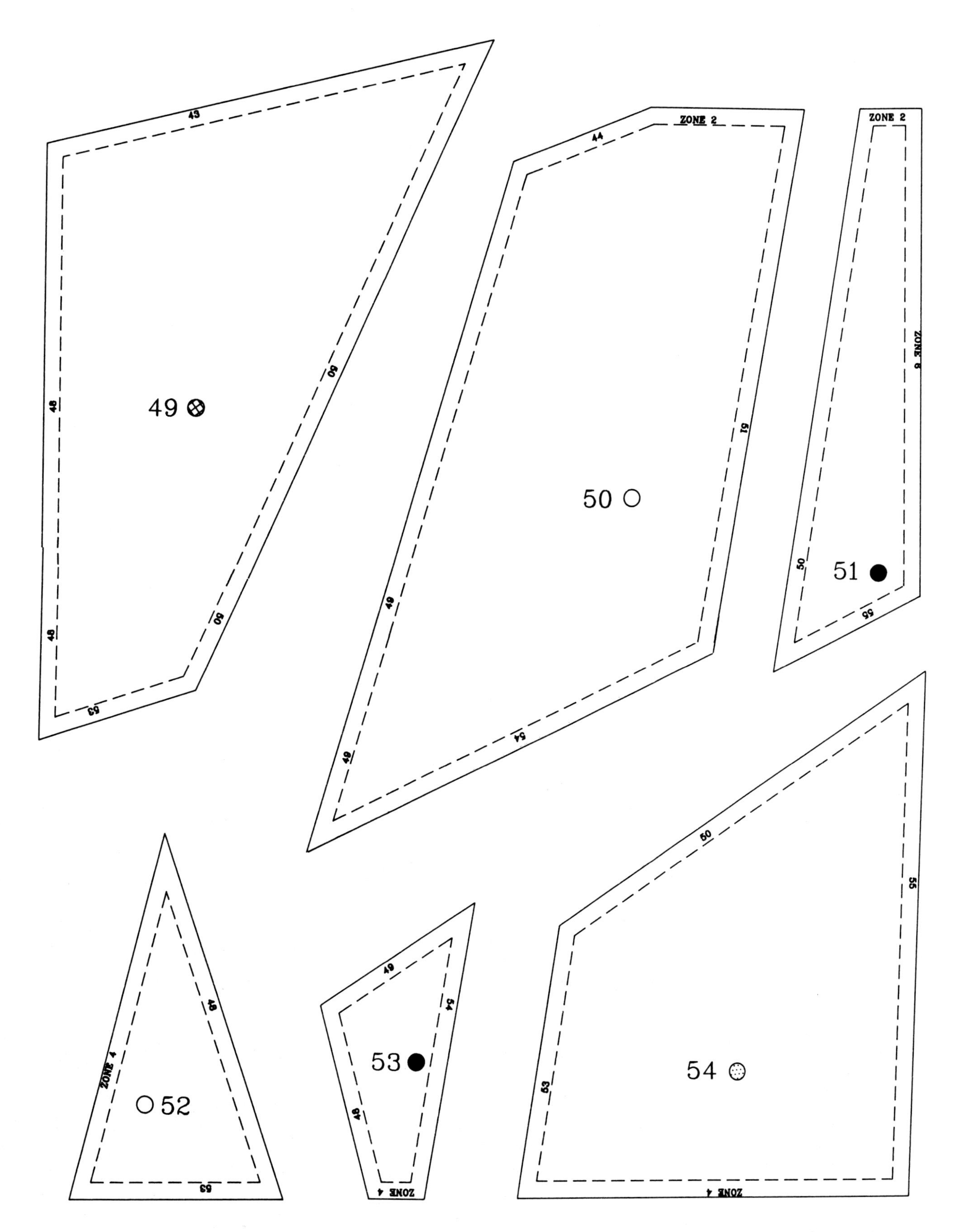
49
50
51
52
53
54
ZONE 2
ZONE 2
ZONE 4
ZONE 4
ZONE 4

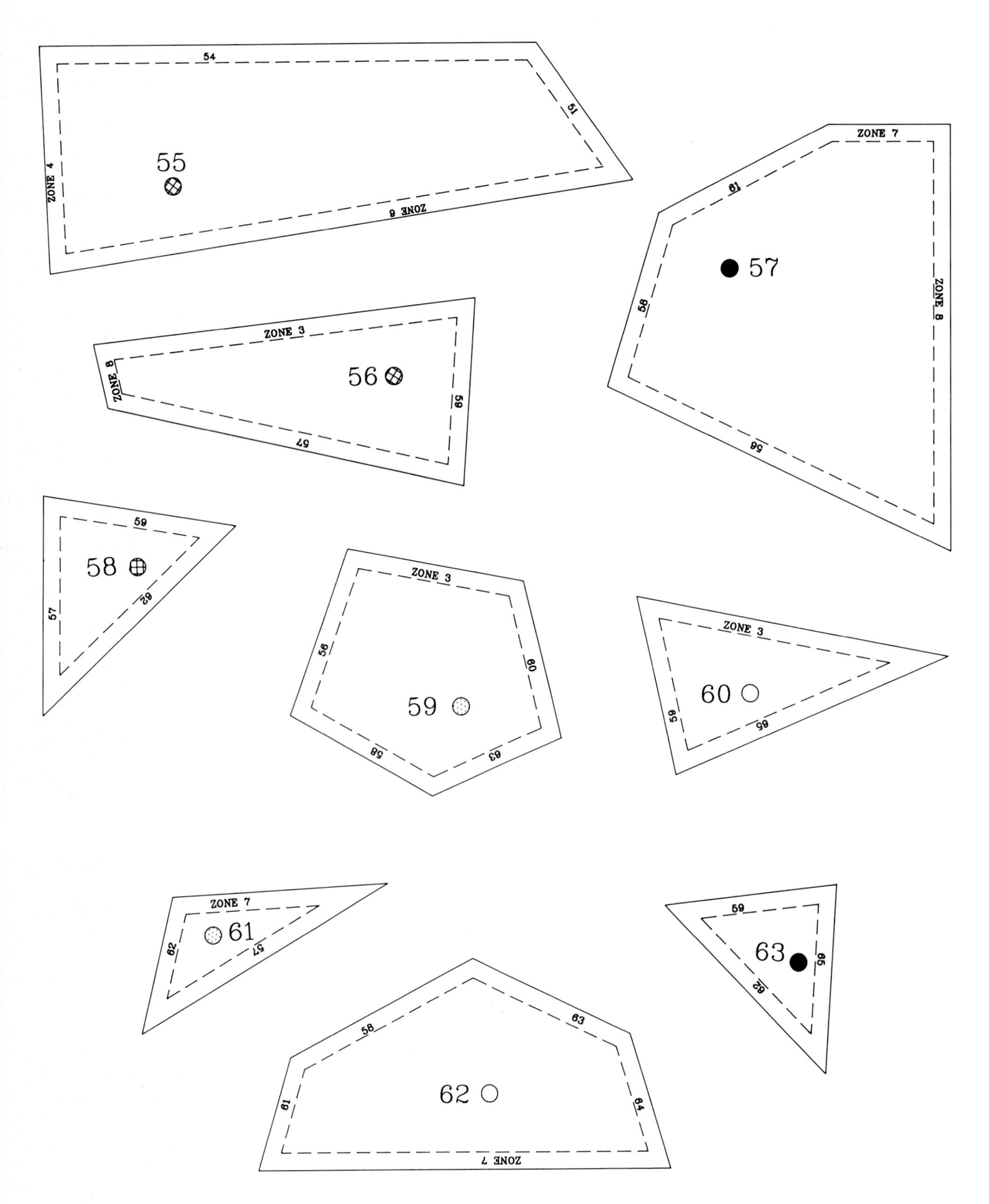
54
51
55
ZONE 4
ZONE 6
ZONE 7
61
57
58
ZONE 8
66
ZONE 3
ZONE 8
56
59
67
59
58
62
57
ZONE 3
56
60
59
58
63
ZONE 3
60
59
65
ZONE 7
61
62
57
59
63
65
62
58
63
62
61
64
ZONE 7

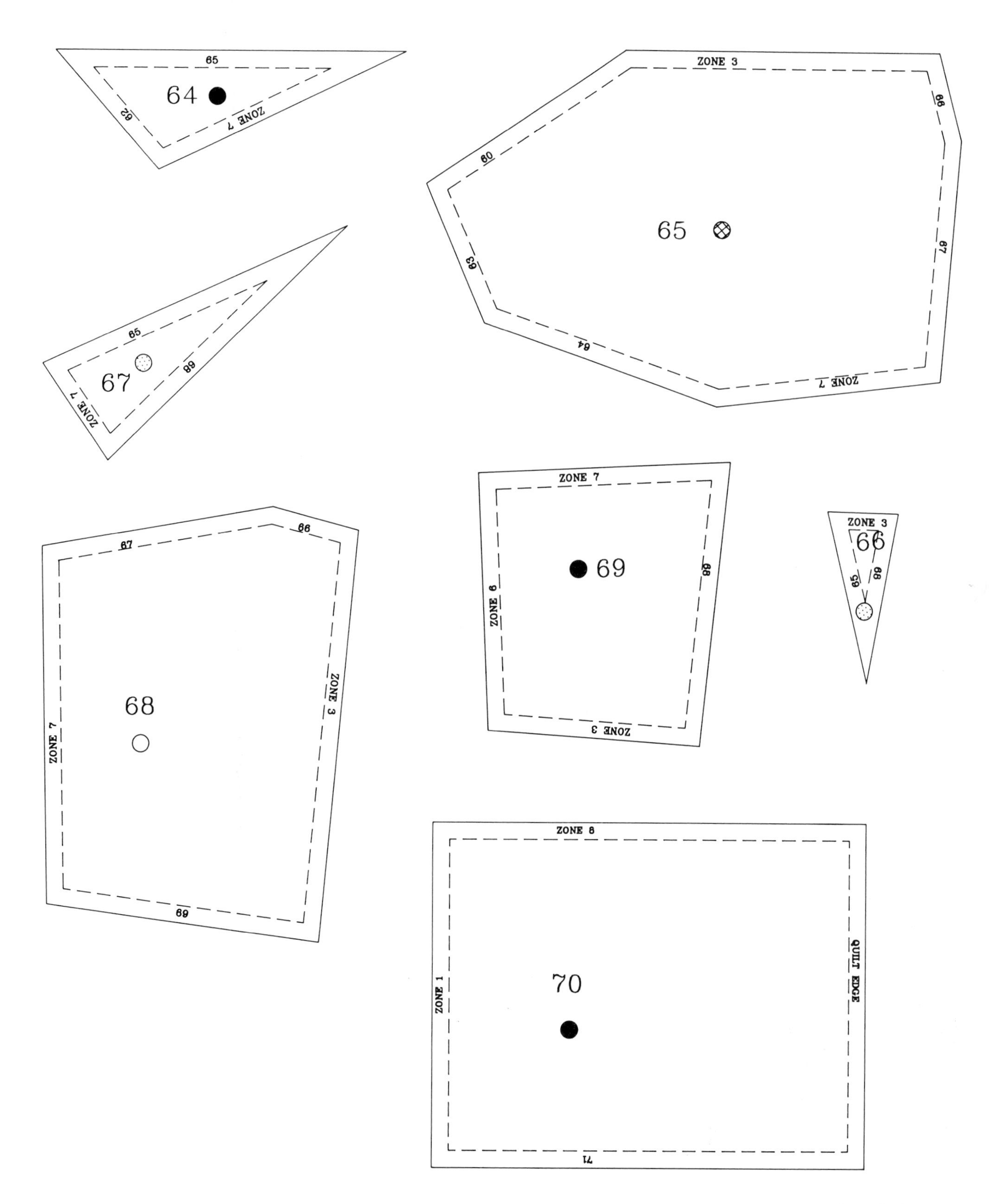

65
64
62
ZONE 7
ZONE 3
66
60
65
67
63
64
ZONE 7
65
68
67
ZONE 7
ZONE 7
ZONE 3
66
65
68
ZONE 6
69
68
67
66
ZONE 7
ZONE 3
68
69
ZONE 3
ZONE 8
ZONE 1
70
QUILT EDGE
71

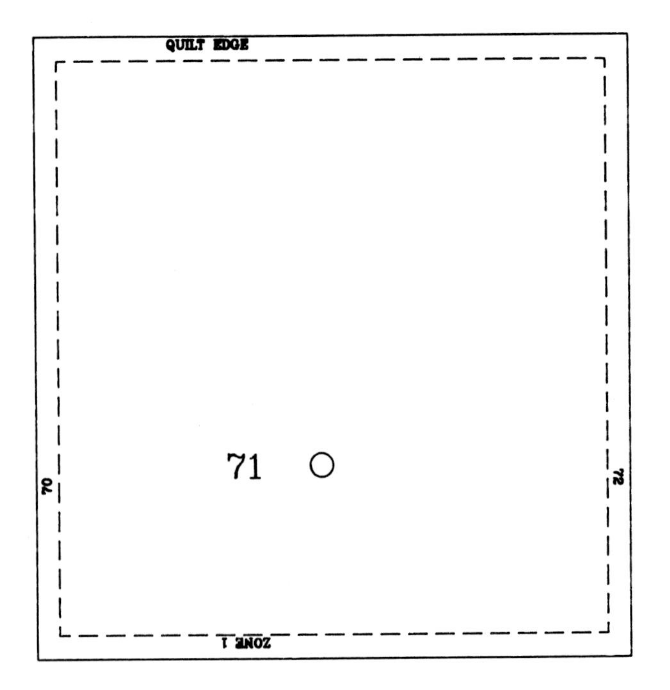
QUILT EDGE
71
70
72
ZONE 1

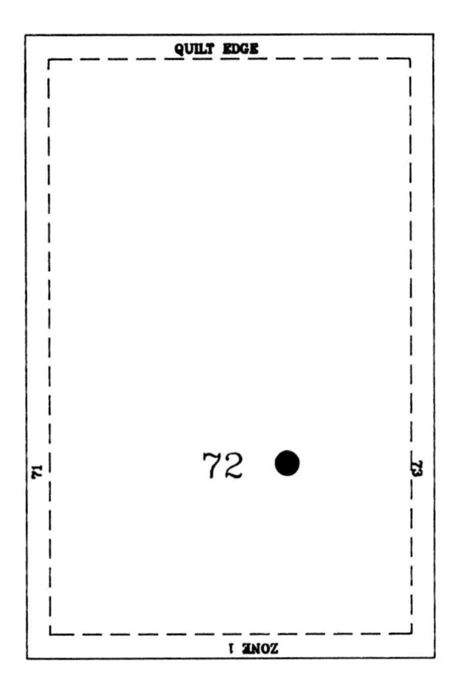
QUILT EDGE
72
71
73
ZONE 1

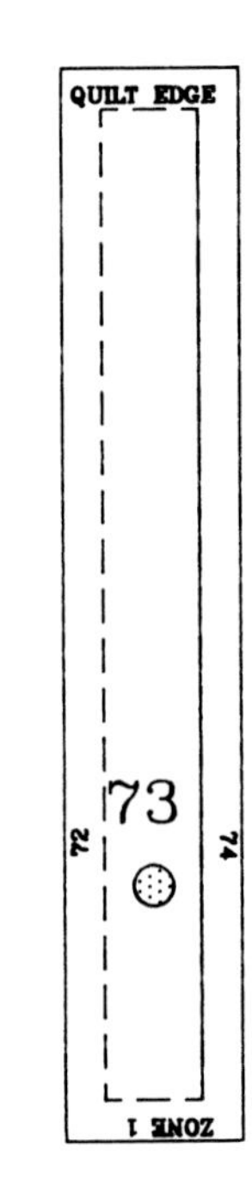
QUILT EDGE
73
72
74
ZONE 1

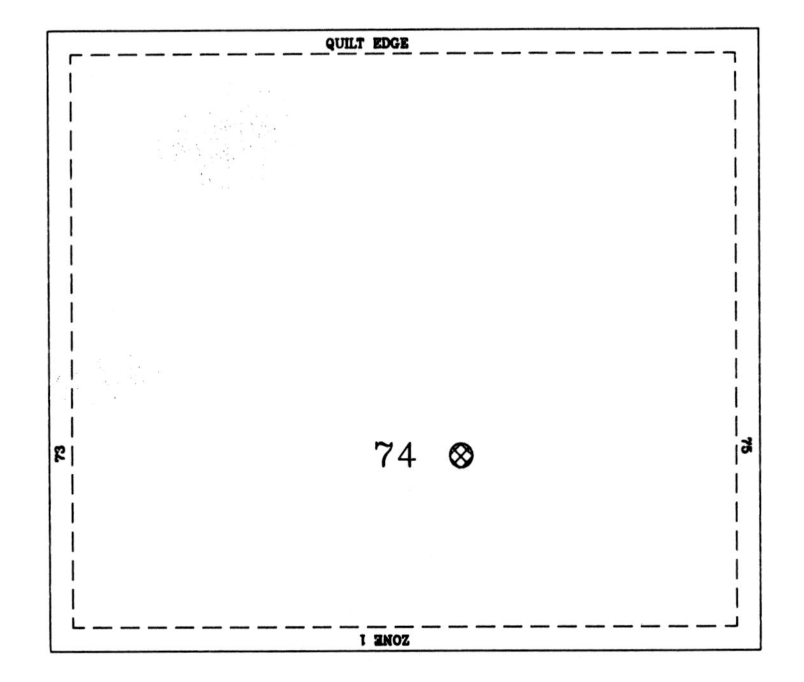
QUILT EDGE
74
73
75
ZONE 1

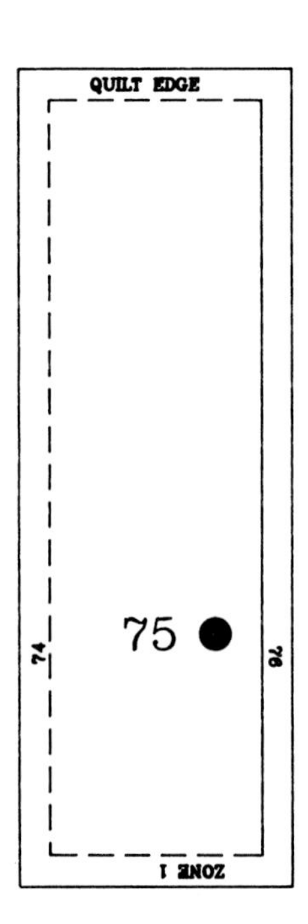
QUILT EDGE
75
74
76
ZONE 1

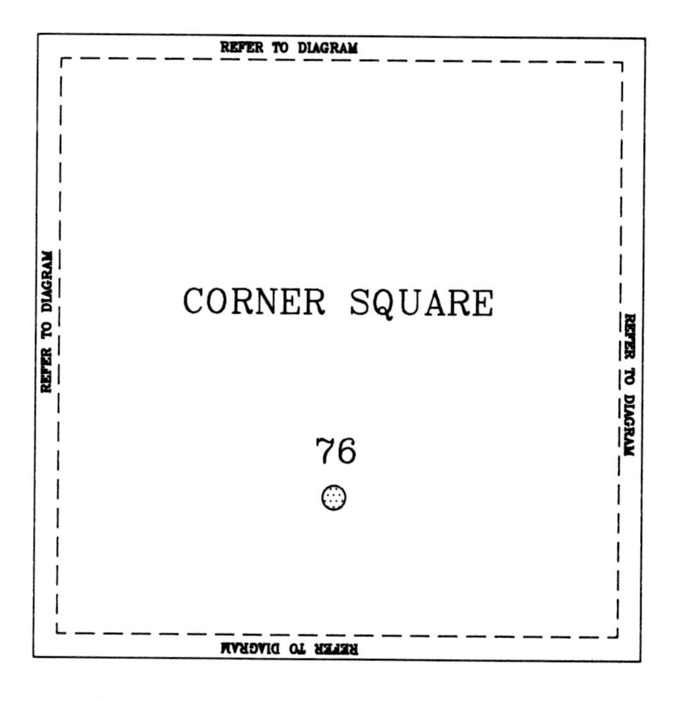
REFER TO DIAGRAM
REFER TO DIAGRAM
CORNER SQUARE
REFER TO DIAGRAM
76
REFER TO DIAGRAM

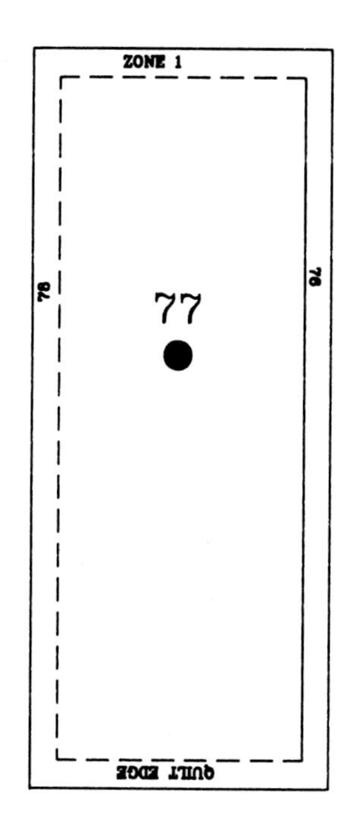
ZONE 1
78
77
76
QUILT EDGE

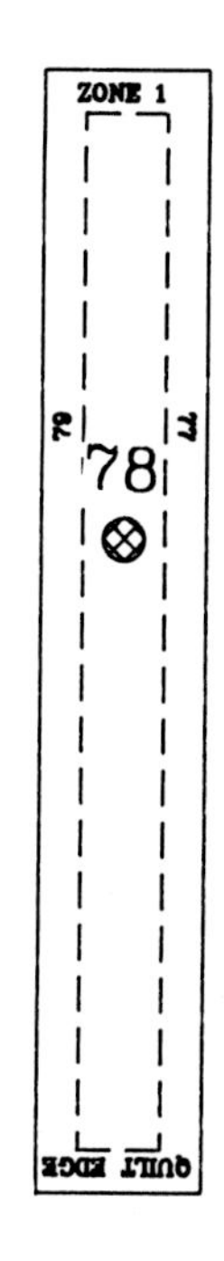
ZONE 1
76
78
77
QUILT EDGE

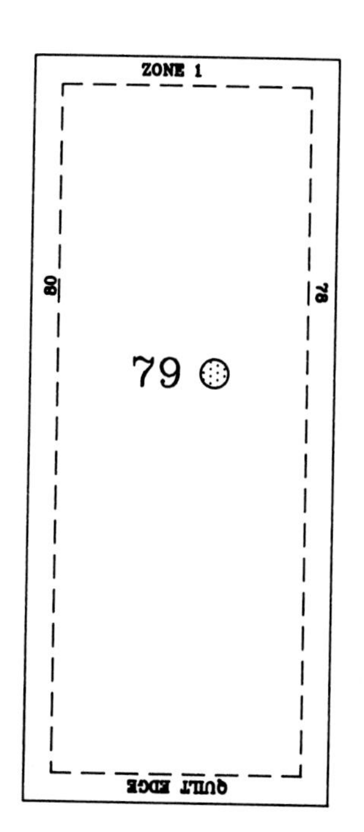
ZONE 1
80
79
78
QUILT EDGE

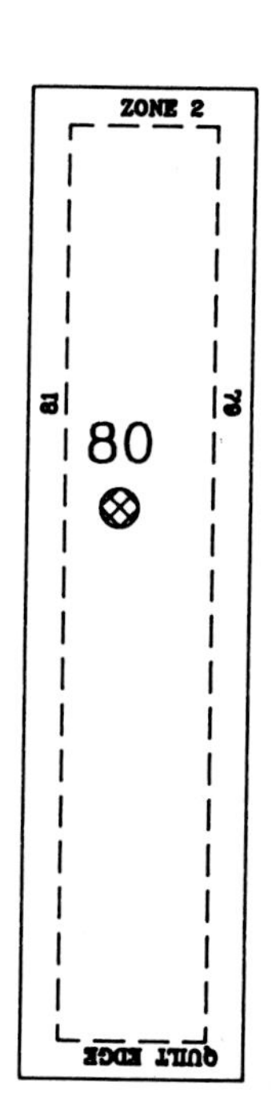
ZONE 2
81
80
79
QUILT EDGE

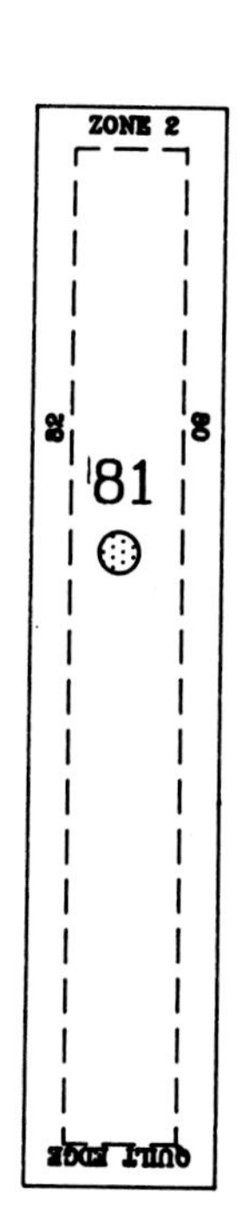
ZONE 2
82
81
80
QUILT EDGE

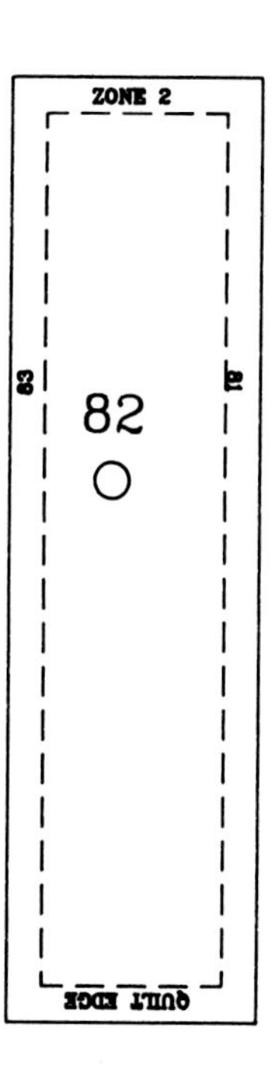
ZONE 2
83
82
81
QUILT EDGE

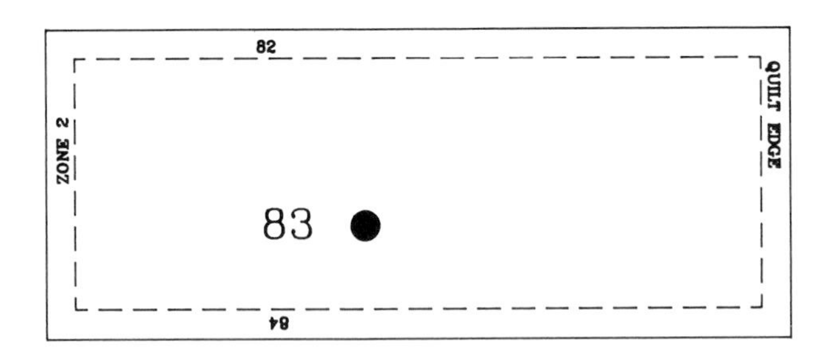
82
ZONE 2
QUILT EDGE
83
84

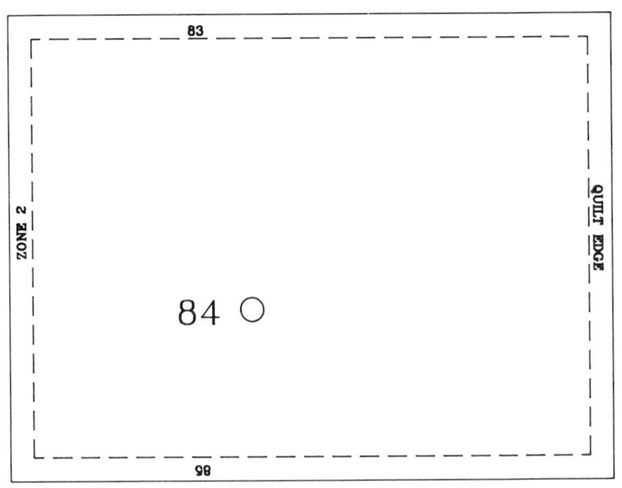
83
ZONE 2
QUILT EDGE
84
85

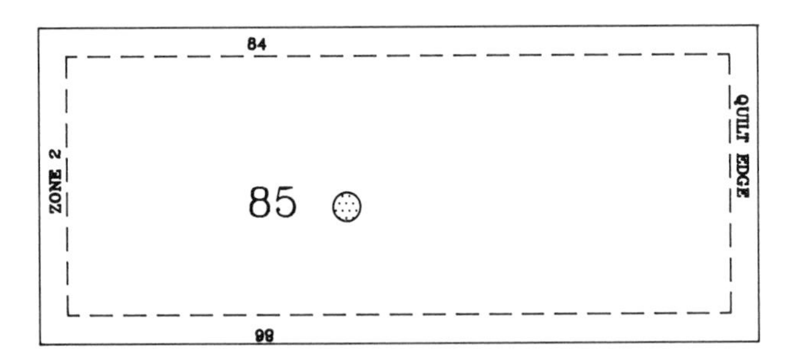
84
ZONE 2
QUILT EDGE
85
86

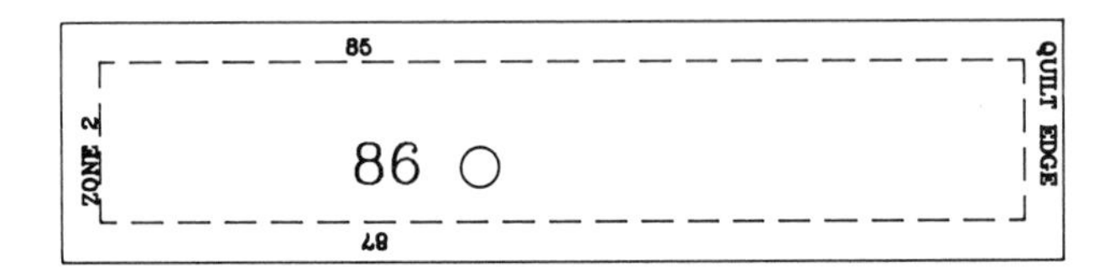
85
ZONE 2
QUILT EDGE
86
87

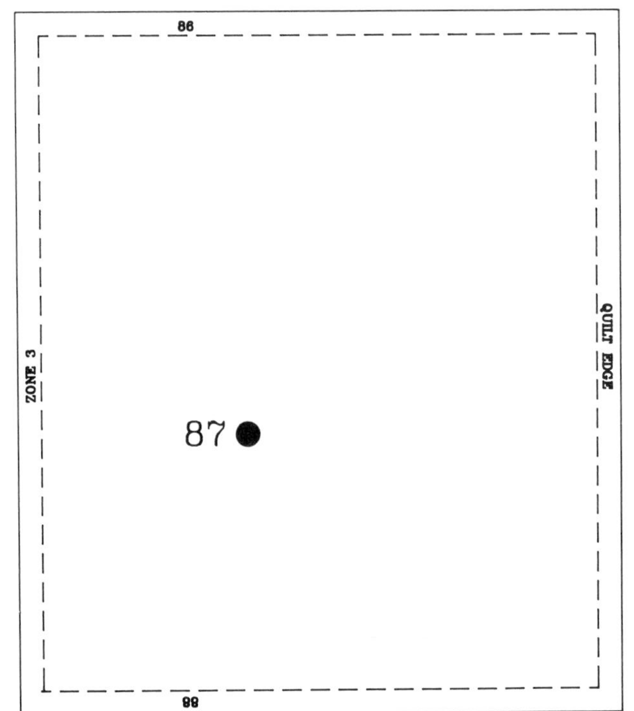
86
ZONE 3
QUILT EDGE
87
88

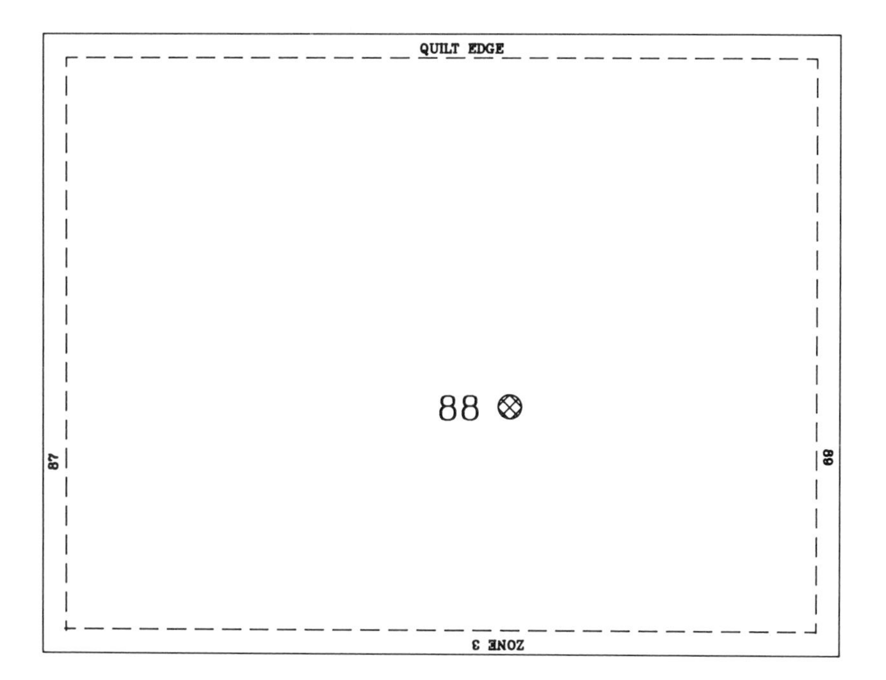
QUILT EDGE
88
87
89
ZONE 3

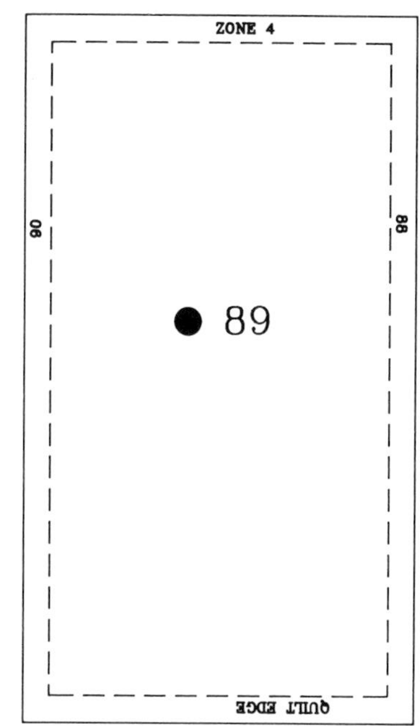
ZONE 4
89
90
88
QUILT EDGE

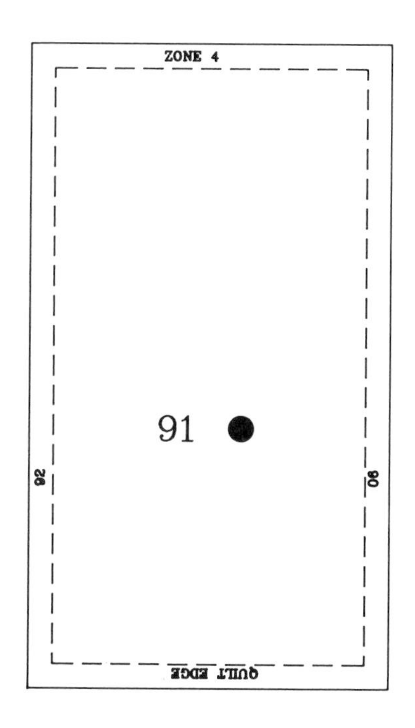
ZONE 4
91
92
90
QUILT EDGE

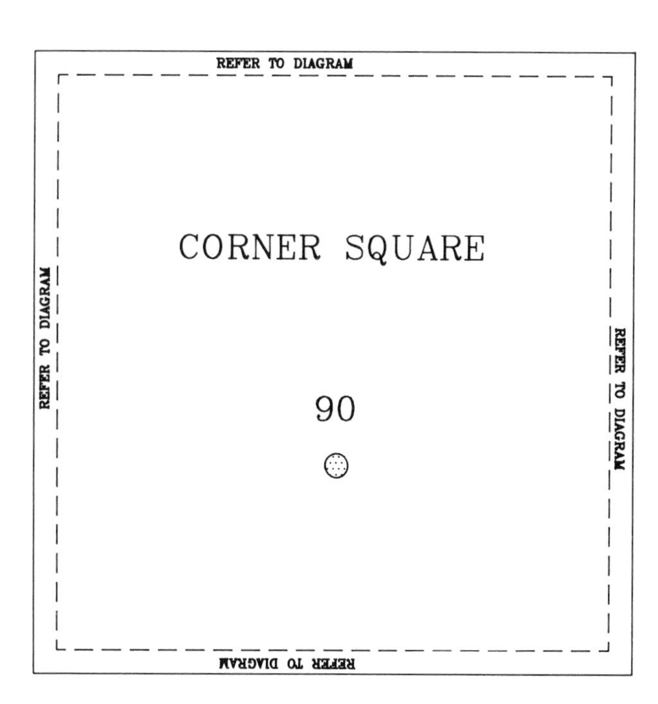
REFER TO DIAGRAM
CORNER SQUARE
90
REFER TO DIAGRAM
REFER TO DIAGRAM
REFER TO DIAGRAM

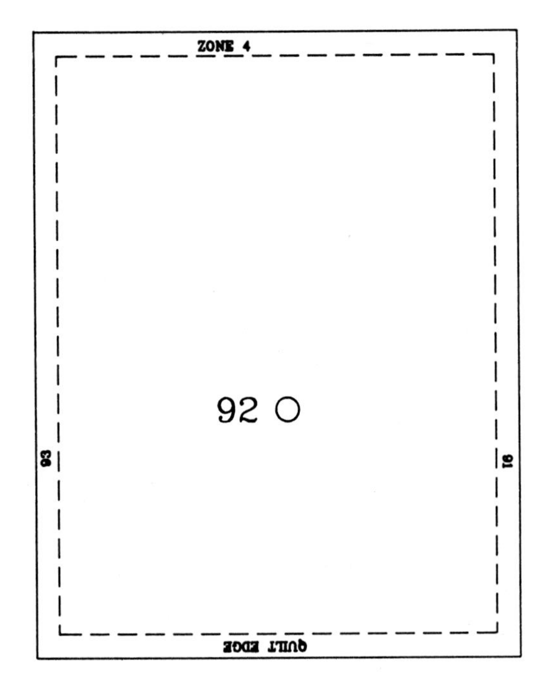
ZONE 4
92
93
91
QUILT EDGE

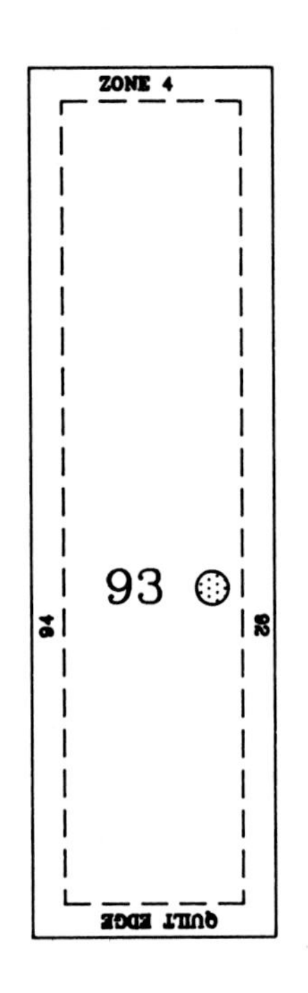
ZONE 4
93
94
92
QUILT EDGE

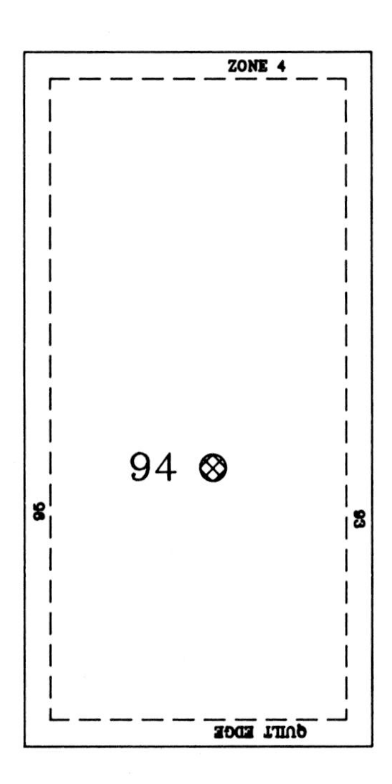
ZONE 4
94
95
93
QUILT EDGE

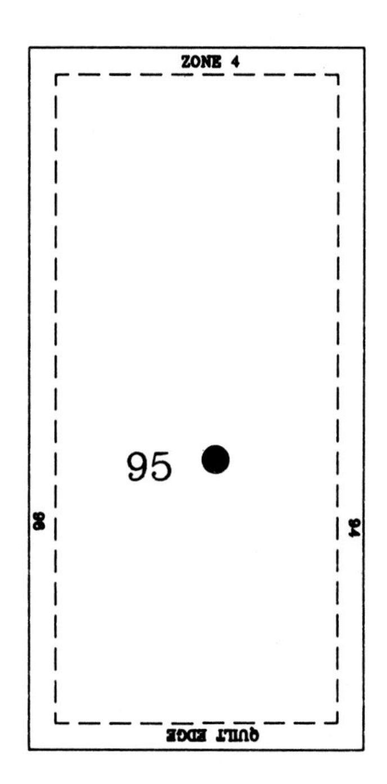
ZONE 4
95
96
94
QUILT EDGE

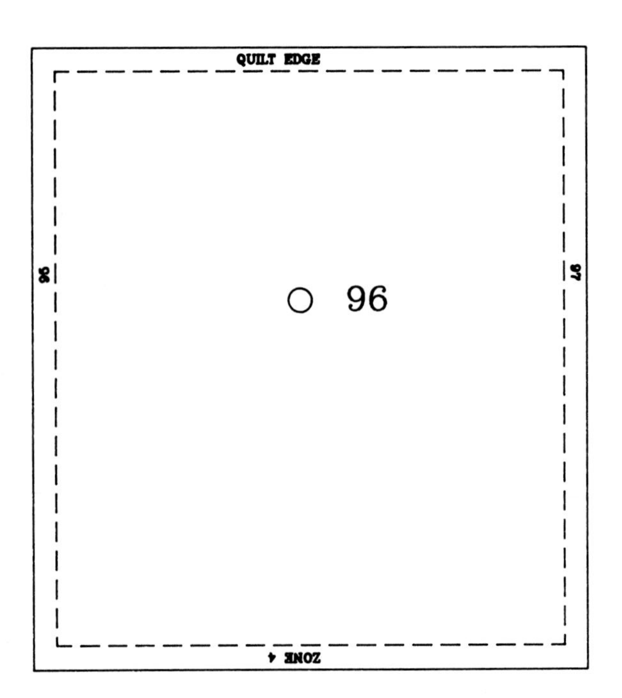
QUILT EDGE
96
95
97
ZONE 4

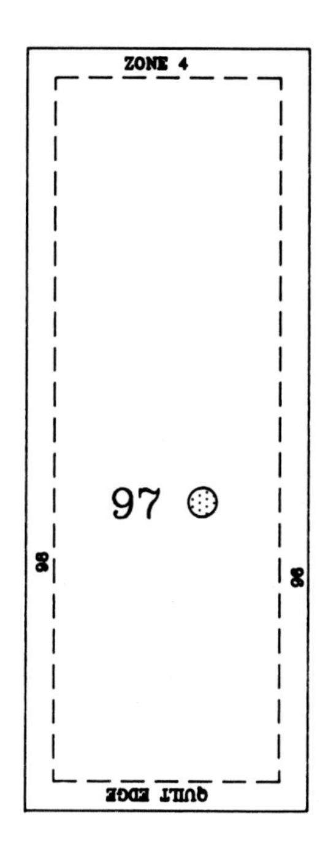
ZONE 4
97
96
98
QUILT EDGE
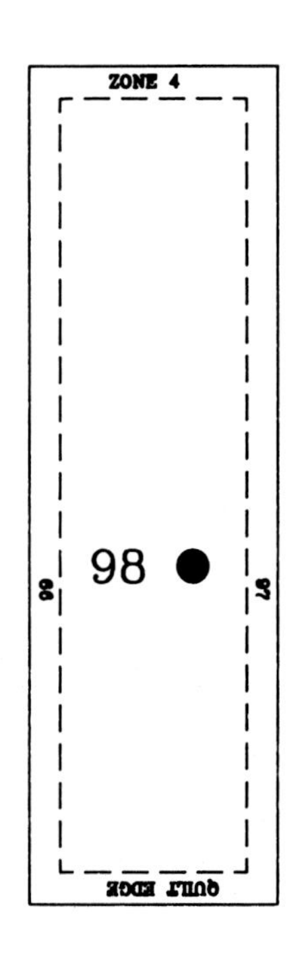
ZONE 4
98
99
97
QUILT EDGE
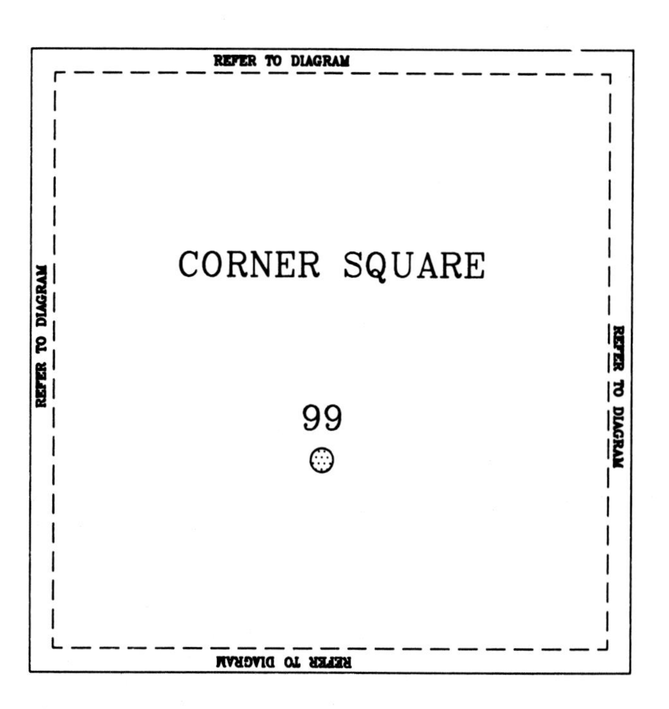
REFER TO DIAGRAM
CORNER SQUARE
99
REFER TO DIAGRAM
REFER TO DIAGRAM
REFER TO DIAGRAM
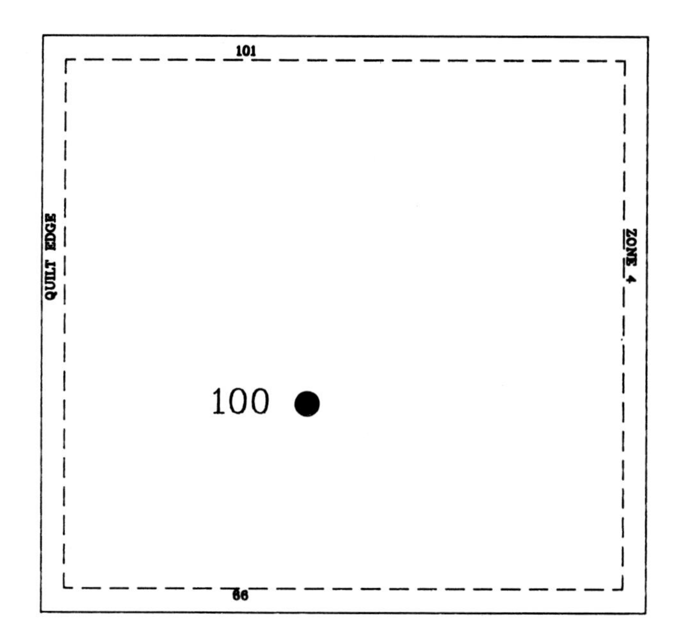
101
QUILT EDGE
ZONE 4
100
99
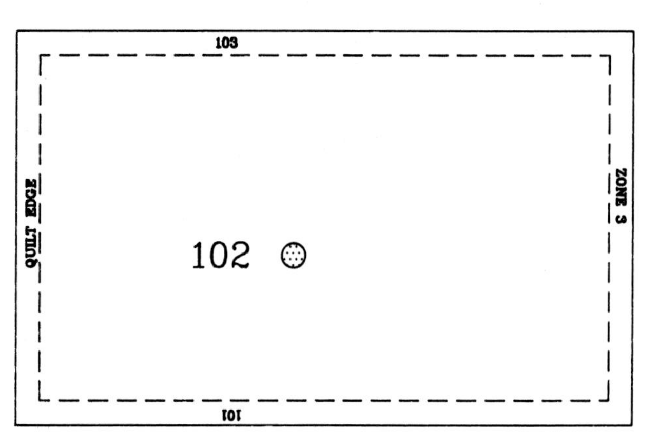
103
QUILT EDGE
102
ZONE 3
101
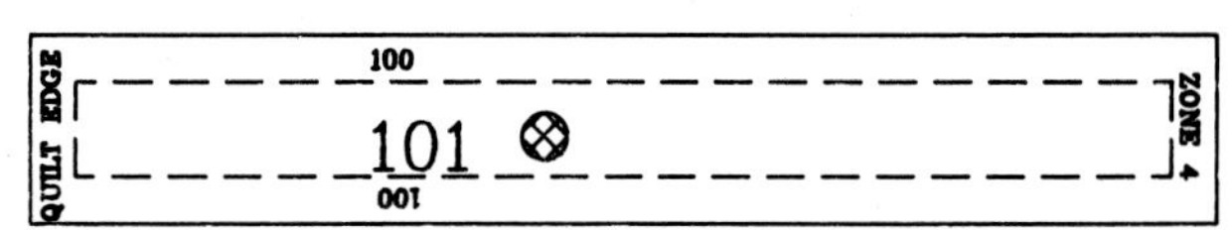
100
QUILT EDGE
101
ZONE 4
100

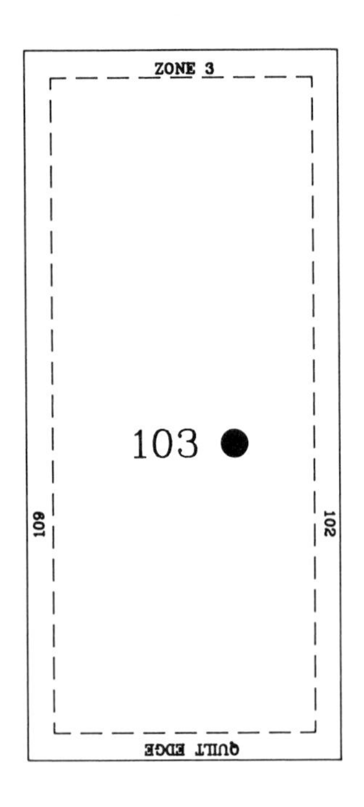
ZONE 3
103
109
102
QUILT EDGE

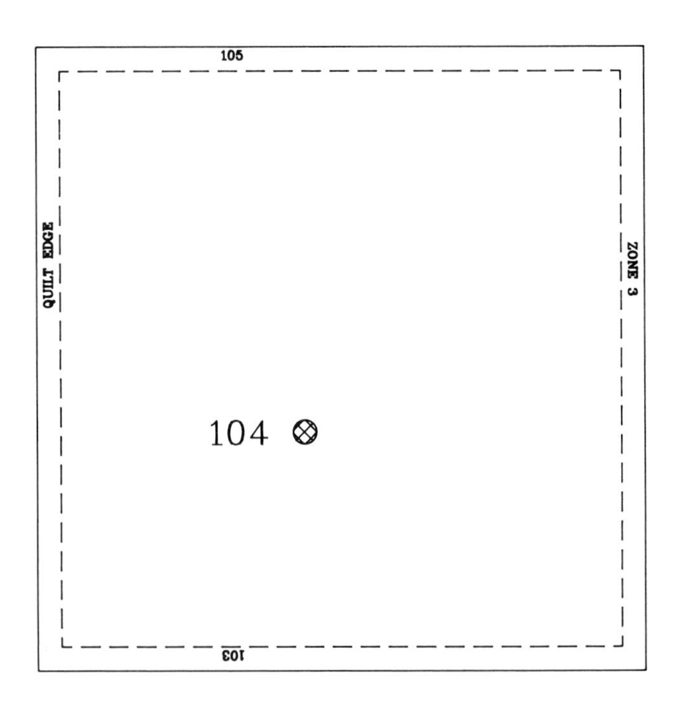
105
QUILT EDGE
ZONE 3
104
103

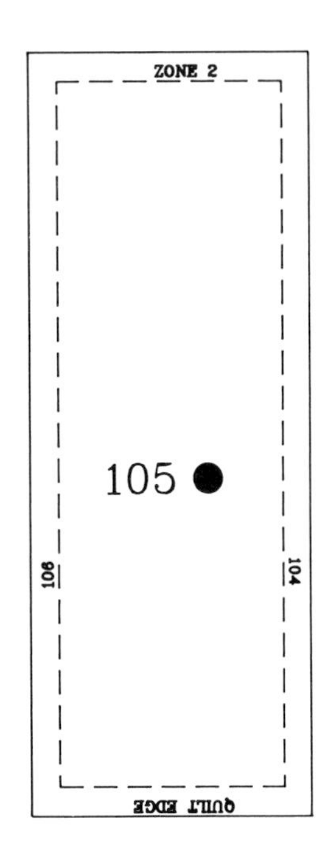
ZONE 2
105
106
104
QUILT EDGE

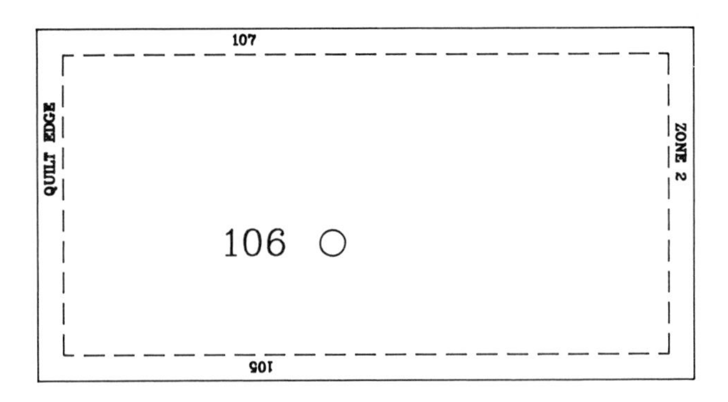
107
QUILT EDGE
ZONE 2
106
105

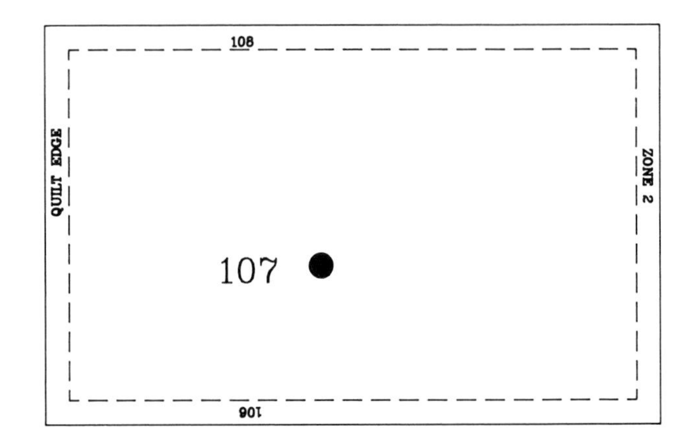
108
QUILT EDGE
ZONE 2
107
106

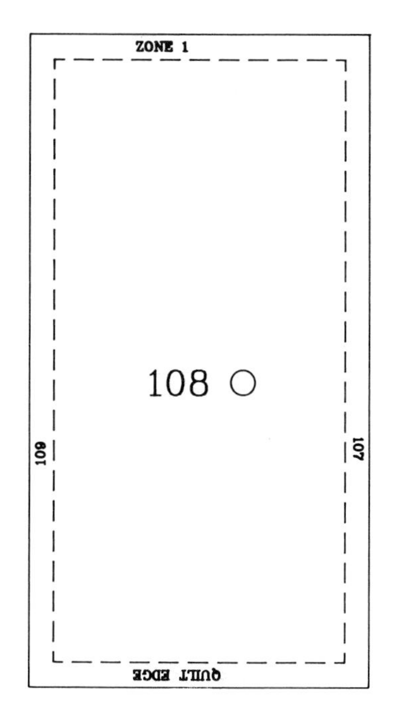
ZONE 1
108
109
107
QUILT EDGE

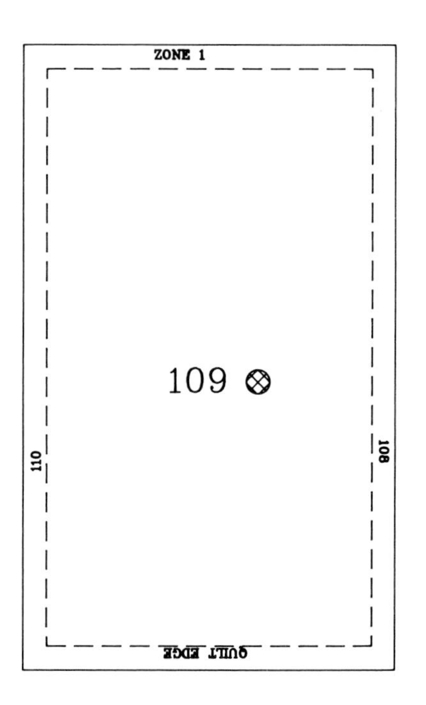
ZONE 1
109
110
108
QUILT EDGE

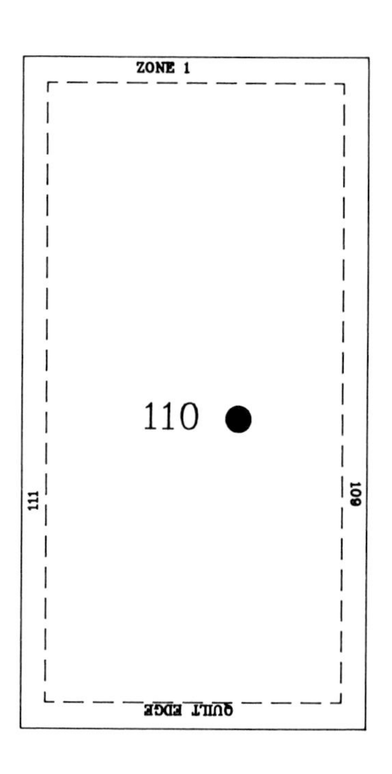
ZONE 1
110
111
109
QUILT EDGE

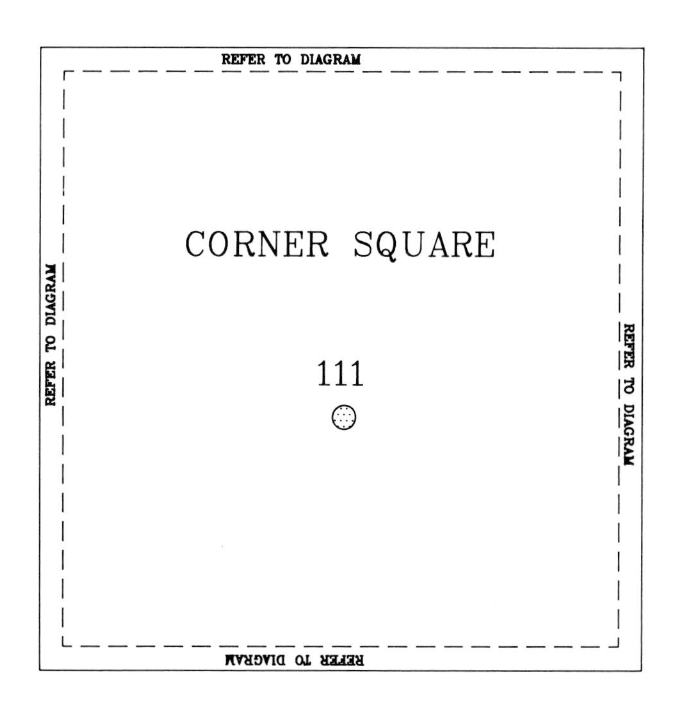
REFER TO DIAGRAM
CORNER SQUARE
111
REFER TO DIAGRAM
REFER TO DIAGRAM
REFER TO DIAGRAM

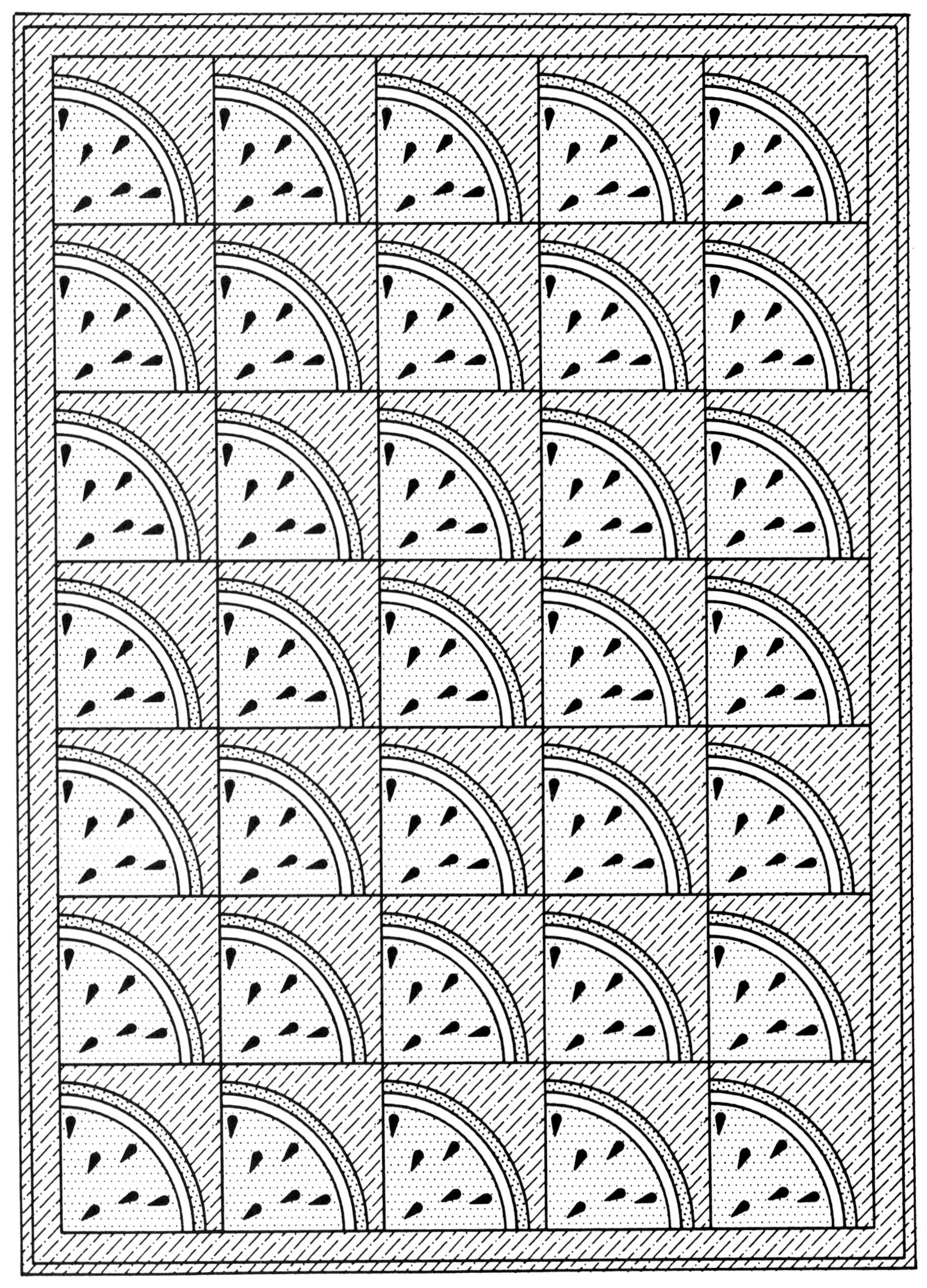

Finished quilt, 38" by 52"

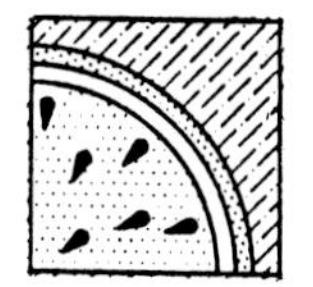

10. Watermelons

The watermelon is summer's most distinctive fruit. It suggests picnics, holidays, and family gatherings. It has remarkable visual appeal. It cuts cleanly into a circle, semicircle, or wedge. Each piece has neatly arranged dark seeds set into the redness of the melon and protected by a mottled green rind.

With these qualities and associations it is not surprising that watermelons show up in folk art, paintings, and carvings. But they appear only rarely in quilts, and then either as an embroidered image lost on the surface of a crazy quilt, or deformed into a triangular piecework shape to fit into the overall pattern.

This simple design sets a quarter circle of plain red cloth—calicoes or prints would diminish the effect—against a printed green background. Recessed beyond the face of the melon are the seeds, made of dark printed material and done in reverse appliqué. Two nested arcs, one white and one plain green, complete the unit. It is important that the fabrics on the cut face of the melon are plain and those beyond it are prints. This differentiates between the two surfaces, pushes the printed elements back from the visual surface, and makes the design sharper and crisper.

Like most asymmetric units in other quilt designs, the melon blocks could be combined in several different ways. The blocks could be assembled to make full-circle melons or half-circle melons. The version illustrated here is less representational. All the squares have the same orientation, and the quarter-circle melons make an arrangement reminiscent of fan quilts of the Victorian period.

Instructions

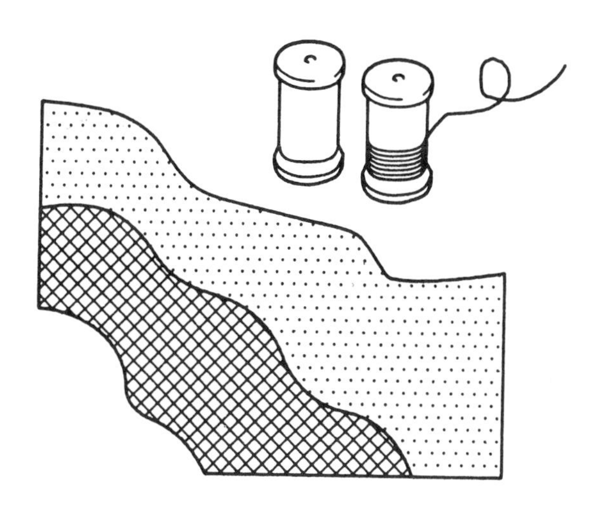

1. Materials:

   1 yard of solid red (watermelon centers)
   1 yard black print (seeds)
   ½ yard each of solid white and light green (inner and outer rinds)
   3 yards green print (skin and backing)
   Cotton batting
   White and green thread
   5 yards of black piping

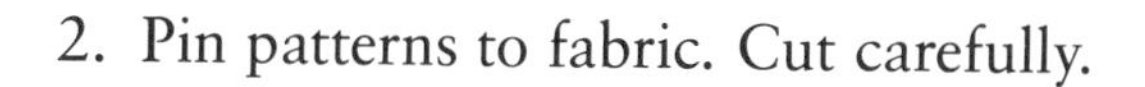

2. Pin patterns to fabric. Cut carefully.

   From the green print, cut two border strips, 2″ wide and 36″ long. Cut two more, 2″ wide and 50″ long.

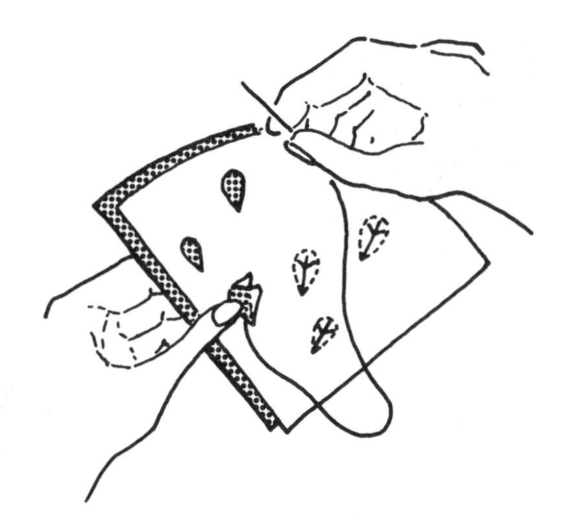

3. The watermelon seeds are reverse appliqué. Pin the red cloth over the black print. Cut a hole for each seed as shown on the pattern. Stitch along the seam line.

4. Sew the white and green arcs to the red and black quarter-circles.

   Sew the green print skin to the light green outer rind. Clip seams as required.

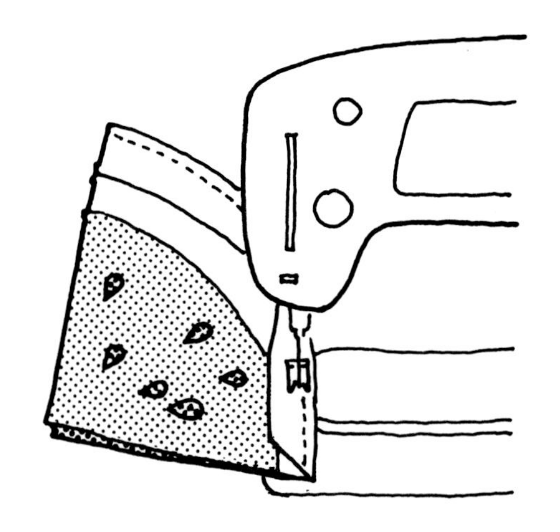

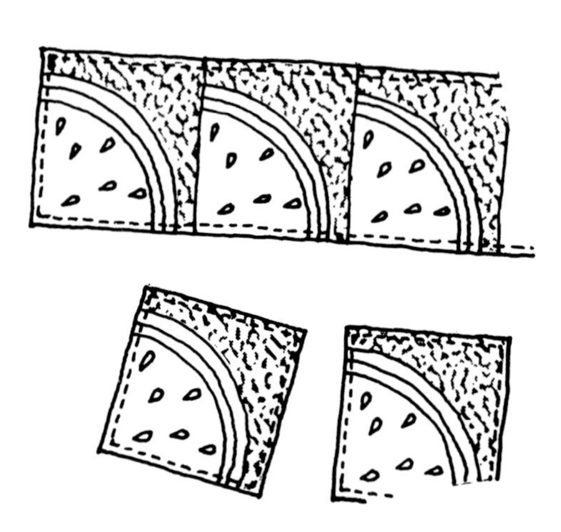

5. Sew the watermelon blocks into rows. Sew the rows together, matching all seams carefully.

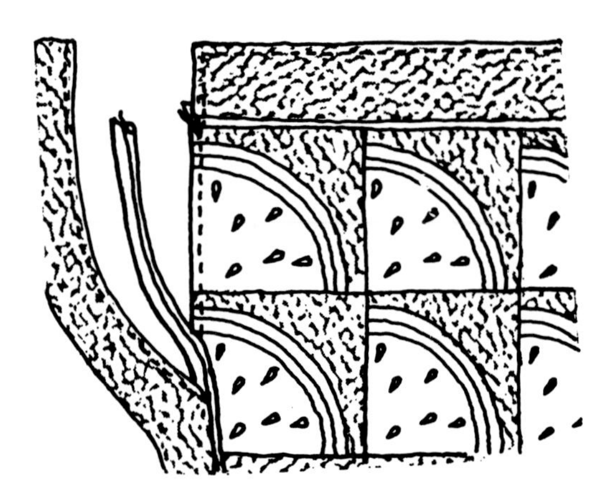

6. Pin the piping to the edges of the watermelon assembly. Sew the border strips and piping to the quilt top.

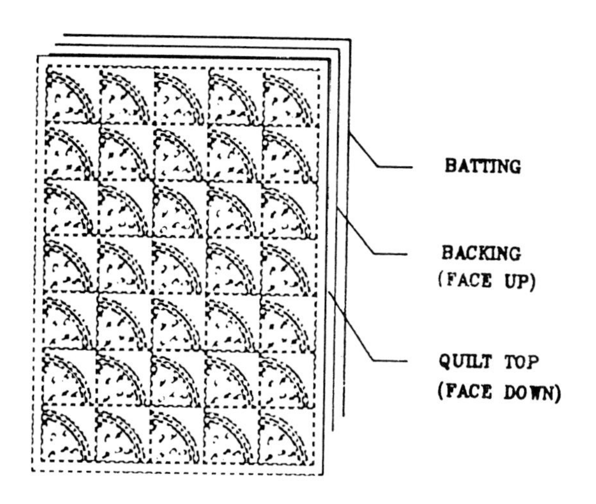

7. Lay the quilt batting on a large table or work area. Lay the backing, face up, on top of the batting. Lay the quilt top, face down, on the backing. Pin through all three layers. Machine stitch along the edge of the quilt top, leaving an 8″ gap at the end. Trim close to the seam.

8. Turn the quilt by pulling it through the 8″ gap. Sew the gap closed by hand.

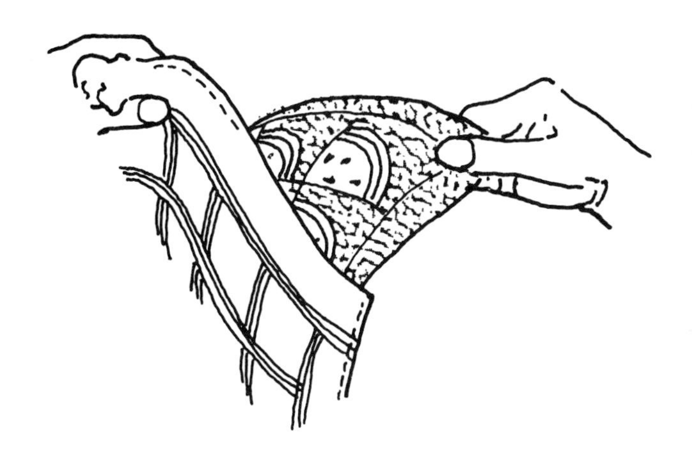

9. For quilting the three layers together, hand stitch a quarter circle that follows the edges of the red watermelon center to the light green outer rind. Then stitch along the edges of the skin element. Finally, sew diagonal lines, 1″ apart, through the green skin as shown.

Pattern Pieces

Shown one-half actual size

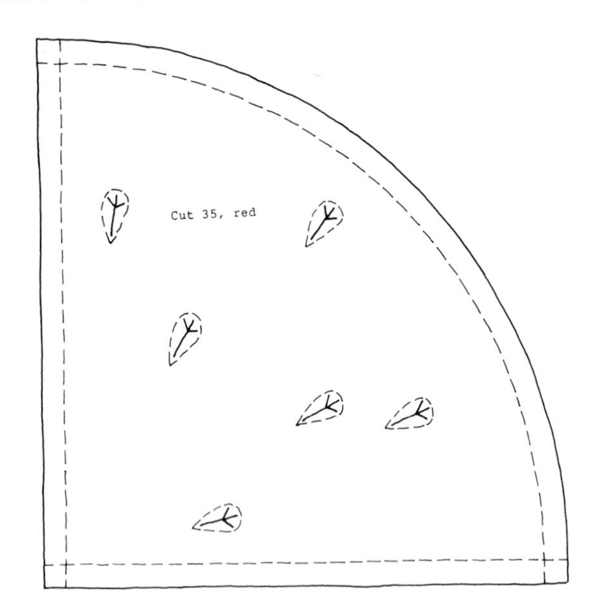

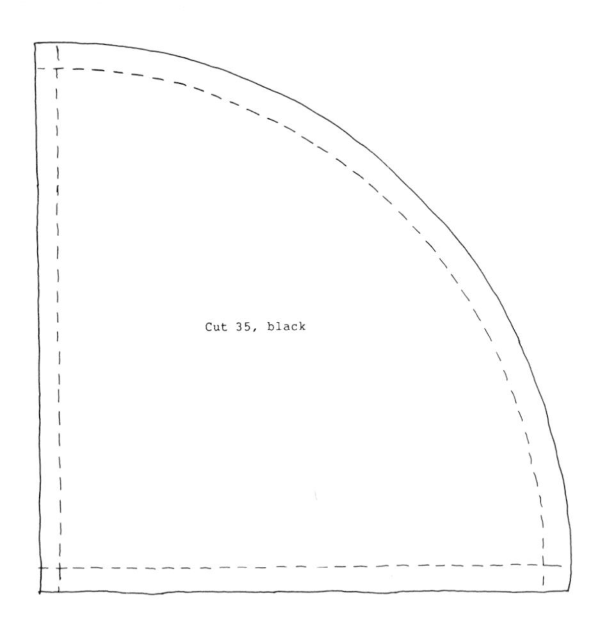

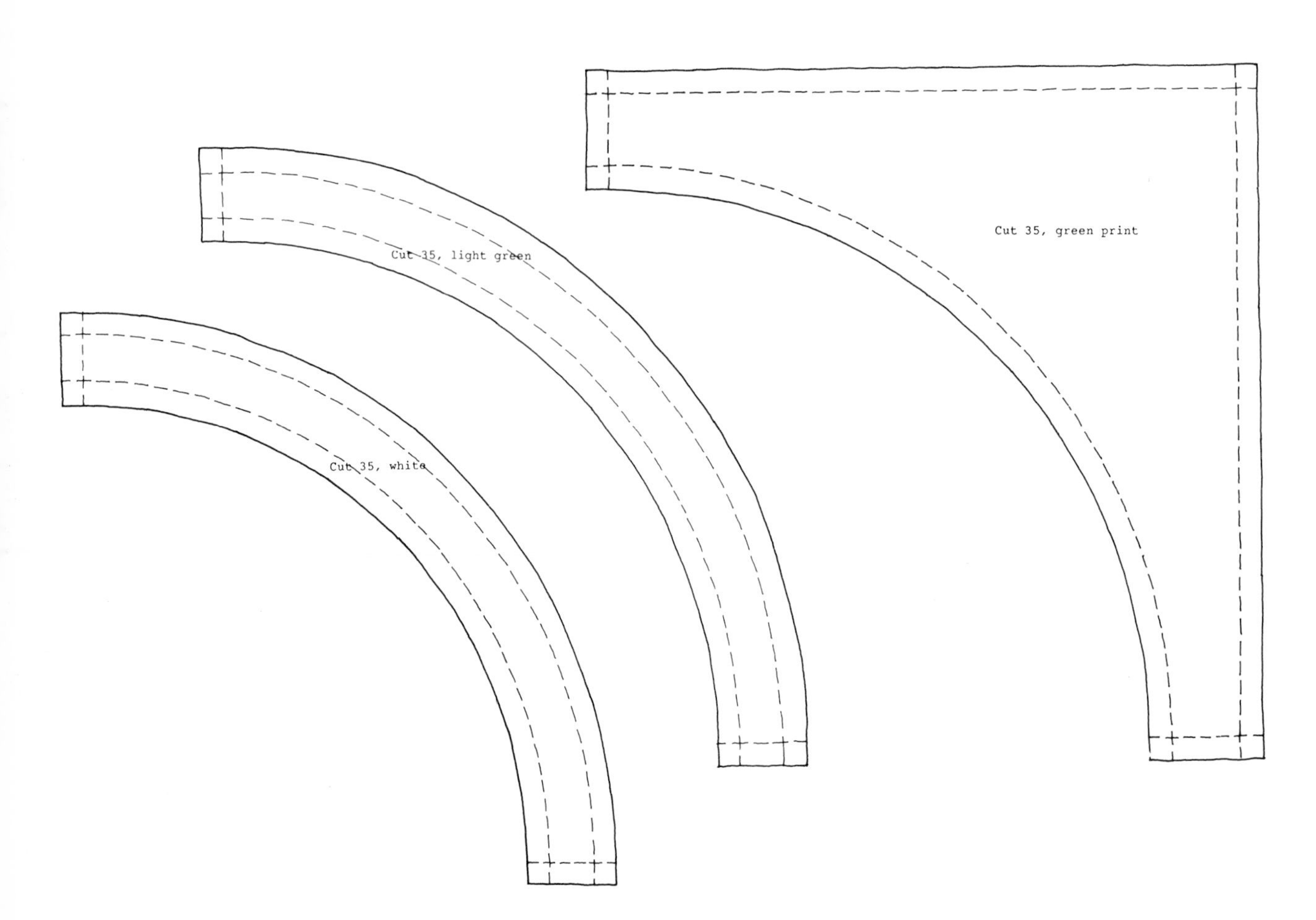

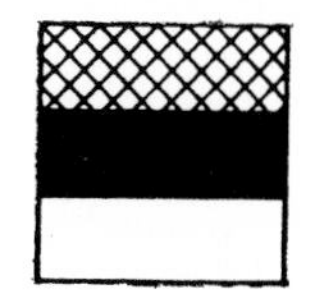

11. Fence Rail

Certain quilt patterns generate optical illusions. They create the appearance of motion or turbulence, or the suggestion of three dimensions. Typically, these illusions depend on pattern asymmetries, either in color, tone, or line. In spite of the complexity of the illusion, the lines of these quilts are usually very simple.

Among the most striking examples are the Tumbling Blocks design, the Pinwheel quilts, and the Log Cabin and Fence Rail groups. In the Tumbling Blocks pattern, identical diamond-shaped pieces are colored with light, dark, and intermediate tones. The blocks appear to tumble off the surface of the quilt because of the arrangement of shades. If the elements were colored uniformly, or even randomly, the dynamic would be lost. Pinwheel quilts, including designs like Crazy Ann and Whirlwind, rely on anti-symmetry to suggest turbulence and motion. They are usually composed of triangular elements and executed in two colors. As with the Tumbling Blocks design, the arrangement of colors is critical. Were the triangular pieces done in different tones, the illusion would be gone. The Log Cabin and Fence Rail patterns are inherently symmetrical, and depend for effect on coloring. The actual lines of these designs are simple—both are composed entirely of strip elements.

Fence Rail has only one block. It is a square divided into three bands. The blocks are sewn together in such a way that vertical and horizontal bands alternate. The visual power of the quilt comes when the bands of similar color or tone join up across the block seams to create zigzag lines.

This version of Fence Rail acknowledges, even encourages, this reading by using a strong orange-red shade for the dominant zigzag color. A secondary line is cream. The third color—it is the middle stripe in each block unit—is dark gray. The dark gray bands do not join up because of the red and cream elements. They do not form a jagged line, only an interrupted one. On this surface, the solid dark color seems to be a deep shadow of the other lines.

Finished quilt, 37″ by 46″

Instructions

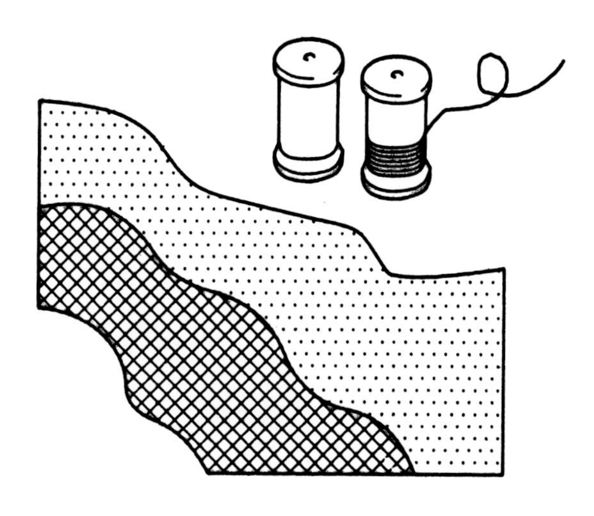

1. Materials:

   $2\frac{1}{4}$ yards solid red cloth
   $\frac{3}{4}$ yard solid gray cloth
   $\frac{3}{4}$ yard solid cream cloth
   Cotton batting
   Cream and red thread

2. Set aside $1\frac{1}{2}$ yards of red cloth for quilt backing.

   Cut the remaining red cloth into 9 strips, 2″ wide, 45″ long.

   Cut the cream cloth into 9 strips, 2″ wide, 45 ″ long.

   Cut the gray cloth into 9 strips, 2″ wide, 45 ″ long.

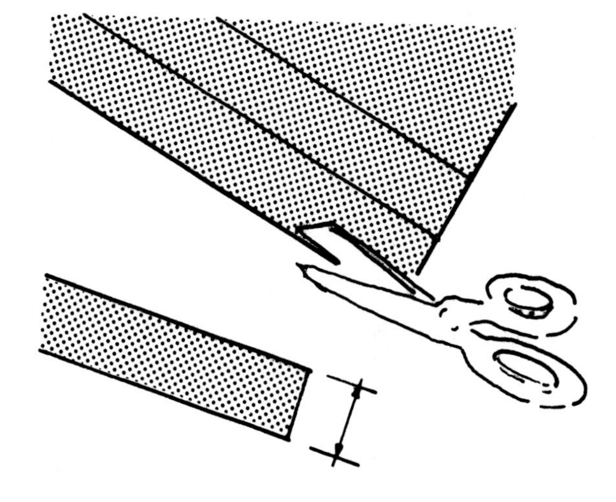

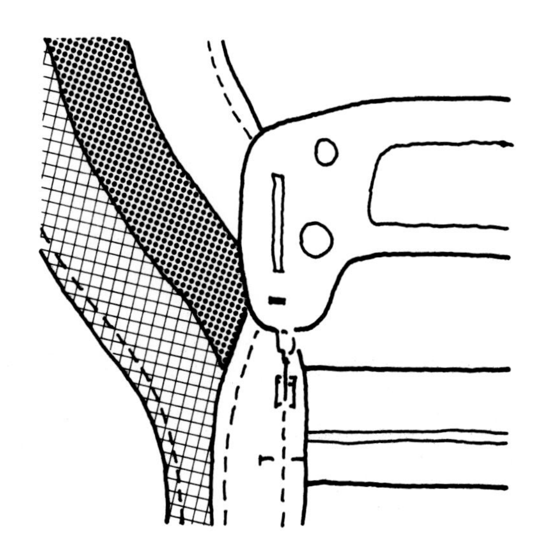

3. Sew the strips together in groups of three. Each group should begin with a red strip, then have the gray one, and then the cream one.

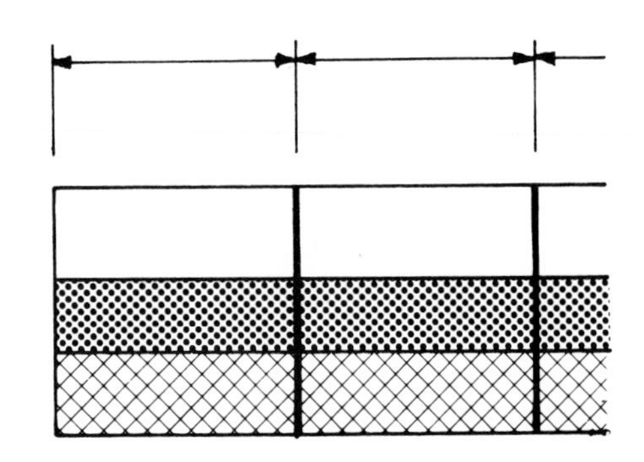

4. Measure and cut across the seams in the strips just sewn. Cut 9 squares from each strip. The squares will be 5″ by 5″.

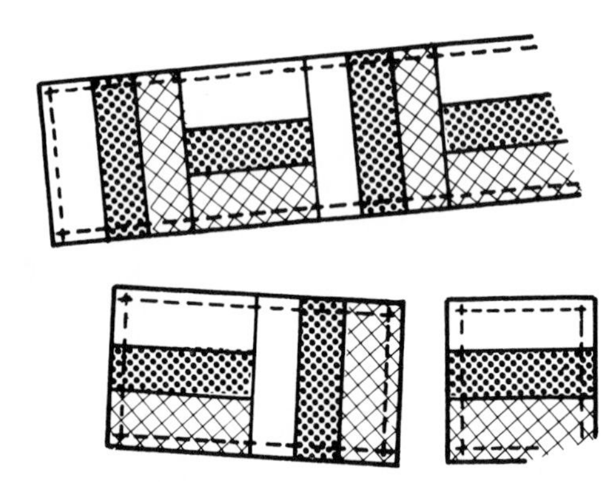

5. Sew 8 squares together to make a strip of squares. Alternate the squares as shown. There will be ten strips of squares, five of which begin with vertical elements and five with horizontal ones. There will be one extra square left over; discard it.

   Assemble the quilt top by sewing the strips of squares together, matching seams carefully.

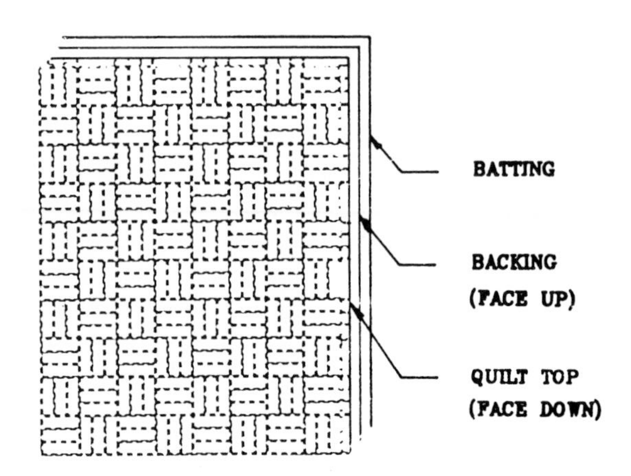

6. On a large table or work surface, lay the quilt batting down. Lay the backing material, face up, on top of the batting. Lay the quilt top, face down, on the backing. Pin around the edges.

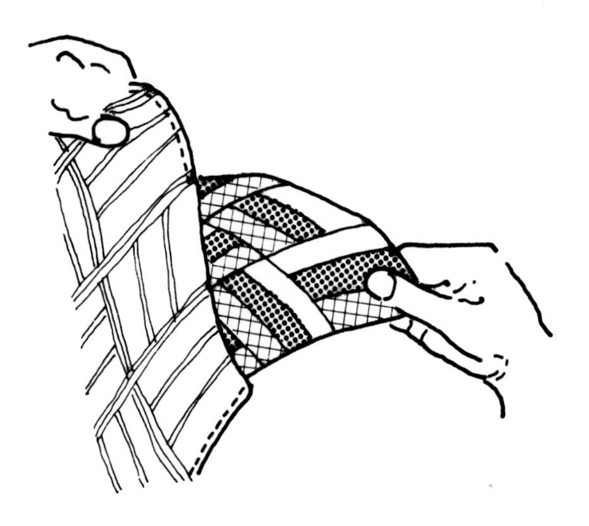

7. Sew around the edges, leaving an 8″ gap at the end. Trim the seams.

   Use the 8″ gap to turn the quilt right side out.

   Hand sew the 8″ gap closed.

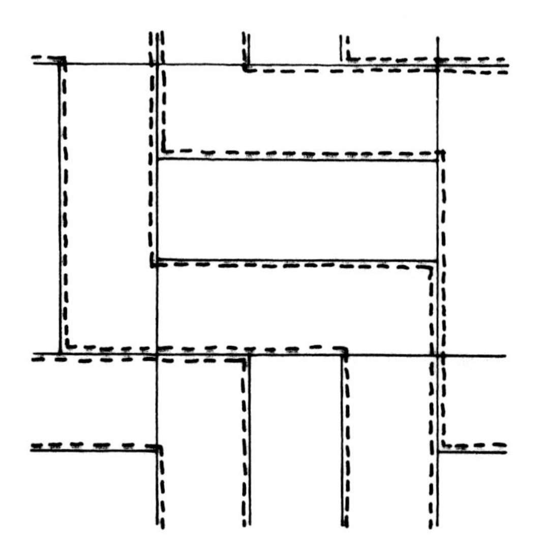

8. To emphasize the geometry of the quilt, hand stitch along the edges of the red and cream elements as shown.

12. Apple Pie

Geometric quilt patterns are those which use regular geometric elements—squares, rectangles, and triangles—in some consistent overall organization. In the long history of geometric designs the individual variations are too numerous to count. But certain families of patterns can be identified. For example, the Log Cabin family uses long strips to make various types of blocks. Courthouse Steps, Windmill Blades, and Pineapples are members of this group.

The Apple Pie quilt belongs to a family in which each block has a central rotated square. This pattern has some similarities to the "Shoo-fly Pie" pattern of Amish quilters. Central rotated squares are flanked by triangles and strips. The corners of the strips are broken down into little triangles. These tiny triangles are the "flies" which buzz around each pie.

Early quilts were often done in contrasting prints, most often in a dark blue and a white calico print. Printed cloth was a manufactured good, not always easy to get, and certainly not available in the rainbow of shades and patterns offered in stores today. A bolt or two, bought once a year, would be used for that year's dresses, shirts, quilts, and curtains.

A limit of two colors was not a hardship for pioneer quilters. Their quilts are as rich and interesting as some of the later ones that exploit a wider palette.

The quilt stitching for this piece superimposes four concentric circles over the blue-and-white squares. The circles are one inch apart. The first circle fits just inside the central rotated square, and the successive ones cross through the strip and triangular elements.

Instructions

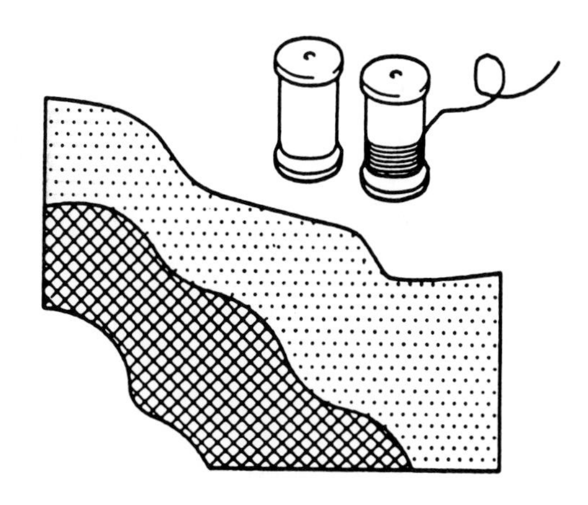

1. Materials:

   $2\frac{1}{4}$ yards dark blue print
   $1\frac{1}{2}$ yards white and blue print
   Cotton batting
   Blue yarn or thread for tacking

2. Set aside $1\frac{1}{2}$ yards of dark blue print cloth for quilt backing.

   Pin pattern pieces to cloth. Cut carefully.

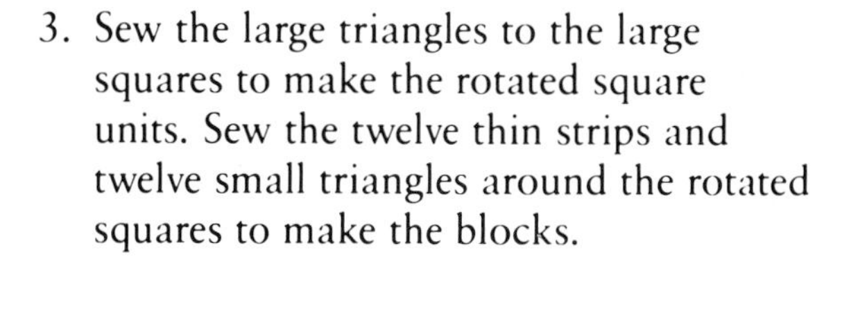

3. Sew the large triangles to the large squares to make the rotated square units. Sew the twelve thin strips and twelve small triangles around the rotated squares to make the blocks.

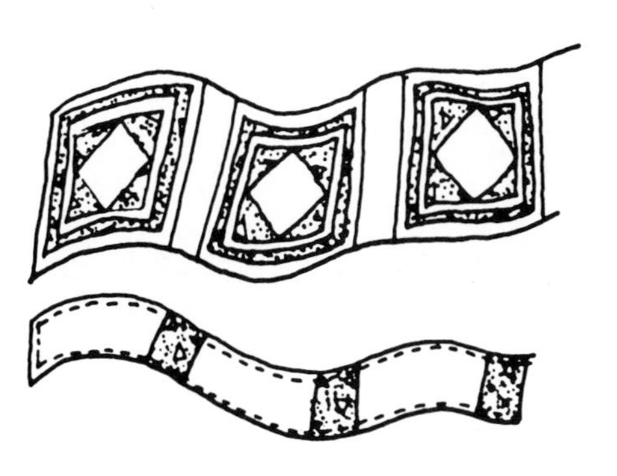

4. Sew the blocks and lattice strips together to make rows of squares. Sew the lattice strips and squares together to make lattice strips.

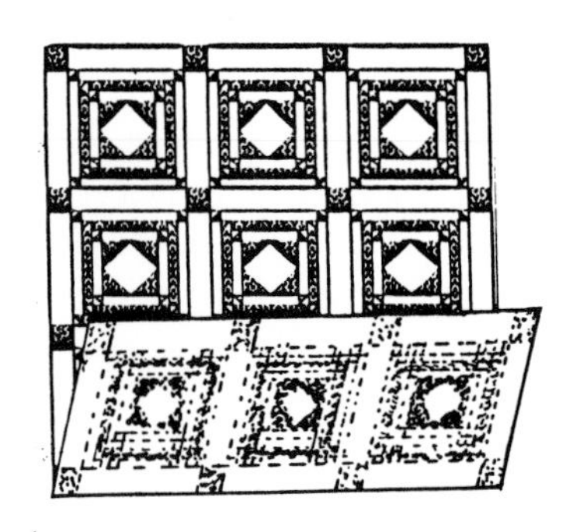

5. Assemble quilt top from rows of squares and lattice strips, matching seams carefully.

6. On a large table or work surface, lay the quilt batting down. Lay the backing material, face up, on top of the batting. Lay the quilt top, face down, on the backing. Pin around the edges.

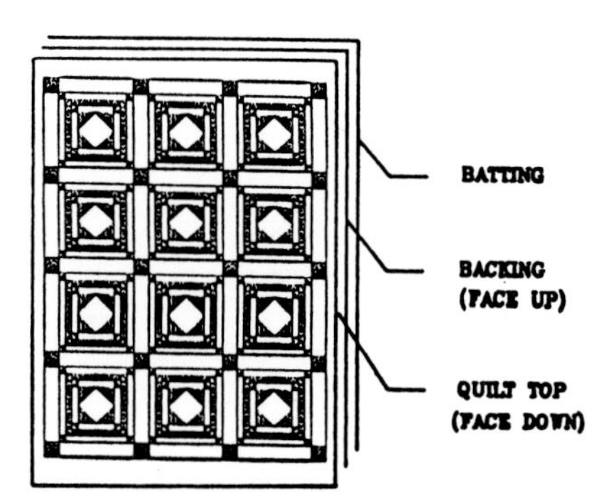

7. Sew around the edges, leaving an 8″ gap at the end. Trim the seams.

   Use the 8″ gap to turn the quilt right side out.

   Hand sew the 8″ gap closed.

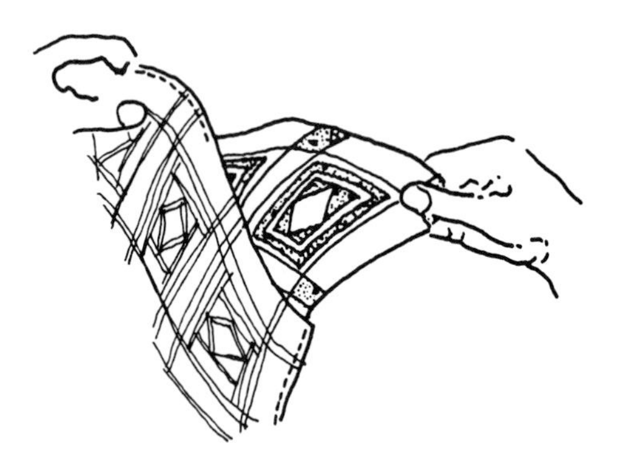

8. For quilting, stitch four concentric circles one inch apart on the blue-and-white squares. The first circle begins inside the central rotated square, and the successive ones cross through the strips.

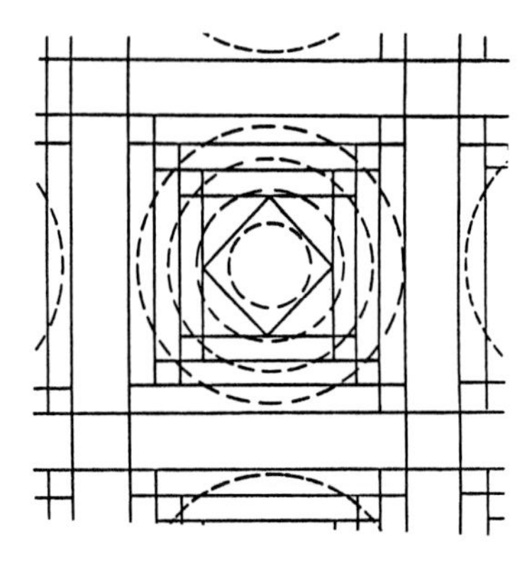

9. Using the heavy blue thread, tack quilt layers together at the corners of the pie blocks.

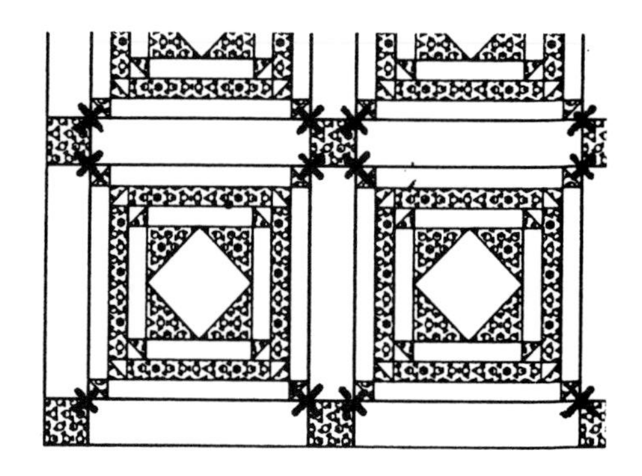

Finished quilt, 34″ by 45″

Pattern Pieces

Shown one-half actual size

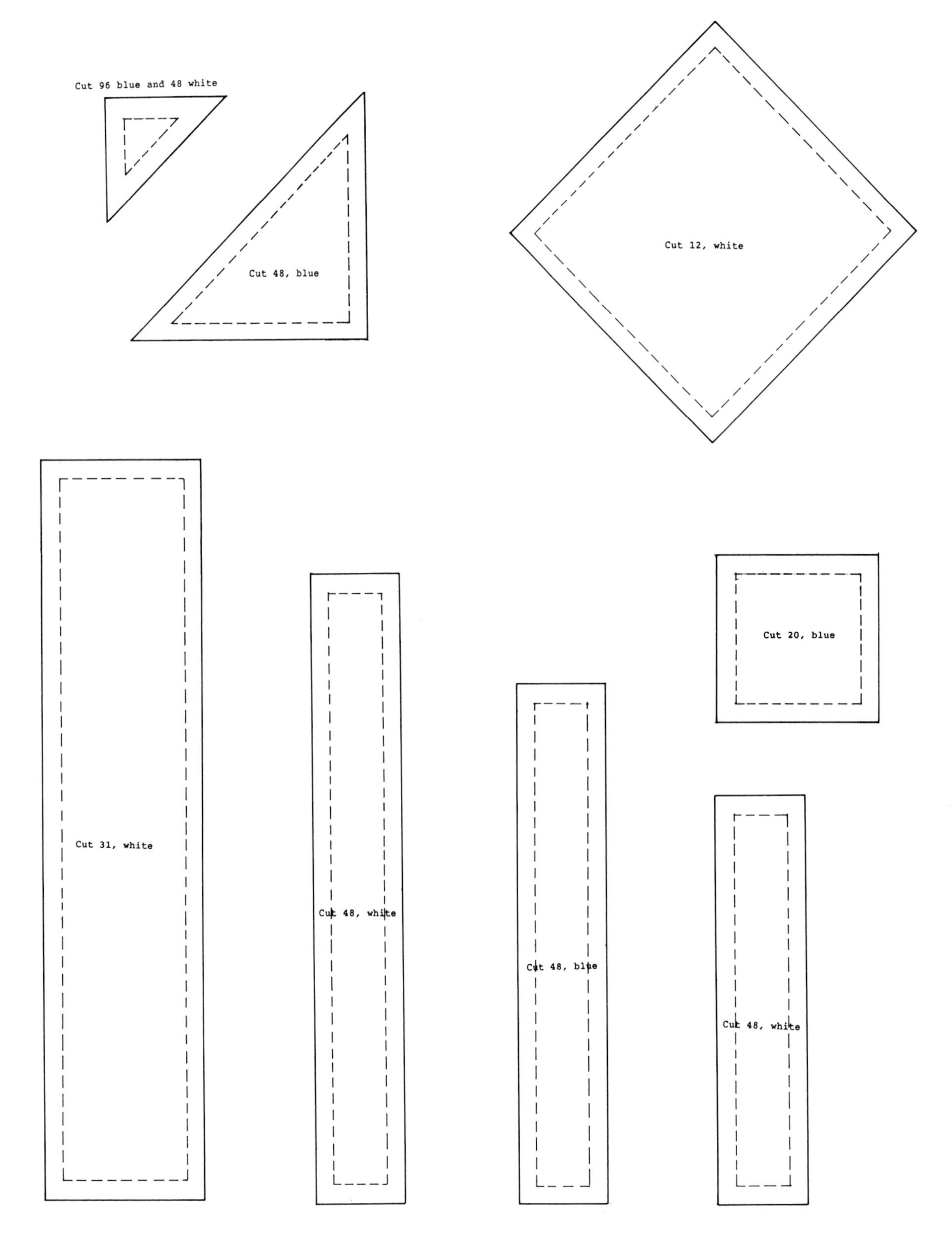

13. Fire

Three-dimensional quilts are rare. The techniques of using stitching and stuffing to create high and low points are very demanding and difficult. There are two basic methods for creating three-dimensional relief. The first method, known as trapunto, uses top and bottom cloth layers that lie flat against each other. The stitching and varying amounts of stuffing create the three-dimensional effect. The second method is a sculptural one. In sculptural quilts, the top cloth does not lay flatly against the bottom one. It has built-in, sewn-in valleys and ridges. The stuffing fills the volume between the top and bottom cloths, and the stitching holds the quilt together.

The fire quilt is a three-dimensional, sculptural piece. It uses four solid materials—red, orange, gold, and yellow—to make a field of low-relief pyramids. Each pyramid is independently stuffed.

The quilted surface is lively and active. The colors and shapes dazzle the eye. The texture and contour become especially apparent when the quilt is draped or folded.

Solid colors enhance the three-dimensional effect. Prints would tend to obscure the lines. They would superimpose a fine pattern which would read across the edge and vertices, and which would effectively flatten the surface. In this quilt, the colors also intensify the low relief by implying shade and highlight.

This design could be executed in many different colors. In blue and purple shades it might resemble jewels; in whites the effect would be like ice and snow. Here, the reds, yellows, and oranges are used to suggest the colors of hot coals and embers. The whole quilt has the glow and tone of fire.

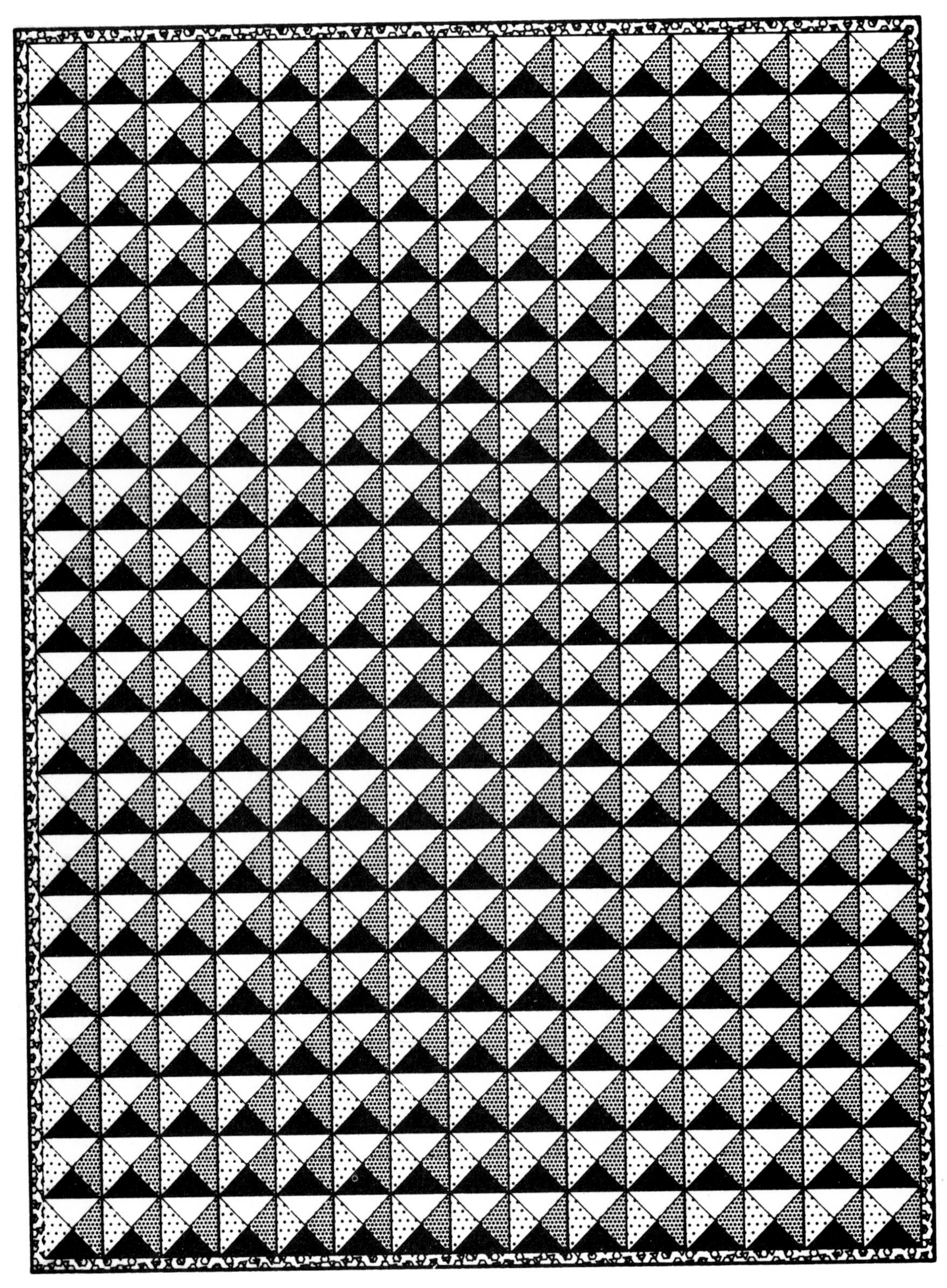

Finished quilt, 35″ by 47″

Instructions

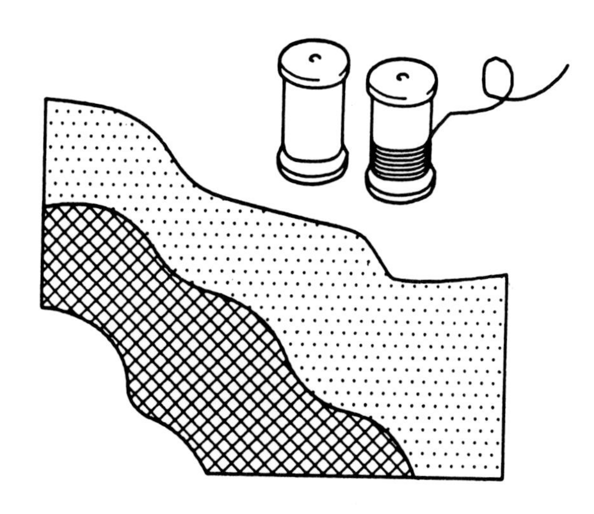

1. Materials:

   ¾ yard each of solid yellow, gold, orange, and red
   1¾ yards of red and orange print
   Cotton batting in both quilt and stuffing form
   Orange and red thread

2. Cut triangular pieces from solid colored fabrics. The easiest way to do this is to cut 2¼″-wide strips and then to cut a series of triangles from each strip.

   Cut a long edge strip, 4″ wide and 14′ long, from the printed material.

3. Sew the triangles together to make pyramids. Note that the pyramids will not lie flat.

   All the pyramids should have the same arrangement of colors—going clockwise from the top, yellow, gold, red, orange.

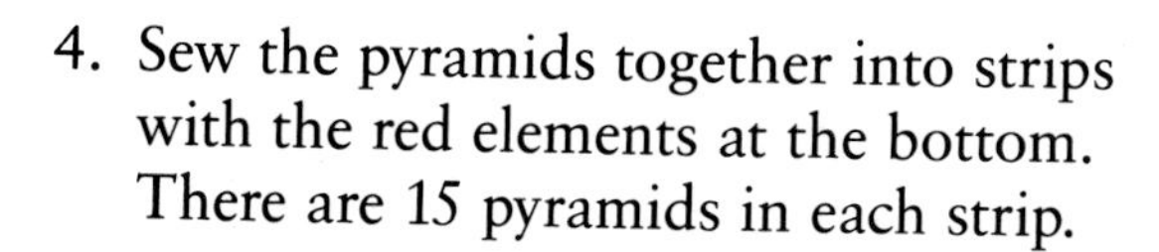

4. Sew the pyramids together into strips with the red elements at the bottom. There are 15 pyramids in each strip.

   Sew the strips together, matching seams carefully.

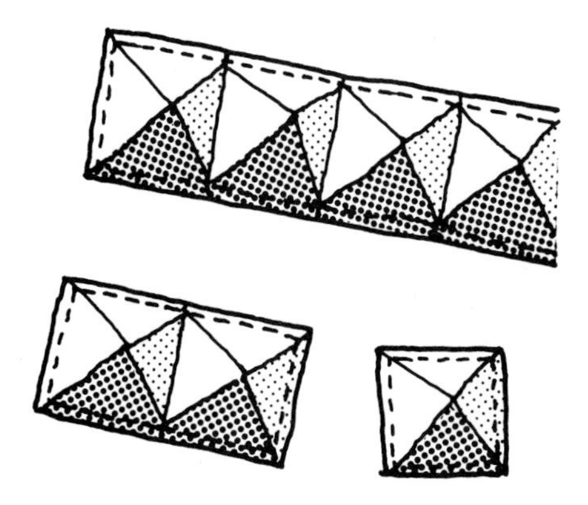

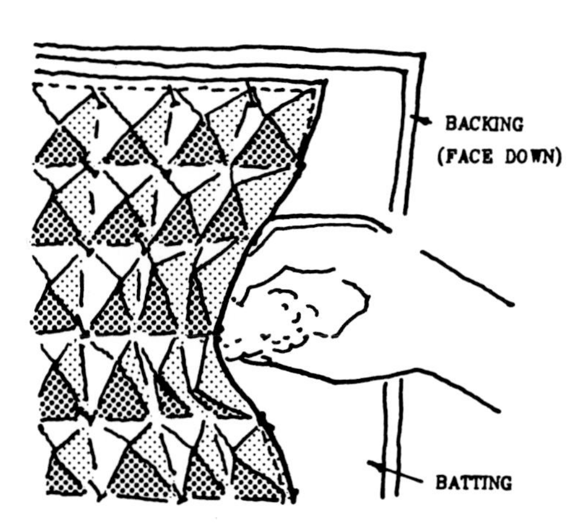

5. Lay the quilt backing face down, on a large table or work area. Lay the batting on top of it. Lay the quilt top on it, right side up, and pin through all three layers along the orange edge of the top. Insert a clump of stuffing between the quilt top and the batting under the first pyramid and pin at all corners. Repeat until all pyramids are stuffed.

6. Using the red and orange thread, sew by hand along all the valleys between the pyramids. Trim the quilt assembly around its edges.

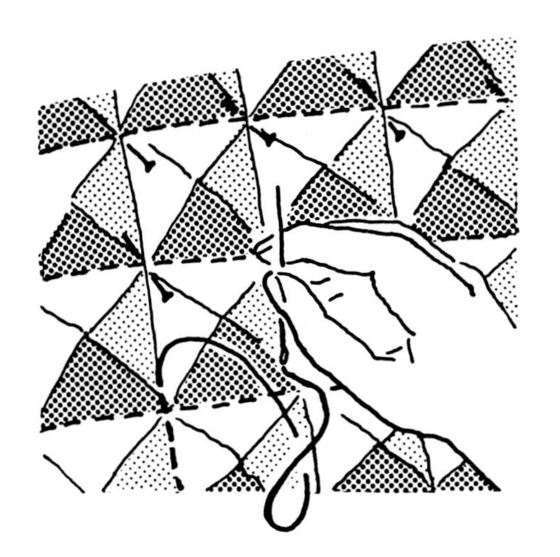

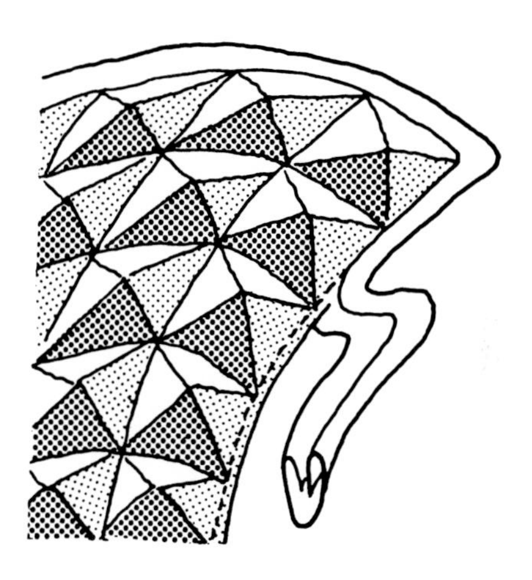

7. Press the seam allowances of the edge strip under. Hand stitch the strip around the quilt assembly.

Pattern Piece

Shown actual size

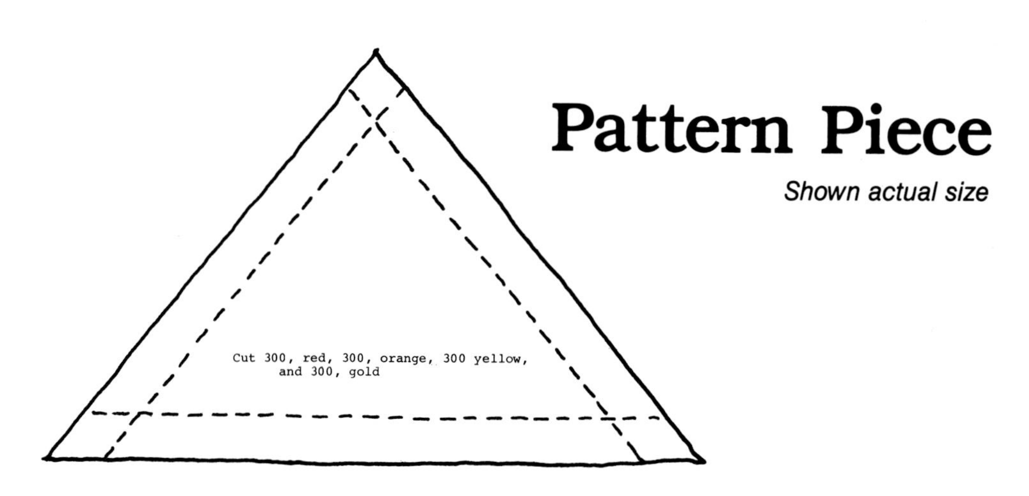

Finished quilt, 40″ by 50″

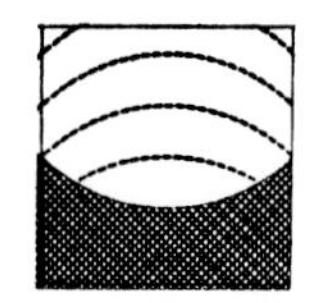

14. Waves

Very few pieced quilts have curving lines. The curve is both difficult to work with and uneconomical to cut. Orange Peel, Steeplechase, and Drunkard's Path are among the few traditional pieced, curved designs.

This quilt uses two solid colors and a simple, shallow arc in each block. The arc joins with adjacent inverted arcs to create regular wave patterns.

The design would be rather flat without the quilting. Stitching lines one inch apart run across the waves, mirroring the crests and troughs. The stitching is done in alternating bands of blue and white to match the fabrics, but the lines appear and disappear as they cross from white to blue at the wave lines. The stitching bands are five lines wide; that is, there are five white lines followed by five blue.

Instructions

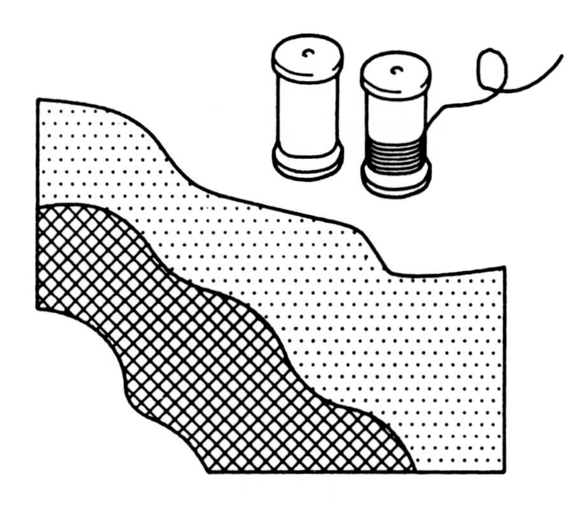

1. Materials:

   2½ yards of solid blue cloth
   1 yard of white cloth
   Cotton batting
   White and blue thread

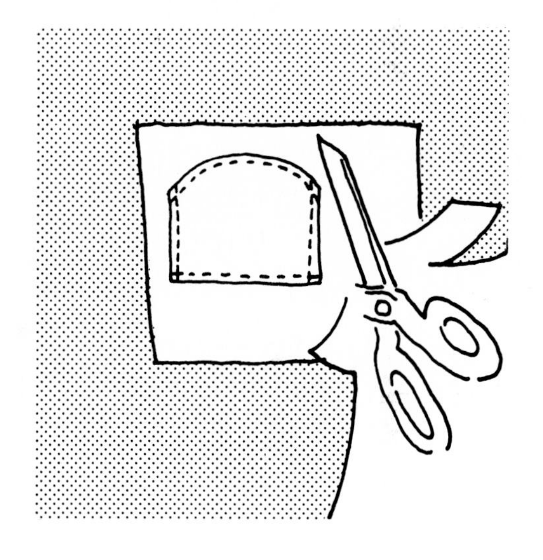

2. Set aside 1½ yards of blue cloth for backing.

   Pin patterns to fabric. Cut carefully.

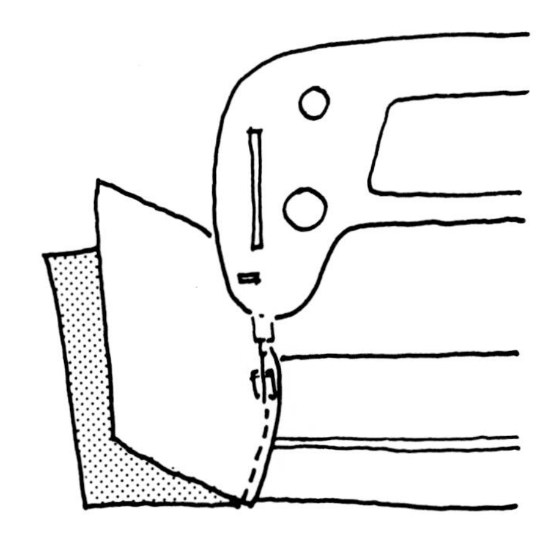

3. Sew white and blue pieces together to make blocks. Clip along curves as required.

4. Sew blocks together to make rows, matching seams at the waves.

   Assemble blocks to make quilt top, matching seams carefully.

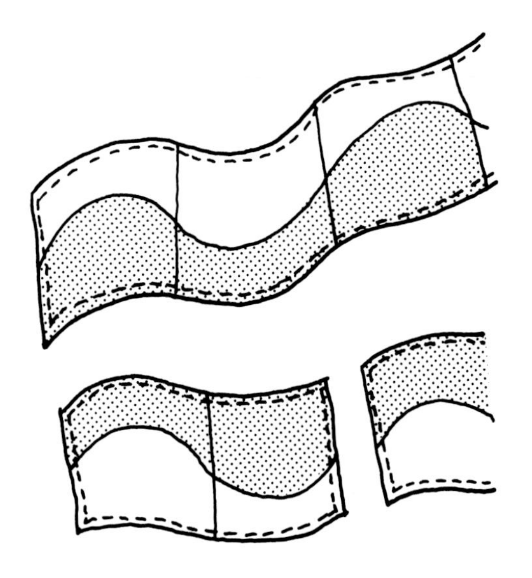

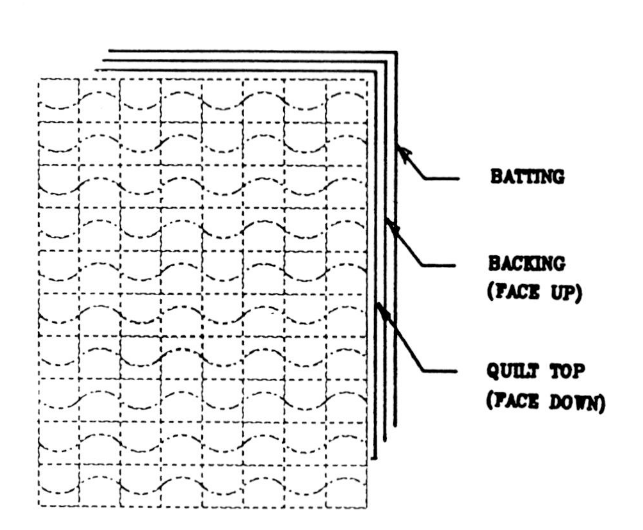

5. Lay the quilt batting on a large table or work area. Lay the backing, face up, on top of the batting. Lay the quilt top, face down, on the backing. Pin through all three layers. Machine stitch along the edge of the quilt top, leaving an 8″ gap at the end. Trim close to the seam.

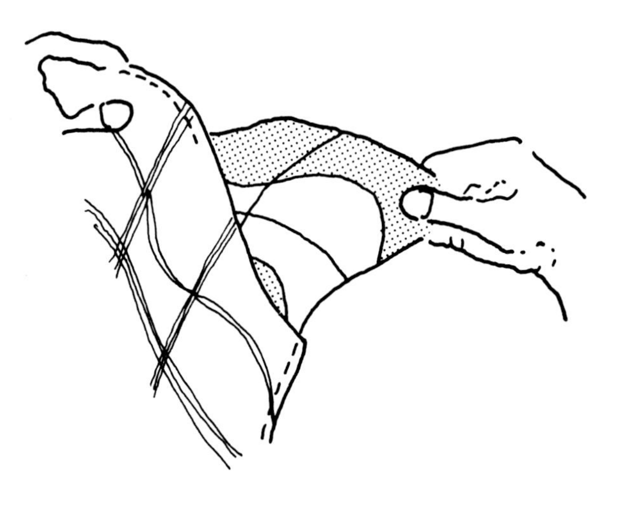

6. Turn the quilt by pulling it through the 8″ gap. Sew the gap closed by hand.

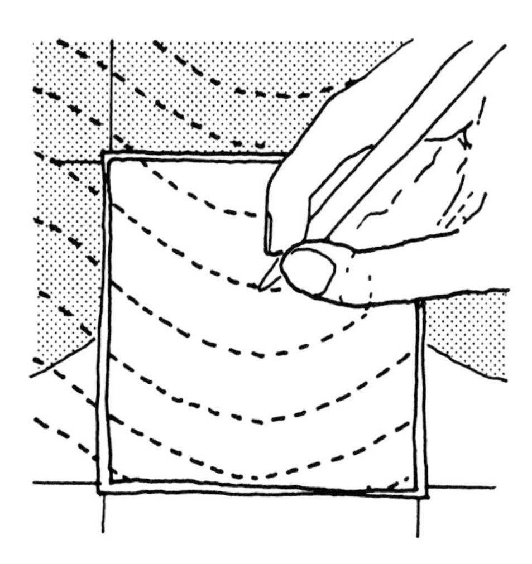

7. Mark quilting lines on the quilt top, using stitching pattern and quilter's marking paper. The quilting stitching runs across the wave lines as shown.

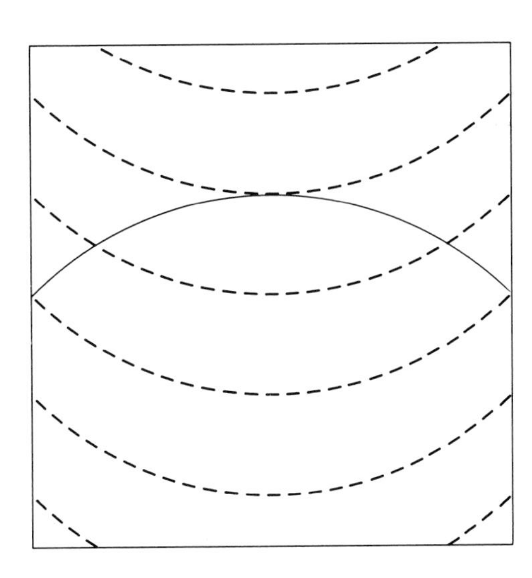

8. Stitch along the quilting lines. Use white thread for the first five quilting lines, then use blue thread for the next five lines. Alternate thread colors until entire quilt is quilted.

Pattern Pieces

Shown actual size

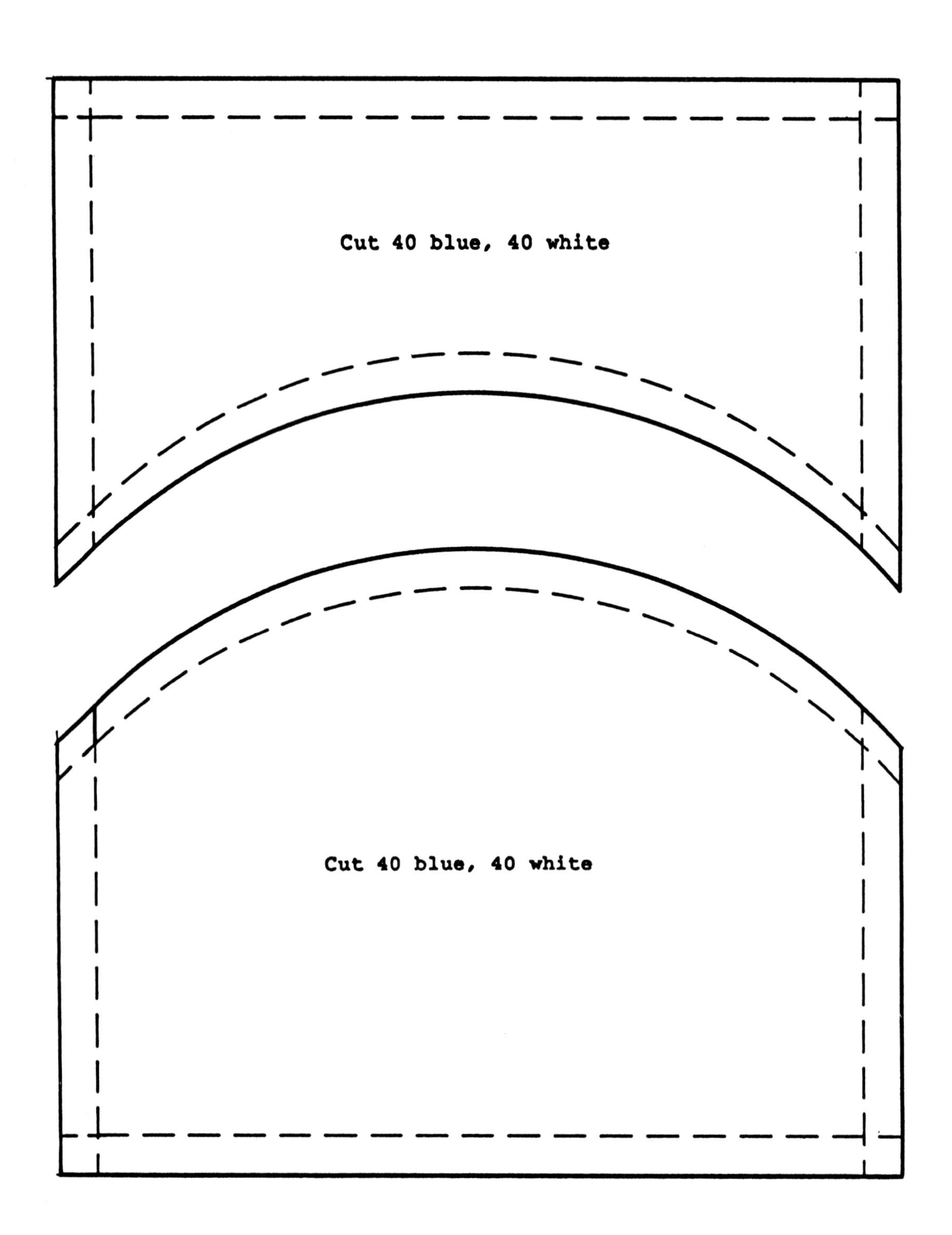

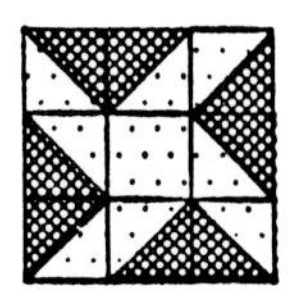

15. Pinwheels

The Pinwheels pattern is a member of a large family of spiraling, illusionistic designs. Other members of the group include Old Maid's Puzzle, Windmill, Seesaw, and Next-Door Neighbor. All these designs lack familiar axial symmetry: each block has a rotational symmetry instead.

This quilt is intense and dark—the red pinwheels jar against the blue/black field. As in Amish quilts, the darkness of the field sparks the quilt surface and makes the red seem extra vivid. This quilt departs from Amish traditions in its use of printed fabrics rather than solid colors. The prints are subtle ones. Fine black lines, in an irregular crackled network, add texture to the red and blue forms.

The whole quilt has a jagged, unsettled quality to it, rather like graffiti.

Finished quilt, 34" by 45"

Instructions

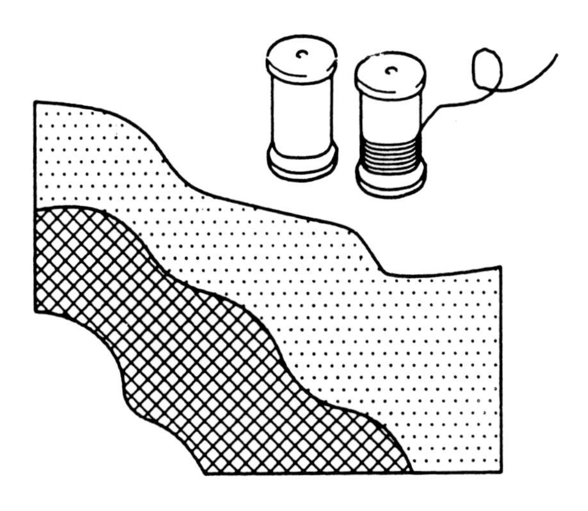

1. Materials:

   3½ yards dark blue print
   2½ yards bright red print
   Cotton batting
   Blue yarn or thread for tacking

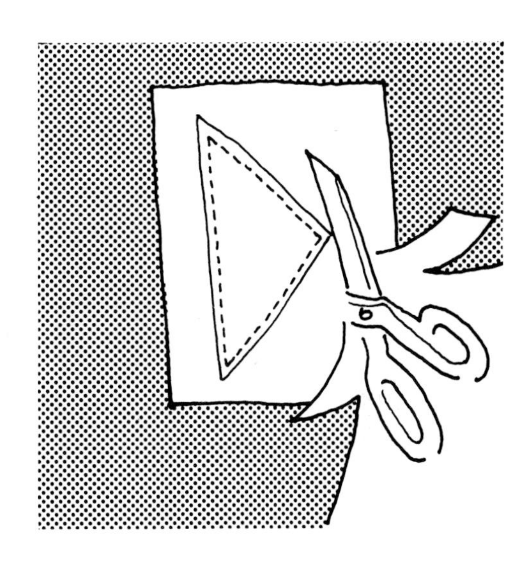

2. Set aside 1½ yards of dark blue print cloth for quilt backing. Pin pattern pieces to cloth. Cut carefully.

   Cut 2 blue border strips, 2½″ wide and 41½″ long, and 2 additional blue border strips, 2½″ wide and 34½″ long.

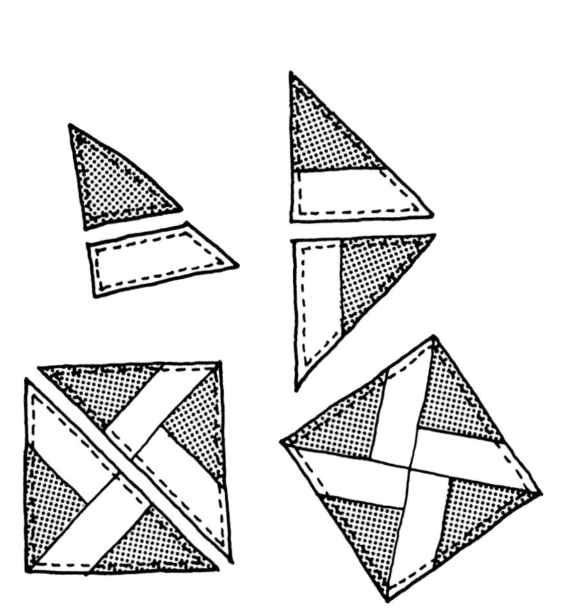

3. Sew the triangles and quadrilaterals together to make pinwheel blocks as shown.

4. Sew the pinwheels together to make a strip of blocks. Assemble the strips of pinwheels to make the quilt top.

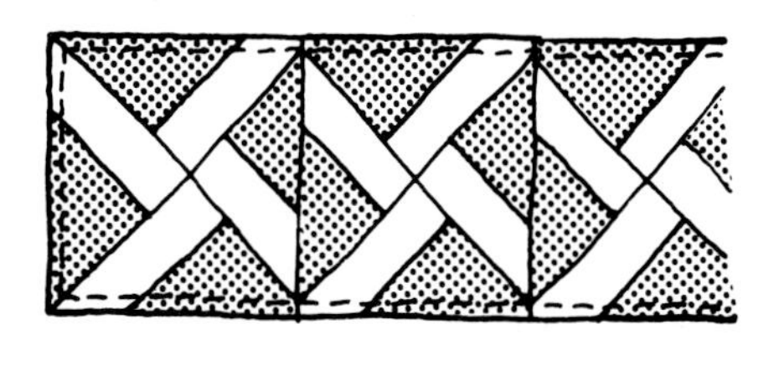

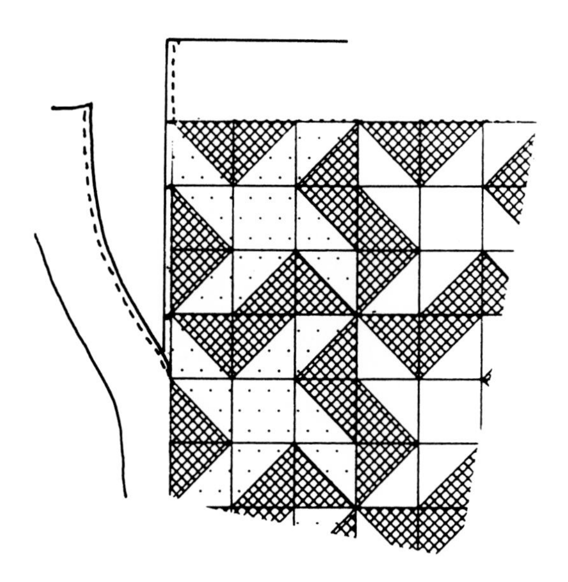

5. Sew border strips to edges of the quilt top.

6. On a large table or work surface, lay the quilt batting down. Lay the backing material, face up, on top of the batting. Lay the quilt top, face down, on the backing. Pin around the edges.

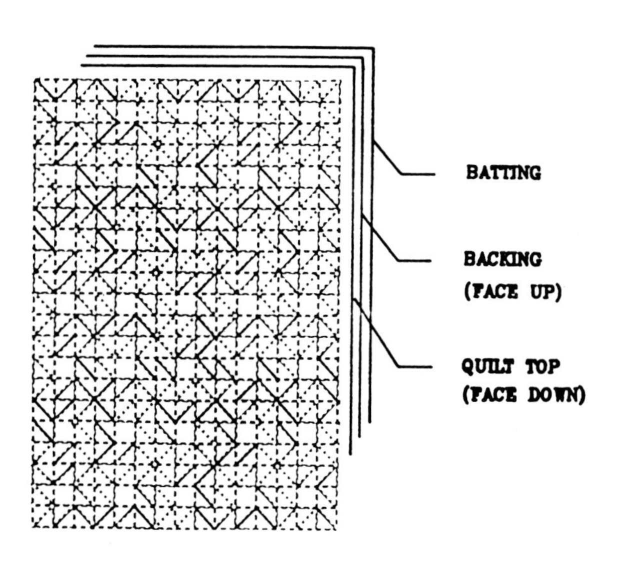

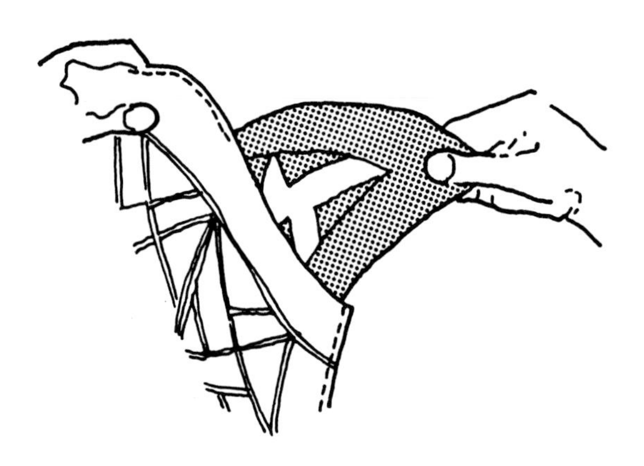

7. Sew around the edges, leaving an 8″ gap at the end. Trim the seams. Use the 8″ gap to turn the quilt right side out. Hand sew the 8″ gap closed.

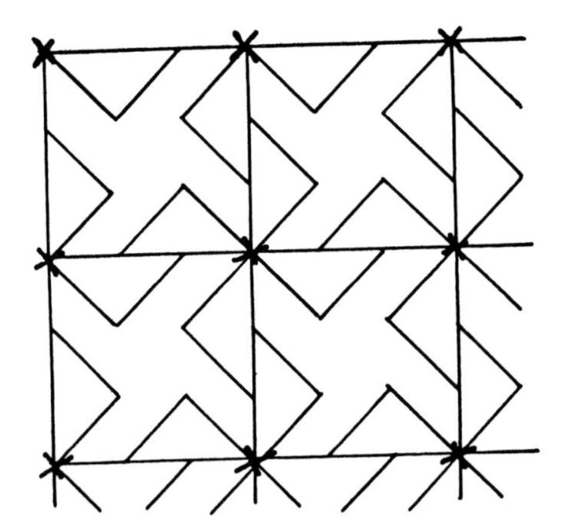

8. Using the heavy blue thread, tack quilt layers together at the corners of each pinwheel block.

Pattern Pieces

Shown actual size

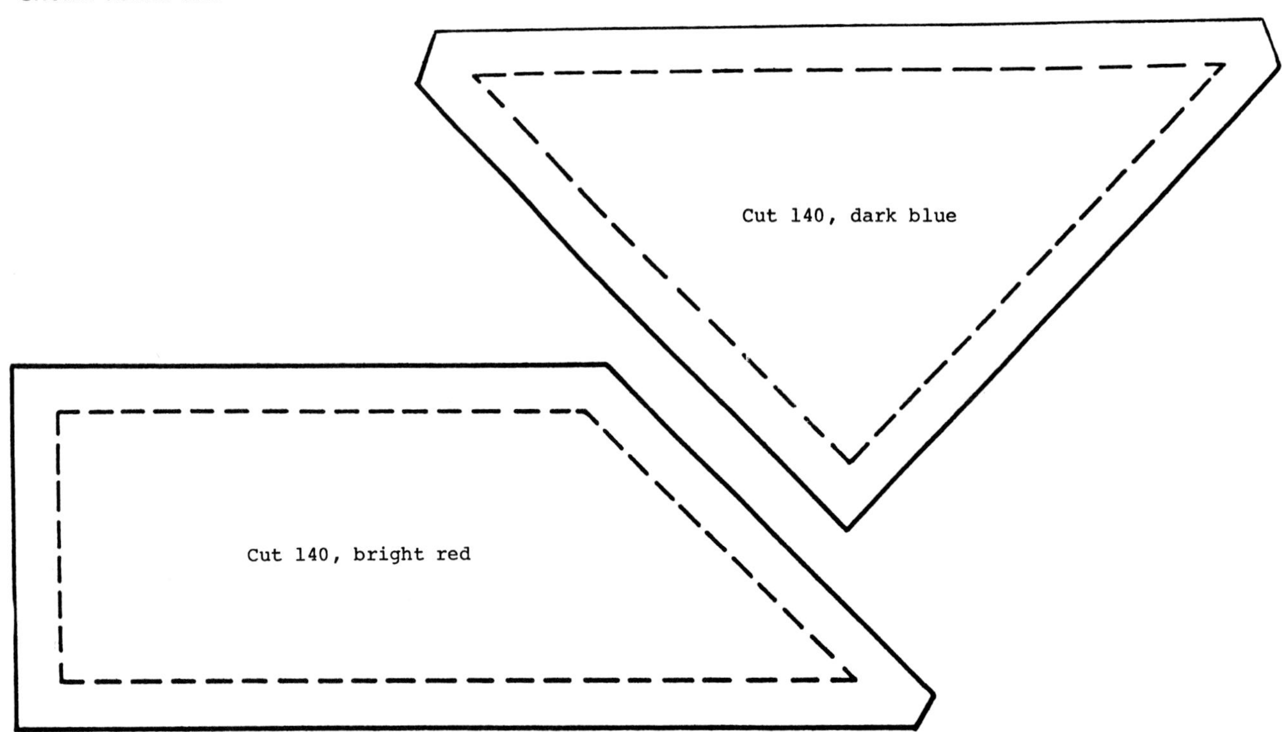

Acknowledgments

The following people and institutions were particularly helpful to me while I did research on the history and design of crib quilts: Anita Jones and Nancy Press of the Baltimore Museum of Art, Leona Bicker of the Brooklyn Museum, Janey Fine of the Museum of American Folk Art, Barb Abrams of the Germantown Historical Society, Amelia Peck of the Metropolitan Museum of Art, Blanche Greenstein of Thomas K. Woodard Antiques, Laura Fisher of Laura Fisher Antiques, and Faith Ringgold and Jan Myers, both of them quilt makers.

At The Main Street Press, Lawrence Grow, Vicki Brooks, and Beth Kalet worked to make the manuscript into a book. Photographers William Taylor and Joan Ford took most of the photographs that accompany the quilt projects. The design arrangements in each case were my own work. William Taylor took the pictures for projects 1 and 3 through 14. Joan Ford photographed quilt project 15. Three young models posed with certain quilts. Alexandra Suarez sat with the Hearts and Hands quilt. Megan Ronning posed with the Nine-Patch quilt. And Halley McDaniel posed with the Fence Rail quilt. Sharon McGinness and Steve McDaniel helped with the drawings and sketches.

Bibliography

Bacon, Lenice Ingram. *American Patchwork Quilts.* New York: William Morow, 1973.

Bishop, Robert, and Elizabeth Safanda. *A Gallery of Amish Quilts: Design Diversity from a Plain People.* New York: E. P. Dutton, 1976.

Colby, Averil. *Patchwork Quilts.* New York: Charles Scribner's Sons, 1971.

Cooper, Patricia, and Norma Bradley Buferd. *The Quilters: Women and Domestic Art.* Garden City, N.Y.: Doubleday & Co., 1977.

Fisher, Laura. *Quilts of Illusion.* Pittstown, N.J.: The Main Street Press, 1988.

Gutcheon, Beth. *The Perfect Patchwork Primer.* Baltimore: Penguin Books, Inc. 1974.

Haders, Phyllis. *Sunshine and Shadow: The Amish and their Quilts.* Pittstown, N.J.: The Main Street Press, 1976.

Holstein, Jonathan. *Abstract Design in American Quilts.* New York: The Whitney Museum of American Art, 1971.

————. *The Pieced Quilt: An American Design Tradition.* Greenwich, Conn.: New York Graphic Society, 1973.

————, editor. *Kentucky Quilts 1800-1900.* Louisville: The Kentucky Quilt Project, 1982.

Johnson, Bruce, et al. *A Child's Comfort: Baby and Doll Quilts in American Folk Art,* New York: Harcourt Brace Jovanovich in association with the Museum of American Folk Art, 1977.

McMorris, Penny. *Crazy Quilts.* New York: E. P. Dutton, 1984.

The Quilt Digest. San Francisco: The Quilt Digest Press, 1985.

Pellman, Rachel and Kenneth. *Amish Crib Quilts.* Intercourse, Penna.: Good Books, 1985.

————. *The World of Amish Quilts.* Intercourse, Penna.: Good Books, 1984.

Safford, Carleton, and Robert Bishop. *America's Quilts and Coverlets.* New York: E. P. Dutton, 1972.

Schorsch, Anita. *Images of Childhood.* Pittstown, N.J.: The Main Street Press, 1979.

Woodard, Thomas K. and Blanche Greenstein. *Crib Quilts and Other Small Wonders.* New York: E. P. Dutton, 1981.

Provincetown. Glistening bodies . . . crashing surf. A shifting seascape of muscular men . . . women of pulse-stirring beauty . . . vulnerable teenagers. Where frantic sex and mindless violence can begin anytime.

Where rage screams when the moon rises . . . and can end with murder.

PROVINCETOWN
THE SHOCKWAVE NOVEL OF
EROTIC LOVE
BY BURT HIRSCHFELD
AUTHOR OF *ASPEN*

Bantam Books by Burt Hirschfeld

ASPEN
PROVINCETOWN

Provincetown

Burt Hirschfeld

PROVINCETOWN
A Bantam Book / June 1977

2nd printing

ISBN 0-553-11057-8

Published simultaneously in the United States and Canada

Bantam Books are published by Bantam Books, Inc. Its trademark, consisting of the words "Bantam Books" and the portrayal of a bantam, is registered in the United States Patent Office and in other countries. Marca Registrada. Bantam Books, Inc., 666 Fifth Avenue, New York, New York 10019.

PRINTED IN THE UNITED STATES OF AMERICA

Provincetown

1

The Emporium was built for drinkers. Day and night, the bar was jammed. Men, mostly, serious imbibers of whiskey and beer. Some gin people, some on white wine, one or two on brandy. No martinis here, no daiquiris or screwdrivers.

Lots of talk about a man's last Great Tear. About long-distance boozing. About the legendary giants of the Drinking Profession. There was talk about Incredible Hangovers and about the Crazy Creatures that inhabited the besotted brains of certain Drinking Men. There was boasting about stretched-out days, and nights of sexual athletics (which nobody believed, but nobody questioned). There was talk about the most Pernicious Puke, and great laughter brought on by tales of failed bladder control.

Guys got looped in the Emporium, tanked, pissed, fractured. And nobody ever asked why. Nobody analyzed a man's reason for being there. Good old drinking buddies, that's all. That was enough.

Sexton was at home in the Emporium. One of many such places he visited, depending on mood and where he happened to find himself. He hunched over his glass like a great protective predator. He sipped a little bourbon, tracing its warming run across his tongue, into his throat, until it was lost in his belly. Drinking until the meanness commenced its sticky flow out to where his nerves ended, and this time he did nothing to staunch the seepage. His muscles tightened and his skin tingled, and he sensed the irregular vibes he was giving off. Always the message was dispatched, and always there was a receiver nearby to decode and respond.

What this time? Who? There was an exceedingly rare pleasure in not knowing. An exquisite anguish in the wait. He drank more bourbon and stared into the glass, neither perceiving anything there nor expecting to. Inevitably there was movement to Sexton's left, a human form easing into the space at the bar alongside him.

"I have been watching you for some time."

A woman, voice grating with the promise of sensual delight. In the invitation was a note of challenge. Was he man enough for her? Sexton caressed his glass with great bony hands.

"I haven't seen you before."

You haven't looked, was his silent response.

"You're real cute."

Cute. Sexton couldn't recall when anyone had last used that word to describe him. Perhaps in his boyhood, or adolescence.

There was a manly, burnished cast to his face, the features clearly defined and strong. His jaw was lean but without delicacy, his nose bony and aggressively angled. His mouth was full, sensuous, and wideset eyes were set deep in shadowed sockets. A hard and handsome amalgam, softened only once in a while by a smile. When it came, it was quick, wide, showing a clench of large white teeth. It was the kind of smile that made other people smile back. Or cringe, when Sexton was angry, giving off a thin awful flash of white.

Perched now on a barstool, he cut a fine figure of a man meant for action. There was an insistent balance to his body—the wide shoulders and trim waist; the full, strong thighs; the hands, veined and sinewy, fingers twisted from considerable violent use.

Sexton was the kind of man other men were drawn to. In admiration. Or in challenge. And women. From his earliest years, women had sought him out, catered to him, loved him. And nearly always were hurt by him. But they kept coming, and none of them ever told him he was cute. Except this one. . . .

"Buy a lady a drink?"

Sexton drank for the pleasure of drinking. He enjoyed the taste of booze. The deepening stages of satisfaction it provided, never twice the same. He did not drink in order to be sociable. Or to meet women. Or seduce them.

Drinking softened things for Sexton. Damped down the undercurrent of anger that was otherwise always present. Eased tension. Lowered him into a gentler way of being. More often than not, Sexton leveled off right there. Loose, cool, digging whatever came down.

But not always. Danger sometimes took on a peculiar appeal. A craving for action activated stinging acids in his nervous system. A burning need for physical release. He'd protest and oppose the desire until, like oxidized metal grown old and feeble, he lost the ability to resist. Then he looked for trouble.

"Come on, willya?"

Sexton shifted around. She'd lived hard in her years. Scruffy at the edges. Bloated, shaky, too long abandoned on threatening ground. In the old days, she'd been a beauty.

"A friendly little drink?" Her voice was shrill, leaning into hysteria, ready to laugh, to please, and begging.

Sexton didn't want to hurt her. "Wrong guy."

"One drink?"

Her weakness, her fright, scorched the meanness

around the edges. Made him sharp. "Find another sucker."

"Ah, come on. Look, you don't want to hang around here, I understand. I like you, I really like you. We can split, go to my place."

There was no kindness in him. "No."

"Please."

The corners of his mouth turned down, and his eyes glazed over. No pity here, not for anyone. "Go away."

She failed to heed the warning. "Too good for me! That's it, isn't it? Your kind, I know the type. Always drunk, can't get it up anyway . . ."

The frozen set of his perfectly beautiful face told her that she'd gone too far, and she backed off. It was possible to describe the tilt of Sexton's mouth as a smile, but it was devoid of mirth or encouragement.

She wanted to make one last sally. Something to put him finally down. Something to bolster her pride. But fear overcame all else, and she turned quickly and left.

Sexton went back to his drink and killed it. Ordered another. He made it last. He knew what he was doing. He drank in order to arrive at certain attitudes of comfort, never to get drunk.

When the glass was empty, Sexton left the Emporium. He walked easily, with what might be mistaken for a swagger. His toes pointed straight ahead as if he were balanced on a high wire.

Turning a corner, he left the dock area. The street was empty, a single lamp dropping a cone of yellow light halfway up the block. His bladder was full, and he resisted the pressure. A prideful man, drinking or not, did not piss in public. Even when no one was watching. He scanned the street for a taxi. Maybe he could make it back to the studio in time. No cab anywhere.

He went faster. He was almost to the cone of yellow light when the two men showed up. Out of an alley they came, taking up solid positions to cut off Sexton's line of march. Legs spread, arms stiff at their sides, chins tucked down as they glared balefully his way. Just like in the movies.

"Goddamn," Sexton muttered. He stepped off the sidewalk, trying to go around them, knowing better. They sidestepped into his path.

"Men, I been drinking. Gotta pee something fierce."

"Tough." The taller of the two had spoken. He wore a handlebar mustache and reminded Sexton of a gunfighter in a John Ford western. Sexton decided that a visual imagination could be a curse.

"Let's face it, men, I'm too old to do it in my pants."

"Tough," Gunfighter said again.

A one-note man, Sexton remarked to himself. Hard on the ears but easy to anticipate.

"I'm going around," Sexton said.

"No way." The shorter man was built low to the ground, wide, with no sign of a neck. A good pulling guard, no doubt. Hard to bowl over.

Sexton clamped his mouth shut. Words wouldn't do it. They had made up their minds, had worked all of it out. Gunfighter was about three strides to Sexton's front and left, Guard about the same distance to his right. The three of them formed an almost perfect triangle. Not as good as front and back, but strategically sound, nevertheless.

Sexton held his hands out. "I don't have much money, men. Just a couple of bucks. It's not worth the work." He smiled.

"You think it's funny?" Guard said, getting ready to charge.

"Not yet," Sexton said. The anticipatory sap had broken out, rolled in waves across his gut. He felt light, airy, easy to maneuver. His smile grew wider, teeth showing in a strong clench, an awful greeting to two new friends.

"You insulted my lady," Gunfighter complained.

"At the bar? You pimp for her?"

"You make it a pleasure," Gunfighter said.

"You gonna get it good," Guard added.

A vision of Mike Berger flashed into Sexton's head. Old Mike had taught him the folly of waiting too long, of allowing *them* to control the action.

Mike knew about such matters. He had learned all there was to learn in the million and one bars he had drunk in, plus a like number of cathouses and back streets. Mike had wandered the world—even as Sexton had for so long—and he had revealed certain fundamental truths to Sexton.

"Sooner or later the bastards will come after you," was the way Mike Berger had put it, his voice an amused screech. "You're big and good-looking, and that's enough reason for some of them, full of hate and envy. The real studs'll come alone, and they're the hardest to deal with. They don't intimidate, and they don't back down, and they're good at what they do. So you got to be better.

"And then, the others, the herd animals. Come in groups, they do. Find their strength in each other, their guts. They'll stomp you and break you up, they get the chance. So you either run like hell or take them down in a hurry."

Good advice, and Sexton had followed it whenever possible. Too bad old Mike had neglected to do likewise. He'd still be around if he had.

Sexton had no doubt. The pair of goons facing him down in the street was intent on busting head. His head. Sexton spread his hands, as if in helpless surrender, and almost smiled. Oblige the mothers now, he commanded himself.

He put a move on Guard, who made a very bad mistake—he backed away. Sexton was on him in the middle of his second stride, delivering a solid kick between those thick, slow thighs. Guard grunted and threw up all over his shoes. Sexton slugged him twice at the base of his skull, and he went down and out.

Gunfighter came to fight. Sexton accepted his charge with a rolling block and scrambled, beat his man up. From the kneel, he pumped short and straight. Gunfighter took one in the Adam's apple, another on the chin, and bounced off the asphalt. Sexton hit him four or five more times around the face, and that ended it.

He never heard the prowl car glide up. Or the cops padding up behind. The words were clear, however. "Try this for size, fuckhead!" A nightstick put him flat, and somebody delivered a boot to his kidney. As a result, just before he lost consciousness, Sexton wet his pants. Which made him mad as hell.

O'Day sat with his back to the wall, on the dark wood table in front of him a glass of Irish whiskey. No ice. Between the tobacco-stained thumb and forefinger of his right hand, a smoldering Gitane.

When in New York, O'Day always stayed at the Plaza. O'Day had a deep respect for tradition and age in places and in people. Unfortunately New York had been transformed into a city of glass monoliths without style or dash. The Plaza was a remnant of a more gracious period remembered fondly by O'Day.

This bar, with its paneled walls and rubbed wood tables, gave off a dense, musty, masculine presence. No cocktail bar, this. No lounge for fashionable ladies taking time out from visits to Bergdorf's and Saks. An old-fashioned place where a man could be with other men. Allowing women to drink here had been a bad mistake.

O'Day shifted his attention to the entrance. Where was Vicky? Attention would be paid when she appeared. Sidelong glances in some cases, bold stares in others. But all would look. Men and women alike.

Vicky Pierce really turned people on, as the kids said. She could give a statue a hard-on.

O'Day recalled some of the great beauties he had known. Actresses, society belles (did anyone say that anymore?), four or five princesses, an army of hookers at different price levels, and many elegant private ladies. Dames of every size and hue and sexual preference. Some of them had possessed some qualities that made them special. Vicky Pierce had it all.

She had the grace of a natural athlete. Not studied and slick, not rehearsed and trained. More like Henry Armstrong, boring in all the time, throwing punches on the go, unable to stop, doing what nature had intended him to do.

The best of them had it. Not talent, not technique, not necessarily intelligence. Just nature's gift.

Garland had had it, along with that fabulous voice. Gable, of course. The Duke. Bill Fields, that old misanthrope. Marilyn. Harlow before her. A few others, most forgotten by now.

Star quality.

The good guys didn't always have it. But those who did were special, exciting to be around, to work with, different from ordinary folk. Anyway, who were the good guys?

A waiter approached, and O'Day felt premonitions of disaster. Some monumental calamity that would ruin his present and subvert his future, such as it might be. He sipped his drink. Irish whiskey always softened his reflexive pessimism. Which, he supposed, was why the Irish drank so much.

"Phone call, Mr. O'Day." The waiter showed no obsequiousness. They were accustomed to movie people in the Plaza.

It had to be Vicky, and that would mean trouble. He didn't need trouble, but he did need Vicky. She was right for the role, righter than anyone else he could think of. He had battled Pike like hell for her, and after all of that, she was going to back out. Just when he needed her most.

"Shall I bring an extension?"

"I'll take it at the bar."

"Vicky," he began. "Where are you? I hate getting sloshed all alone." He worked a grating edge into his voice, the ordinarily rough, but protective director's voice that promised a safe harbor for those within his perimeter. "You all right, my love?"

"I can't make it, Little John." Even the sound of her was thickly sensual, enriched by a plaintive lilt.

She wanted out. Meant to quit on him before they started. Without Vicky Pierce the picture would necessarily become less. Her absence would make it bland, lacking in that special provocation she alone possessed. His work would be made more difficult, his burden heavier, his return to glory more uncertain. *Don't give her an inch. . . .*

"You sick, Vicky?"

"It's not that, Little John."

"Where are you, Vicky?" he said, knowing damn well where she was.

"At the house."

"You're half an hour late now." Stick it to her.

"The lines were busy."

"I planned my day around our meeting, Vicky." A shot of raw guilt. Vicky handled guilt less effectively than most people. What the hell, he *needed* her.

"It's been so long."

"Too long. People ask me when—?"

"I warned you, Little John. Don't count on me, I warned you."

"I am counting on you. I need you." He could hear her breathing. Rapidly. And he imagined those fantastic eyes fluttering shut in moral anguish. Beautiful. "Without you, this picture is zilch, Vicky."

"I hear Lana might be interested."

"I want you, Vicky. The part is perfect for you. Get on the train, come on in. We'll talk."

"I can't do it, Little John."

He swallowed his anger and put a smile into his voice. "Fair enough, I'll come out there."

"It won't do any good."

"It's been a long time. What the hell, if old friends can't talk . . ."

She replied in a softly sardonic manner. "Little John, you is one great big sumbitch."

"Sumbitch is right." He gave her his best friendly laugh. "I'll be on the next train out of Grand Central."

"Maybe," she said wistfully, "there'll be an accident."

"No way. My luck, she is running good."

Downing had the mind of a night clerk, arranged in neat compartments and slightly soiled. He'd been described as a shark, when in fact he was a pilot fish, willing to accept the droppings of his betters. His stock in trade was distortion and exaggeration. Lacking imagination, he substituted a competent memory, drawing on the work of others for his best efforts. Downing was a movie press agent, and he'd been born to the trade.

He sat now in a windowless cell in front of an old Remington, fingers poised, giving the ring of truth to an ancient lie about a new motion picture based on an old story. He was on the point of creation when the phone rang. He examined it suspiciously. On this job, he received few calls. Nobody knew where he was. Nobody knew what he was doing. He wanted it that way. Writing handouts for B&B Productions' television shows, of which there were many, was hardly a status symbol. Downing had taken a long step backward, and it galled him. He had to submit every story he wrote to J. C. Bolton himself for approval. Not only that, he was on the temporary payroll, never knowing from week to week how long he'd be kept on. So it had been for almost a year, turning out garbage by the ream. But what choice did he have? Jobs were in short supply these days. Downing picked up the phone.

"You're wanted in Mr. Leon's office," said an impersonal female voice.

"Oh," he said. "Oh, yes." Leon was executive vice-president in charge of independent financing. The money man. A man of immense and absolute power in the studio, second only to J.C., of course. "What's he want?" he dared to say. But the phone was dead in his hand.

Braced for trouble, Downing hurried up to the executive floor. Leon's secretary—the face matched the voice—indicated he was to enter the great man's private office. Downing stepped inside, leaving hope behind. He looked around.

No Arthur Leon. A man in a white suit stood at the bay window looking down onto the western street below. Downing recognized him at once.

"Hillary, what are you doing here?"

The man in the window turned, and Downing kept his distaste buried. Hillary Pike had a vaguely androgynous look, pale, hairless, his serpent's eyes oddly fixed. Downing perceived him as a product of a sci-fi film, an unearthly creature belonging to no one, created by clever technicians and burnt-out chemists. He was, in Downing's view, slimy, a product of the primeval ooze.

"Hello, Lee," Pike said.

"Gee, Hillary, I wasn't expecting to find you here. How are you?"

"Arthur said it was all right to use his office."

"You doing something for the studio?"

"An independent production. B&B does not have the resources I require."

Which meant, Downing interpreted, that Arthur Leon had turned down Pike's project. The thought pleased him, and he placed a commiserating smile on his feral face.

"How would you like to work for me?"

Hillary Pike could give a man a coronary. But then, who couldn't in this business? Hillary Pike was rough to work for. Which of the bastards was easy? Hillary Pike was unstable, addicted to paying off at fifty cents on the dollar.

"I got a job, Hillary."

"Not for long, Lee."

Downing blanched. "Why . . . why do you say that, Hillary?"

"B&B has its problems. Three series have been terminated. You didn't know that? Check it out. Economizing. Everybody's economizing. First to go are the temporaries like you, Lee. You're out."

"Well, that's okay with me. I've had an offer from Metro. Unit stuff, steady work, good pay . . ."

"I do my homework, Lee."

"Hillary, I—"

"In two weeks you'll be back on the unemployment line. I know. I am doing a picture. Going big time. I need a good unit man, and you are good."

That pleased Downing. "Well, thank you, Hillary."

"I want lots of ink, Lee, all the space you can get."

Downing remembered. Pike had produced four movies, artistic stiffs, financial busts. Downing had worked on the first two. Slave labor.

"If shit were poetry, Hillary, you'd be a laureate."

The white cheeks took on color, a hint of blue, fading quickly. "You're in a subservient position, Lee, always have been. This may be the best opportunity you'll ever have."

"You've got the production dough?"

"That's my function, to get the money."

"You don't have it all. What about distribution?"

Pike flicked his tongue. "This business is not what it used to be, Lee. Jobs are hard to come by. And people do not like you very much."

Downing felt his blood pressure rising. "That's not a nice thing to say, Hillary, not nice at all. I've made a point of getting people to like me, and they do. They really do."

Pike pressed the fingertips of his graceful pink hands together. "What matters is that if you put out, you can do the job I want done. I'll pay you well."

Money had always had a tranquilizing effect on Downing. "Seven hundred a week?"

Pike hissed, eyes slitted. "This picture, it'll be a big deal. Put me where I belong, top of the pile. This picture, pure beauty.

"Audiences are starved for emotional experiences. For love stories. The impact of true feeling. This is special, this picture. A story I can care about. Two frightened people, lost. The woman older, experienced, but lonely, can you see it? The man is young and fragile, hasn't been around much. A natural drama . . ."

"Yeah," Downing drawled.

"They meet. They reach out and fall in love."

"Beautiful."

"Yes. Fantastic emotional impact. Nothing like it since Irene Dunne and Charles Boyer."

"Are you sure they worked together?"

"What's it matter! You get the message? This picture concerns me deeply. It must be made. I must make it. The story is essential to today's cynical and unloving world. Downing, do you understand what I'm telling you?"

"Sure. You got what looks like a hot commercial property here, and—"

Pike's pale features drew together, the eyes frozen

in a malevolent stare. "You've been getting paid three-fifty here. I'll pay four."

"Five."

"Four, on a six-month contract."

"Four, but for a year. A full year."

"Very well."

"When do I start?"

"Finish the week here. The picture's called *Provincetown*. Based on a novel by a guy named Reynolds, you read it?"

"I'll read it again," Downing lied.

"All shooting will be on location on Cape Cod. O'Day is directing."

"John O'Day? I thought he was dead. Why not Altman or Scorsese or—?"

"O'Day is the director. And it looks like Vicky Pierce—"

"A couple of has-beens."

"Joe Crespi has the male lead."

"He's a good one. But O'Day and Pierce, they're tough. I ought to get more money."

"Do the job, and there'll be a bonus."

"Will you put it in writing?"

Pike raised his hairless brows. "You'll never amount to anything, Lee, unless you learn to trust your fellow man."

2

The apartment was small, only a single room with a Pullman kitchen. French doors opened onto a tiny garden. It was one of those unexpectedly warm days that come to New York in early April, and Bruno opened the doors so that the cat, small, sleek, and black, could wander in and out.

"I should've guessed you'd have a garden," Crespi said. "You always had this thing about plants."

"Makes me feel good to be surrounded by growing things."

"Like the cat."

"I like him. He reminds me of you, Jojo. Wouldn't you say he looks like you?"

"I wouldn't say so, no."

Crespi stared steadily at Bruno, his luminous eyes large and unblinking. Once, during one of those frequent arguments they used to have, Bruno had said that he looked like a Keene painting. Hardly a compliment, Crespi had decided. Still, his eyes were a very important part of his acting equipment, perhaps the single most vital factor in his mounting success. Next to his talent, of course.

"Don't stare," Bruno said.

"You needn't have run away."

"Jojo, I did not run. I simply left. Departed. Packed

up and came to New York in order to pursue my own career."

"You could have a career in pictures."

"I'm a dancer."

"My agent would get you work on TV. There are musicals . . ."

"I'm a trained dancer. Classical ballet. I've spoken to Balanchine, he likes me. I don't want to do any more of those silly commercials. Or provide background for some stupid girl singer. I want to do honest work, Jojo."

"You might at least have said good-bye."

"I said good-bye a hundred times. You didn't listen."

"I miss you, Bruno."

"I miss you, Jojo."

"Then come with me to P-town."

"Uhuh. That's your thing, not mine."

"You know how I feel about you."

"No. No, don't come over here, Jojo. It is over for us. You're a movie star, I'm a gypsy."

"I need you."

"Everybody talks about need. You want to own me, and I am not ownable. Go on, go to P-town. Make that movie. First thing you know, it'll be Joe Crespi, superstar! A growth industry all by yourself. Another Bette Midler."

"That's not funny."

"The way your career is going, you do not require an obvious queen like me hanging around."

"I've been thinking about coming out."

"Don't be stupid, Jojo. America hasn't been prepped for its first gay leading man. Can't you hear the giggles when you plant a French kiss on your leading lady? . . . There goes all credibility."

"Change your mind."

"Run along, my dear, and become a superstar."

"Why don't I stay? At least for tonight. Then, tomorrow . . ."

"That would be impossible."

"You've got somebody coming?"

"Man does not live by dance alone."

"You always were a cruel bastard, Bruno."

"Tempus fugit, dear one. Ta-ta—it's off to P-town for you. I hear the place is loaded with rough trade, so stay cool and keep a tight asshole."

Sexton led the way up the creaking stairs to his studio. On the landing outside his door, he looked back down to where Novick had paused to catch his breath.

"You're a mess, Miles. Half my age, you don't drink, smoke, or do anything dirty, and look at you. Shape up, man."

Novick resumed the climb. "I'm ten years older than you are, and I'll bury you yet."

Sexton ushered the other man into the studio.

"Not much," Novick said.

Sexton began taking off his clothes. "You say that every time you visit, Miles. It's a palace compared to the drunk tank. Hustlers, homos, and sadists. That makes a man edgy."

"You want to know what I think?" Novick collapsed into a chair, chest heaving. "I think you are not such a tough guy as you make out."

Sexton, wearing only Jockey shorts, located a bottle of bourbon under the kitchen sink. "Have a drink, Miles."

"You'll become an alcoholic yet."

"By definition, I've made it."

"Why do you drink? That stuff will kill you."

"What else is there to do? Don't worry, Miles, I've got it under control."

"That's what they all say. I say you drink too much."

"Just enough."

Novick smacked his heavy lips. "You are a great deal of trouble to me."

"You mustn't bother with me, Miles."

"What kind of a thing is that to say! You're my friend, I'm your friend. What is a friend supposed to do—not to bother?"

Sexton put on his most awful grin and indicated a square of canvas perched on the easel near the window. "Take a look, Miles. My latest masterwork. Make me an offer now, and you can have it. Wait, and it'll cost ten times as much. I'm fated to become next year's fashion. I'm going to take a shower."

"I'll look at it," Novick said.

Sexton remained in the shower for more than twenty minutes. He scrubbed himself vigorously with a stiff brush, shampooed his hair. Finished finally, he wrapped a towel around his middle and went out to where Novick waited.

He lifted his glass. "Well?"

"You don't need the drink."

"I don't need a lecture."

"After twenty years, if I lecture once in a while, it's all right. Give up the whiskey . . ."

"Bourbon."

". . . make something of yourself. There's still time. You're a young man still."

"A fading forty."

"You kept your figure, your hair. You got all your teeth?"

"I am not a slave up for auction."

"Find a steady job, a girl, settle down, and live a little."

Sexton touched his jaw. "I think I'll shave."

"A man like you in jail. Is that sensible? How many times have you been arrested? Times I don't even know about. A lot, isn't that right? You could rot in that place if I don't show up."

"Did I neglect to thank you?"

"You have a nasty streak. Anybody ever tell you you have a nasty streak?"

"Many people."

Novick rocked back and forth as if in prayer. "All right. You ready to go to work?"

"Same as last year?"

"And the year before that, and the year before that. How many summers you worked for me?"

"Too many."

"Nastiness. Nobody is nice anymore. If not you, I can always get somebody else."

"I thought I'd paint this summer."

"And starve all next winter without the money I pay you."

"Lend me five thousand dollars, Miles."

"Not only nasty, but crazy. The trouble is, you got no respect for money."

"And you've got too much of the stuff."

"Who ever heard of having too much money?"

"Every year another Cadillac. You live in a duplex up near the sky, and you eat supermarket luncheon meat on Wonder Bread."

"I like Wonder Bread."

"Those galleries of yours, Miles. Filled with junk."

"Now you insult my artists."

"You're an art pimp running a stable of paintbrush whores."

"Oh, it's difficult to be your friend."

Sexton took up a position in front of the easel. "It's good," he said. "I'm good."

"Maybe great, for all I know. You could make a fortune."

"If I painted the kind of garbage you want me to."

"If you painted what people want to buy."

"Same thing."

"Maybe in a hundred years they'll talk about you, write long critical reviews about your work. Who can guarantee such a thing?"

"Painting is what I do, Miles. I do it *now*. Posterity doesn't matter to me."

"It matters that you're alive. It matters that you got to have a mouthful of food to put in your belly. A little money to put clothes on your back, to pay rent. You want some fun out of life, not be in jail all the time."

Sexton turned his attention to the painting. "I'm on to something, Miles. Maybe I haven't got it down yet, but I'm getting there."

"Yes." Novick stepped alongside the other man. "The trouble is, if I hung it on Madison Avenue, nobody would buy."

"You're sure of that?"

"Look at that, looks like somebody's schlong. Are those breasts? A regular jumble, a garbage dump of human parts. It distresses me that you have such a dirty mind, because I know you want to be a good man."

"There is no goodness, Miles."

"No goodness!" Novick shook his head in despair. "Look at you, the face of a movie star. Or an All-American athlete, at least, and you say terrible things like that. That's what your father taught you?"

Sexton blinked once. His father had been a man of immense natural gifts. Six and a half feet tall, with the sleek and sexual beauty of a jungle beast, a man who recognized no personal responsibilities, no obligations, no duties. He lived in the present for his own sensual gratification. Liquor, gambling, women.

Why Sexton's mother had tolerated it all, he had never understood. And as the years passed, the situation had become increasingly devastating to the young boy, more emotionally shattering. He came to fear and eventually to hate his father, and to despise his mother for tolerating him.

Sexton confronted Novick, his eyes flat and without life. His voice grated when he spoke. "It's the bad guys and the worse guys, nothing else."

"That's what you learned in forty years!"

"A man experiences a very little bit of life, Miles. The rest is just hearsay. Books, the philosophers, the words of people you know."

"Don't you believe in anything?"

"Give me an example."

"God." Novick pronounced the word as if afraid he'd be overheard.

"I believe," Sexton said soberly, "that no matter how hard you try, a man ends up being a bewildered accomplice to his own undoing."

"What the hell does that mean?" Novick knuckled his eyes as if to clear his vision. "Ach! Trouble is, you're too smart for your own good."

Sexton grinned.

"You think too much!"

The grin grew wider, more of a challenge.

"You're your own worst enemy."

"You could get a hell of an argument on that point. In any number of bars."

Sexton gazed out of the huge window that looked down at the Charles River. Points of light sparkled on the water. A scull went skimming upriver in an effortless series of thrusts. He went back to where Novick stood in front of the painting.

"Gloomy," the art dealer said. "Work some color into it."

"That's your advice?"

"I know what people like. What they buy. They want to hang you in MOMA, okay by me. But where else?"

"Nobody paints the way I do, Miles."

"That's true." He went back to his chair. "Okay, let's say you're a genius, but even a genius has to eat."

"Right on."

"So. You take the job again this season, manage the store in Provincetown for me."

"I don't know."

"You want me to, I'll give you money. But it's better if you take the job. You'll paint up there. After all, it's an art colony."

Sexton smiled, and his face seemed young again. "It's a summer clip joint, we both know that."

"I got some good kids from the Art Students League on the payroll. Sunsets, fishing boats, whatever. You want surrealism, I got it for you. Impressionists, minimalists, fauvists. I got one guy can deal up a Picasso in twenty minutes. A Lichtenstein in an afternoon. You want a Van Gogh, a Rubens, you got it. Three days to ship is all the time I need, so you make calls direct. Faster and cheaper. I deliver the merchandise, Jim, you sell the paintings."

Sexton started to respond, thought better of it. He sipped some bourbon.

Novick spread his hands. "You get a long season in the sun, some beach time, and you make some money. Maybe you even have some fun with the ladies. Is that bad?"

"Not bad, Miles."

"Stick around Boston, and what have you got? More trouble is what. Well, am I wrong, or am I right?"

Sexton raised his glass before answering. "Right again, Miles."

Kiley felt sick. Choking on confusion and impotence. His brain was suffocating in a swamp of poisonous matter. Nothing worked right. Nothing felt right.

He had been victimized by a shrewd and unknown enemy.

Only another biker could sympathize with his loss. Understand his rage. The obscene fear that gripped him. He had no memory of ever feeling so defeated. Deprived. Empty.

The Harley was his. The only worthwhile thing he had ever owned. The best thing he had ever done. That bike—he had conceived it as a dream that could never come true. Worked it over on paper until it was right, *perfect.* And when the time came, he had built it with his own hands, a living part of himself.

Six months of labor. By himself. Transforming a 1953 hulk of ugliness and uselessness into a righteous sanitary creature of beauty. Hustling for old parts that could be reclaimed and reworked until they fit. Accumulating bucks in odd ways in order to buy new parts. Going at it day and night until he had shaped that distant dream into a shining reality.

The ultimate bike. *His* bike.

Low lines, a stripped-down expression of speed and manliness, a beautiful mount. He had extended the hardtail a couple of strategic inches, raked the neck by a cool five-eighths. And look here—a twelve-inch overstock springer on a nineteen-inch wheel. *Outta-sight.*

The engine was a compressed fount of beauty, power, dependability. H 'd ported the heads, polished them, inserted aluminum push rods and solids, tooled a shifter pedal out of a small piston rod. Just below the gas tank, between the heads, he had put down a brand new speedometer. And personally chromed every one of the removable parts. *Neat.*

And now . . .

And now some vile and rotten motherfuckers . . .

They had boosted the Harley. Stolen his bike.

The brothers, the Straight Arrows, were properly understanding. Bikers all, they went out into the streets and searched for the Harley with Kiley. Along the streets of the Village, east and west. Through the junkyards up in the Bronx and among the dealers out in Queens. They talked to other bike clubs, as far away as Ohio and south to Georgia. They even reported the theft with a suitable description to the pigs. And came up empty.

Inevitably the search ran dry. The brothers lost interest. The pigs did nothing. Sympathy and understanding withered away, and the other Straight Arrows began to avoid Kiley as if he were somehow to blame for the loss of his own bike. As if he had become less than he was. A biker without his bike. A hollow man.

Kiley went out and got stoned. Stayed so for a week. He crammed bennies into his mouth and sniffed coke and smoked pot and beat up a few dudes and mugged a black fag for his expensive watch and the gold cross he wore around his neck. None of it helped. In the end, there was only the bike.

Kiley locked himself in his room and got straight. Ninety-six hours cold turkey, man. No company. No booze or bennies, no grass. Time alone to screw his head back on. Waiting for the click, the click that said he was all right, clean, and it was time to put a move on. He cleaned himself, ate, and began to prowl the streets.

The bike belonged in the neighborhood. Somebody from the neighborhood had lifted it. It remained close by, concealed by cunning minds to keep it from Kiley. But he was determined to break through the wall his enemies had erected.

On the third night of his private search, Kiley ran into Geek. As a rule, nobody paid Geek any attention. He was always there, hanging around, his pale face apprehensive, his skinny body ready to run. Kiley stared at Geek, and Geek looked quickly away. Too quickly. Then back again, manufacturing a very nervous smile. Geek made a move as if to leave, but Kiley blocked his way.

"Hey, Geek."

"Oh. Hiya, Kiley. I gotta go, an appointment. See you around."

Kiley raised one hand, and Geek stopped in his tracks. Geek was like that. Yellow-eyed, runny-nosed, snuffling, and weasly. A snitch, and everybody knew it. Not that it mattered. Nobody told Geek anything worth knowing, which left Geek always on the outside of any real action.

"Whattaya know, Geek?" Kiley said.

"Me? You mean me? What do I know? I don't know nothing, nothing."

"Somebody boosted my bike, Geek."

"Not me."

"Who?"

"How would I know? I mean, how would I know?"

"A week ago when I asked you, you said you didn't know, I believed it. Now . . . maybe you heard something?"

"Ah, Kiley, no. I didn't hear a thing."

Kiley looped one of his heavy tattooed arms around Geek's shoulder, steered the little man into the alley. The Geek began to sweat. It was hot, but not that hot. Kiley pinned him to the wall.

"Talk to me, Geek."

"I got nothing to say, honest, Kiley."

Kiley raised his hand, folded it into a fist. An ominous amalgam of lumps and thrusts. Geek squirmed.

"Talk to me, Geek."

Geek slumped in place. "It's the spics."

"What about the spics?"

"They're singing about it every night."

"Singing! About my bike?"

"You know how they are, Kiley? They make up songs. They're a very happy people."

"What spics?"

"On Ninth, the other side of Avenue C."

"Spiderman," Kiley muttered.

Spiderman led a gang of PRs who called themselves bikers. Kiley called them gutless, sneaky, not out front the way real American bikers were.

"Give it all to me, Geek."

"I'm going to have to leave town, Kiley. They'll kill me."

"Nobody's gonna kill you, not when you got me for a friend, Geek. Talk."

"Spiderman's got the Harley."

"He took it?"

"Him and a pal of his, I don't know his name. It was Spiderman's thing."

"Yeah. He still got it?"

"In the lot behind the house where he lives. There's a little shed, he keeps it in there."

"You saw it?"

"Well . . ."

"You knew about it and said nothing to me!" Kiley hit Geek in the gut, and the little man doubled up and groaned. "You're right, Geek. It would be better if you left the neighborhood. I'm gonna get pissed at you every time I see you for a while. Go right away, Geek, and make sure you don't say anything to anybody."

Kiley went off to do some heavy thinking. It was important to his position in the club that he handle the situation correctly. With a certain style. If he asked for help, the Straight Arrows would come down in force on Spiderman and his people. But that would do very little for Kiley's self-esteem. He meant to get Spiderman by himself, for himself.

When he was certain he had a foolproof scheme, he looked up Jeanine, who had been McPherson's old lady until McPherson bought it out on Interstate 95. The Straight Arrows let Jeanine hang around the clubhouse; she didn't take up much room, and she gave good head to whoever wanted it.

Kiley bought a gallon of dago red and took Jeanine up to his room. He primed her with pills and wine and banged her a couple of times, until she was willing to do anything for him. Kiley set it up for the next night.

Kiley went up to the roof of the building in which Spiderman lived, coming over the rooftops from Tenth Street. He hunkered down behind the kiosk that housed the stairwell and waited. The city air was thick and steaming, and Kiley tried to remember the nicest, coolest place he'd ever been.

Twenty minutes later the door of the kiosk opened, flashing a rectangle of yellow light on the black tar roof. Jeanine appeared, with Spiderman a step or two behind her. Spiderman said something, and Jeanine laughed. They moved over to the far side of the roof.

Kiley maneuvered around the kiosk until he was able to see them. Spiderman wasted no time. He backed Jeanine up against the low wall that circled the roof, his middle grinding against her belly.

Jeanine lifted her skirt and spread her legs, and Spiderman maneuvered into position. From where he stood, Kiley got the impression they were both having a good time. Well, okay. He gave them a few humps to get into it before making his move.

He cleared his throat. "You fuck pretty good, spic."

Spiderman kept rooting away, taking care of first things first. Kiley felt a certain amount of admiration for the little guy.

"Who 'at?" Spiderman said, not looking.

Kiley moved closer. "It's Kiley, spic."

Spiderman, still going at it, laughed. "Hey, Kiley. What you doing here? You belong down the street. Hey, chick, you ever make it with this dude? I bet he's some fucker, too."

Jeanine embraced Spiderman with arms and legs, locking him in place. She closed her eyes and grunted noisily and heaved her buttocks around.

"Hey!" Spiderman cried. "What's going on! Leggo, y'hear! Leggo a me!"

"Get it off, spic," Kiley said. "It's your last shot."

Spiderman drove an elbow into Jeanine's face. She cried out and fell to the roof. He spun to one side, coming around, his swollen member aimed at Kiley, a knife glinting in his hand. Spiderman was laughing again.

"Hey, Kiley, which you want—the cock or the knife? Maybe both. Ah, 'at's too bad, I gotta give you the knife, the sweet, sharp knife."

Spiderman circled quickly from left to right, the knife hand floating on the night air like a wary cobra.

"Why you come here to die, Kiley?"

"You stole my bike, spic."

"Oh, that bike. Yeah, I took it. It's a nice bike, Kiley. I gonna keep it."

"Shit you will."

Spiderman charged. Kiley avoided the first thrust and threw a punch, missed. Spiderman danced away and swung back with an admirable grace. The knife flicked out and cut through Kiley's leather jacket, tasted flesh along his right side. He clamped his elbow down fast and hard, and Spiderman was helpless and within reach.

Kiley hit Spiderman until blood ran heavily from open wounds in the smooth olive face. After a while he stopped punching and allowed the little man to fall.

Spiderman rolled over onto his belly, tried to locate

his knife in the dark, crawling without purpose. Kiley took hold of the Puerto Rican by his belt and by his collar, dragged him over to the edge of the roof.

"Come on, man," Spiderman managed to get out. "Don't do something crazy."

"You stole my bike," Kiley said, and lifted Spiderman over the low wall, letting him drop to the concrete six stories below. Kiley turned around.

From her place, Jeanine giggled. "Beautiful, baby, beautiful. Now, finish it off for Jeanine, what the spic started. Please . . ."

"I can't trust you," Kiley said, going toward her.

"I wouldn't say a word. I set it up for you. Everybody in the club knows how I am."

"That's what I mean."

He got her onto her feet and moved her back across the roof. She began to weep, begging him not to do it. He made no reply. And just before he sent her over the side after Spiderman, she ceased her protests. Dying suddenly seemed like a very good idea, and she went all the way down without making another sound.

When Kiley got back to the Straight Arrows' clubhouse aboard the Harley, the brothers clustered around full of congratulations and questions. Before he could answer, Bear, who was president of the club, drew him aside.

"Tell me first," Bear said.

Kiley, proud of his accomplishment, did.

"Very cool," Bear said. "Only one thing wrong."

"I thought it all through," Kiley said. "There can't be anything wrong."

"Geek, he can finger you."

"He won't."

"He's a snitch. It's what a snitch does."

"I'll find him, close his mouth."

"No, we'll find him. We'll take care of him. But until we do, you split."

Kiley saw the logic in Bear's argument. "Where will I go?"

"You think of a place, but don't tell me where. Don't tell anybody."

"I won't, Bear."

"Have a good time."

"Always do."

3

A wide covered porch extended the length of the old Connecticut house. A stately maple tree blocked off the northern view, its branches heavy with new leaves that trembled slightly in the soft spring breeze; at the other end of the porch were the creamy flowers of a dogwood in early bloom. To the front, the land dropped away steeply, and through the dappled woods O'Day was able to see a winding river splashing over a scattering of rocks in a gush of white water.

"This is nice," he said. "Tony must have enjoyed this."

"Tony never saw it." She served him coffee, black, and some date-nut cookies. "I found it and bought it, did it over. I had this porch built because I knew Tony had a thing about porches. He died a month before we were to move in."

"I liked Tony."

"Stupid man, to die that way. What a waste!"

"You sound angry."

"Why not? He left me alone, and I hate being alone. I miss him." She shrugged and sat down, staring out at the woods. "The last time I saw you, Little John, you were on your way to Vietnam."

"The Academy Award banquet in 1969. What a mistake, that picture."

"What a mistake, that war."

"I didn't think so then. A lot of us didn't. I believed in the old ways, the old values. More changes had taken place than I recognized or understood."

"It's over," she murmured.

He shifted around, gazed at her. In profile, she might have been the youthful Vicky Pierce who had flashed into stardom back when Hollywood was the synonym for movies and glamour and entertainment. Her eyes were the same. Sea-green, tilted at the corners, brimming with human emotion, quick to tears, quick to amusement. Her chin was still high, with a suggestion of wellborn pride. Her skin was smooth, tawny, and her hair was a thick flow, burnished to a high copper gloss. A casual observer would have pronounced her to be a woman at ease in her own skin.

O'Day knew better. Ongoing discomfort was her familiar companion. A simmering dissatisfaction, whatever she did, wherever she went. People put her on edge, sharpened her fears and anxieties, forced her to seek a protective space cushion. The most private of women but her startling beauty and natural grace had raised her up to be that most public of people—a movie star. She had hated it; at the same time, she required its comforts and rewards.

She turned to face him, a slight lift to her voluptuous mouth. And even in that soft afternoon light, O'Day saw the slight puffiness at her jaw, the crinkled splash at her eyes, the fine lines that circled that graceful throat. Time was the great enemy of us all, going unrecognized until nothing could be done. Well, all right, he said to himself, summoning up new energy. He hadn't come expecting to find some blooming ingenue to flash across the screen. He wanted a vintage face tempered by time and experience. Softened by life, with a little fear shining out of those incredible eyes. Those eyes. What they had seen, what they concealed, he would cause them to reveal. Those eyes would give depth and extra meaning to every word of Reynolds' screenplay.

"I never expected to see you again, Little John. When a man owns a castle outside of London . . ."

"Dublin," he corrected. "Just another drafty house. Expensive to keep, and impossible to heat."

"I had visions of you composing your memoirs, surrounded by a bevy of beautiful young girls."

"You flatter an old man."

"So you decided to come back."

"I've been away in more ways than one. Coming back is hard. Ask any prizefighter." He lit a Gitane, watched the smoke drift up to the roof of the porch. "Found out that I'm a thousand percent Yankee Doodle Dandy. Kept the flag waving all the time I was over there. Set back Anglo-American relations by at least a hundred years."

"I figured you'd given up the business."

"Making pictures is what I do. The need nags at me. Anyway, to live like an Irish king costs a hell of a lot."

"Costs a hell of a lot to live, period."

"Pike will pay."

"I turned him down. I'm turning you down, too."

"You're tops, Vicky. The brightest, the best of them."

"Was," she corrected gently.

"Once and forever."

"Flattery will get you nowhere. Why do you want an old lady, anyway?"

"You're not old, and you're right for the part."

"Have you tried Hayworth? Or Olivia? There are others—"

"I want you, Vicky. I need you. We do okay together. A good pair. A dual comeback."

"What a romantic notion."

"Ask for more money. I'm authorized to pay."

"Ah, money. I was never very good about it. Every investment I've made has turned sour. But money isn't everything."

"What counts is what money can do. It can buy years of privacy in this house, Vicky. It can free you from worry, from the need to make economies."

"Are you so sure I'm in that kind of financial shape?"

"Pike is a thorough man. He's done some investigating." He smoothed his thick mustache, puffed the Gitane, took her hand. "You need the money, I need the money. But more than that, both of us need to work. To make pictures. It's what we do, what we were trained to do. It provides satisfaction, a reason for getting out of bed in the morning. For us old hands, there is nothing else to do—except wait to die."

Her smile was friendly, mocking, brief. "I spend a great deal of time reading."

He matched her manner. "Then you read the script?"

"And the novel. The girl is much too young. I can't pass for—"

"Not now. She's mature, divorced, lonely, and afraid."

"Typecasting."

"I see her at about forty years old."

"I used to be forty," she offered. "A year or two ago, if memory can be trusted. It's a lousy book, Little John."

"But it sold. The screenplay needs work still, lots of it. The author will be on location, I'll work with him, push him into excellence . . ."

"You were always super with writers."

"Improvisation is something I've always been able to do. Changes as we shoot, on the set, in front of the camera. You know me, Vicky. Casting is important to me, maybe the most important thing. The right face in the right part. Joe Crespi is the man."

"He must be half my age."

"He's a good actor, and he's got the right quality."

She shivered, embraced herself. "You really believe I can do it?"

"Absolutely. The best accommodations, Vicky. Your own hair stylist, makeup man, dresser. You want a car, chauffeur, you got it."

"I've been away so long."

"You made it back once before."

"Oh, dear. Don't remind me. *Tour and Taste* finished me off back then. What a disaster! Nobody wanted me after that."

"You came back."

"Thanks to Tony. He was a terrific agent, my manager, he took care of me. One big hit and—zap—nothing but trash. Five pictures in three years, and I was finished. Acting, movies—I'd given it all up."

"Stars never stop feeling like stars."

She made an impatient gesture, as if brushing aside his words and her own thoughts. "Don't you see, I am paralyzed with fear?"

He was tempted to let go. To seek elsewhere for what he needed. But no one else would provide as much of what he wanted. She was special in her strengths and her weaknesses. Even her fear could be transformed into a positive factor on film.

"We're both afraid," he said flatly.

"Not you, Little John. You've never been afraid of anything."

He wished it were true, wished he were the supportive rock people took him to be. Immutable, immovable, always present, standing high above the storm. He touched her cheek. "I've had six losers back-to-back. In four years, nobody's offered me anything. I sit on an abandoned spur while the rest of the world rushes by on the main line. Until Pike—"

"He used to make porno films. He's a hustler. He's a cheap, tasteless—"

"To hell with that!" he cried, then worked the anger back down. "Vicky, who else wants a washed-up old director? Pike is my main chance."

"He needs you. Your name and your reputation to give the picture character and authority."

"Yes, I know. And to help him raise money. We need each other, and I need you. It's dangerous on top, Vicky. They all take potshots at you when you're out front. All the young ambitious bastards crowding up from behind. A few years back, I'd have gotten *The Godfather* or *Cuckoo's Nest*. Don't think I didn't go after them. All they gave me, some kind words and a free lunch. Pike is my *last* chance."

She rose slowly, taking up a dominant position where the fading sunlight complimented her elegant face, as if by accident. Or instinct. O'Day knew better. She was an actress. A performer. And like all such people, she was two people, one looking on at all times, issuing stage directions, moving herself about to advantageous marks, displaying her best side.

"What," she said absently, "will my fans think if I make love to a boy?"

O'Day put the cutting edge of authority and cynical experience into his voice. "There are no fans. Not for you. For Newman, maybe. For McQueen, Streisand, and she's the only dame brings in a dime at the box office. For the rest, there isn't even an audience to count on. Good pictures with good actors play in cinemas, my dear, and most of the time they play to empty houses. But this story, Vicky, this picture, will work. You will make it better than it would be otherwise. You could win an Oscar, Vicky."

"I'm concerned about the script."

He sat back, able to relax a little. That was the actress in her speaking, the star using the perquisites of stardom. Stars were more than performers; they gave direction to directors, rewrote the writers, exercised control over casting, costumes, lighting, the musical score. Power, O'Day remarked wryly to himself, was a terrible thing in the wrong hands.

"Depend on me." Stars were also fluttery creatures, suspicious of their own shortcomings as human beings. Their egos required constant shoring up, and reassurance, a strong solid place to rest and feel safe. "I'll take care of it."

"Who will you have on camera?"

"Frank."

She seemed pleased. "Jacoby? I like Frank. He gave me scuba lessons when we made *Mermaids and Murmansk.* I was never very good at it. The ocean is such a fearful thing . . ."

"Frank's excited about working with you again." He'd forgotten that Jacoby and Vicky had made pictures together. "He has a touch for women."

She wet her lips. "What about distribution?"

"Universal, Warner's, I don't know."

"It isn't set yet? Oh, Little John, I'd hate to be in a picture that couldn't get shown."

"The money . . ."

"Yes, the money. Pike mentioned fifty thousand."

"Ask for more, Vicky. Insist on it."

"I must have more money, Little John."

"All right, if you insist. One hundred thousand. You say you want a percentage, you've got it." He gave her his best, most winning smile. Charm, he knew, had always been his best feature. "Best of all, you get back where you belong. Right on top of the mountain. Have we got a deal?"

She shook her head as if in regret. "It's a deal."

He kissed her, hugged her with too much enthusiasm. "You won't be sorry," he said.

Neither of them believed that.

Hillary Pike liked Zeke Bechtol. Or more to the point, he didn't dislike the accountant. He felt comfortable with Bechtol, a round, rosy man with a jolly manner. Or was it that he felt superior to Bechtol, in command, able to snap their relationship as easily as he could snap one of the pencils Bechtol always had in hand?

One of the reasons Pike had selected Bechtol to work for him was his growing girth. Bechtol possessed a craving for food, sweets in particular. He indulged the craving often and at length during any twenty-four-hour period. Pike suspected that a fat accountant was by nature an honest accountant, since he fed all his subterranean hungers with food instead of money.

Bechtol, who headed up his own accounting firm, seemed to possess no further ambition, content with his modest place in the cosmic scheme. He was nothing like Pike, a fact that the producer had not overlooked. Pike never trusted anybody too much like himself.

Bechtol looked like a pink Buddha behind his oversized desk. He tapped his knuckles with a pencil.

"What's with Maidenburg?" Pike, swaying slightly in his seat across the desk, said.

"Not interested." Unlike so many fat men, Bechtol was terse, rationing words as if they were in limited supply.

"Did you explain the proposition?"

"In detail."

"The bastard. He said it was almost a sure thing."

"He's got a cash-flow problem."

"Me too. A cash flow is what I'm trying to generate. What if I talked to him, bought him a lunch?"

"He's on a diet."

"A diet?"

"Yoghurt and a banana for lunch."

"Every day?"

"Every day."

"What kind of a diet is that? To hell with the freak. I got Hackanum for fifty thousand."

"That helps."

"We're still short a hundred thousand at least."

"One ninety-five."

"Shit."

"Postpone production."

"I got people on contract, salary."

"Ants."

"What?"

"Ants. In the pants. That's what gets people into financial trouble."

"Zeke, save the jokes. We are talking about money, and money is never funny."

"Not even funny money?"

Pike's hairless white face stiffened, and his eyes locked in place. "Did you hear from Connell?"

"He wants to see the script."

"The bastard makes hamburger patties, he can't read. He's a greenhorn."

"Thirty years. He's been a citizen for thirty years."

"I'll talk to him. The script stinks, you think I'd show it to him! Next thing, he wants to meet a starlet. What am I, some kind of pimp?"

"I'll arrange a meeting."

"I don't understand Maidenburg. What does he really want?"

"A tax shelter."

"Tax shelter?"

"You want to talk about shelters?"

Pike cracked the knuckles on his right hand, one by one, before he answered. "Let me tell you how I got started in the picture business—putting up tents for a nickel-and-dime carnival. I barked, hustled, sold tickets. I was in charge of security. I managed a dance hall in Wichita, Kansas, which nobody in his right mind should have to do. For two years I operated a musical tent on a lake in upstate New York. I produced road companies that toured forever, until they were never heard of again.

"Sam Spiegel, he began by running a fairground.

And when he got into the movie business, he made some pretty bad product. Did he give up? No! He produced *Bridge on the River Kwai.* You didn't know that?"

Bechtol acknowledged that he was ignorant of Sam Spiegel's accomplishments.

"Also," Pike went on in his thin, sibilant voice, "*African Queen* and *Lawrence of Arabia* and *On the Waterfront*. Fine pictures, admit it."

Bechtol made his confession. "You're right, Hillary. Of course, you're right." Good food and more business than his firm could handle had created a patient man in Zeke Bechtol.

"Sam Speigel received awards. And glory."

"Did he make any money?"

"A fortune."

"Okay, Hillary, we won't talk about tax shelters, even if it is a sure thing."

"When I make a fortune, we'll discuss ways and means of sheltering it. Nothing is a sure thing."

"When you play the game with other people's money, when there is no chance of you losing a cent, when you can only win—what would you call it?"

"A sure thing."

"Exactly."

Pike leaned back in his chair, fingertips touching lightly. "I've got a little time. Can it hurt to listen for a few minutes?"

Following is the now famous interview given by actress Sandy Hayden to Joan Kaufman, the freelance critic and writer, as published in the Village Scream. *The interview appeared the week after the film* Provincetown *was put into release in New York and in Los Angeles. It was during that week that Sandy Hayden went from professional obscurity to stardom, on the strength of her performance in the film.*

GIRL USED; WOMAN BORN
by Joan Kaufman

NEW YORK: Sandy Hayden's been there. Thrust by a world she never made into the lower depths. By men. By the system. Admittedly by a failure of her own nerve.

But she made it back. Little girl lost flexed her muscles finally and became all woman; full, independent, brave.

We face each other under a plane tree near the Sheep Meadow in Central Park. She sits cross-legged, relaxed, and natural in faded French jeans and Frye boots, a sky-blue T-shirt for which her body does wonderful things. Men and women alike pass and look her over; she looks fantastic. The little girl's face—pouty, stunningly sexual in its simple construction—exhibits no makeup. Nothing to detract from her natural woman's look. My Sony is running, and our conversation grows warm and very human as the tape unreels.

"I dig time in the kitchen," she reveals without pretension. Those disarming round eyes fix on mine, and we soon make intimate, meaningful contact, one-to-one. Beautiful.

"Cooking is great," Sandy says. "But not for some dude who believes it's coming to him. Because I enjoy it, because I want to do it. For me and for someone I like being with, you dig it."

"Please go on, Sandy."

"I loathe housework, fussing over *things*, picking up

after people or even myself, cleaning. The point is to put in your time on this mortal coil as you see fit, freely. Right?"

Right on, I tell her. Here she is, zipping up that phony Hollywood ladder two rungs at a time but still being herself, cool, untouched by all the crap.

"Is it true your part in *Provincetown* was enlarged after the location was wrapped up?"

"Yes, it was. Hillary Pike, the producer, and a dear, sweet individual if ever there was one. . . . A real human person. Hillary ordered the new scenes, had them written, the role broadened and deepened, made clearer. Hillary directed the extra scenes himself. I was very proud."

"Obviously you think highly of this Pike fellow. You don't dislike men."

She gives the already famous Hayden laugh, head thrown back, mouth wide and free, the long throat stretched in grace and beauty. "Men are terrific. At least, some of them."

"I've been told that your father—"

"I hate him. Always have, always will. A drunkard . . . he used to beat my mother."

"And you?"

"I'd rather not say what he did to me."

"The people out there, they want to know the truth, the real you. They'll love you for it."

"I understand what you're saying to me. Yes, my father beat me, and more."

"More?"

"I was fourteen. Okay, well-developed physically, but still . . ." Tears turn her eyes into shining orbs beyond my powers of description.

"But still . . ." I prod gently.

"A child."

"Yes."

"He came after me."

"The bastard."

"Into my room late one night."

"Drunk?"

"Stinking."

"You were asleep?"

"He woke me and—"

"Poor dear. Incest is a major problem the Establishment in this country refuses to confront. You were a virgin?"

"I heard my mother in the next room crying. She *knew.*"

"She'd seen him go into your room?"

"He told her what he was going to do."

"It went on?"

"Until I couldn't tolerate it anymore. I hit him. With my ice skate, split his head open."

"Good for you."

She sobbed uncontrollably for a long time before she could regain control. Her now red eyes confronted me. "No more. I won't speak of it again."

We went back to her career. "How did you begin acting?"

"In high school. I acted every chance I could. Later in stock, small parts, anything to gain experience, to master my art. I even did chorus work on Broadway, on tour. In New York I studied with Gene Frankel, dear, dear Gene. On the Coast with Jeff Corey. I owe a great deal to all my teachers."

"And Hillary Pike?"

"Hillary helped me to develop confidence. Putting me in *P-town* meant a lot to me. My first movie."

"You've got the talent and the beauty."

"Talent is a special gift. In every area of human endeavor. To be talented . . . Talented people stand apart, don't they? Separated from the crowd, you might say. A part of society but not there. Aloneness, that's it. All people of talent are ultimately alone. All the rewards, the riches . . . the attention, the swimming pools, the Rollses, the servants, the big houses. What does it finally mean if you are alone?"

"Nothing."

"The day of reckoning comes to all of us."

"Sandy, I must ask this question."

"Anything."

"The publicity on *P-town* makes you out to be sexy and beautiful, which is true, of course. But is that the image you truly want to project in this decade of women's liberation?"

"Until you're established, nobody pays attention. Nobody listens. You have no voice."

"No power?"

"Exactly. Once I'm on top . . . well, it's all political, isn't it? A movie star can reach people, influence them, help turn their heads toward correct thinking."

"Power is vital."

"Only way to go."

"Beautiful, the way you've worked it out for yourself. But work and changing the world are not all a woman lives for. . . ."

"You mean love?"

"Is there someone in your life?"

"You mean a man?"

"Not necessarily."

Sandy laughs a good laugh, full of kind understanding. Here she is, a woman in full control, certain of her femininity.

"Nothing is necessarily good or bad between two human persons. If a woman turned me on . . . well, all right."

"You know what the philistines will make of that?"

Again that finely tuned laughter. "I'm a woman for men, essentially. Let them make of it what they will."

"Is the bedroom a special place for you, Sandy?"

"Come on . . ."

I grow embarrassed. It *is* a stupid question. My confusion compounds my stupidity. "Is it always good? . . ."

She is kind, thoughtful, considers the question seriously. "I suppose," she answers eventually, "that all women are actresses at heart. After all, every female must pretend at some time in her life. Especially in the bedroom. . . ."

Right on.

4

There she is!

Beautiful. Lithe, gleaming, delicate. If she's less than perfect, she's the more appealing for being so humanly and irresistibly flawed.

"Ladies and gentlemen, Audrey Hepburn!"

Applause rises up like a seductive wave, becoming louder, sustained by the collective excitement and an outpouring of affection. Audrey stands modestly. In pristine white, those bony shoulders bare, that mobile smile fading in and out, those immense eyes reflecting her appreciation. She extends one slender arm.

"The envelope, please."

The envelope is given over, and she opens it. A hush settles over the hall, and she gazes out into the eye of the television camera, prolonging the suspense.

"The award for the best screenplay adapted from another medium . . . for *Provincetown* . . . Tom . . ."

"Jesus fucking Christ!"

". . . Reynolds!"

"What?" His wife, slumped against the door, spoke grumpily. "What's the matter now?"

"Nothing, nothing." Reynolds, refocused on the road ahead, paid attention to his driving. The Eldorado purred. All fantasy, a long-held dream so familiar as to be real. What a great moment it would be! He began composing his acceptance speech in his head.

"I want to thank the man who made all of this possible—me!"

Why not? All the B.S. Oscar winners handed down. All for public consumption. What the hell, the writer was the root of all good drama. Literature. The flicks. He, Tom Reynolds, was the writer. The True and Fundamental talent. The Creative Force. The rest were helpless, useless, pointless, without his work.

"I feel sick."

He looked over at his wife.

"You look okay." She looked terrific. Fantastic face, and a body to match. Good enough to eat. Not that she was having it that way, not Wanda. Wanda considered human genitals to be disgusting. Or at least distasteful. Not to be inspected too closely. A portion of the anatomy to be used only when absolutely necessary, and then in a most orthodox manner. But Reynolds had been working on her, pressuring her, and, he was convinced, moving her toward a more mature, healthier attitude.

"I don't care how I look, I feel lousy."

Reynolds knew she cared very much about her appearance. She spent hours in front of a mirror applying makeup, checking up on herself. She had promised to come through for him this time; but would she?

"You in pain?"

She had the look of a high-school cheerleader, which once she'd been. The tight-assed body, the strong round legs, the cropped golden hair and light eyes. She reminded Reynolds of June Allyson or Gloria De Haven. One of those.

They'd met at a college dance and he recalled the faintest nuances of his reaction. He was *ready*. The old tool was cranked up, fat and heavy, ready to *go*. One look at her had turned him on. High-voltage stuff. He went after her like a dog after a bone.

But she held him off, firm in defense of her virtue. She was—he found it hard to believe even now—a *virgin.* And proud of it. As if virginity were an affirmative act. She kept her thighs clenched despite his most passionate entreaties. She did, however, permit him free reign of her incredible firm and well-shaped breasts. Once in a while she deigned to give him a hand-job. She became rather good at it, too.

But her hymen remained intact until their wedding night. There were times when Reynolds perceived his wife as still a virgin, mentally if not physically. He had been able to inspire her to sexual flights of fancy and ecstasy only occasionally, and then not for very long. Reynolds was determined to turn her on. Break her loose. Make her as good in the hay as she looked. He wanted her kinky, freaky, crazy. At least, a little bit of the time.

"It's my stomach," she said, pulling him back to common ground.

"Your stomach hurts?"

"I'm nauseated. My head hurts."

"You have a headache?" He didn't care about her head. Not now. On the road ahead, traffic was slowing down, backing up, coming to a complete stop. Jesus fucking Christ, what now! "Premenstrual," he said.

She sat up straight. "I am not, I am not."

"Whatever you say."

"You always say that, always. Whenever I'm out of sorts. Whenever I disagree with you about something. Premenstrual. That's your explanation for everything."

"Don't be absurd."

"I am not premenstrual."

"You ought to know."

"Sometimes I hate you, Tommy."

"Very nice. Very nice to talk to your husband that way."

"I should never have come along. I don't like the beach. I peel. You know how I peel."

"You said you wanted to come."

"You're the one who'll meet interesting people, do interesting things. While I just hang around. I thought it was going to be special."

"What?"

"Being married to a famous writer."

He considered that. Fame was one of the rewards of his work. He'd always craved celebrity, yearning to be noticed, recognized by strangers. Fussed over in expensive restaurants. Invited onto the Johnny Carson show. One day . . .

All his boyhood dreams were falling into place. He'd written a thousand short stories and dreamed of bursting onto the literary scene like a latter-day Saroyan or Norman Mailer. He received rejection regularly and tried to ignore it, his ambition more powerful than his insecurity. He kept writing. A bad idea for a story grew into a novel, and, surprise of surprises, it was published. Ignored critically, it went unread and unsold.

The hell with it. He wrote another book. It was not as good as the first one, but it sold more copies and was reviewed in the *Saturday Review*. He celebrated by taking Wanda to Provincetown for a holiday and decided it was a good locale for a novel. Also, it allowed him to write the trip off on his income tax.

Success followed. He was hired to write the screenplay. Fame and fortune were coming his way.

He put his eyes on Wanda. "I wasn't famous when we got married."

"Now you are."

"I have a certain celebrity, I suppose."

"Thirteen weeks on the *Times*'s bestseller list, that's famous."

"I guess so."

"But nothing has changed."

"What did you expect?"

She had expected something. Something more. Better. She craved rewards she couldn't name. Pleasures she'd never experiencel. Excitement she was unable to define.

"You'll have a good time," he said.

She knew better. Perhaps if she did some of the things Tommy wanted to do. Some of those wild, crazy, disgusting things. Not that they disgusted her that much; they didn't. In fact, she was curious, more than she let on. She wondered what would happen if she told Tommy some of the things she imagined when they made love. The other men that flashed into her mind. The things they did to her, the things she did to them. But of course she never told him, didn't dare, was afraid to.

Bringing her along was a mistake, Reynolds informed himself. She was going to be a drag. An intolerable burden. This location in P-town was his big chance for fame and fortune. A bigger chance than she could imagine, bigger than he dared to consider. How far he had come!

Thomas Aquinas Reynolds, born in Flushing, raised in Babylon. Queens College, B.A. Nobody else in his class had done so much at such a young age. And he was just beginning.

P-town was going to be a ball. If Wanda gave him room enough. After all, he was the *author*, and people —women—were turned on by writers. Especially successful writers.

"Maybe," Wanda said, "I'll throw up."

"No, don't! I'll pull over."

"Maybe, I said. Not definitely."

"You want to throw up?"

"Nobody *wants* to throw up."

"Don't quibble."

"I am not quibbling. Why are you stopping? We haven't moved for five minutes."

"The traffic is jammed up."
"What's wrong?"
"I don't know."
"Shouldn't you find out?"
"How?"
"Ask somebody."
"Who?"
"The person in the car up ahead."
"He doesn't know any more about it than I do." He fixed his eyes on the temperature gauge. The red needle began to swing toward the high side. He decided not to look any more. He stepped out onto the road. "What's going on?" he yelled to the driver of the car in front.
"An accident up ahead, I think."
"Do you know where we are?"
"Buzzards Bay."
Reynolds climbed back into the car. "An accident," he reported.
"How long will we be here?"
"I don't know."
"I wish I could sleep."
"Why don't you try? In the back seat?"
She put her head back and closed her eyes. Reynolds looked at her. What a face! No man could resist her. He remembered how Jerry Wheeler had turned on when they met at the Wyeth exhibition at the Lincoln-Brown Gallery. Kept trying to look down the front of her dress all night. Wanda, Reynolds said to himself, you are the key to the lock, my entry into the club. A honking horn drew his attention. A battered Chevrolet had pulled up alongside, the driver gesturing to Reynolds. He rolled down the window.
"Hey, pal," the driver of the Chevy shouted, "you're spilling gas by the gallon."
"What?"
"Gas. You're losing gas."

"Oh." Reynolds felt a glob of despair form in his chest. It burned as if to break out of the darkness. He burped and nodded his thanks, closed the window. He maneuvered the Eldorado off the road and into a filling station.

Wanda sat up. "What's wrong?"

"We're losing gasoline."

"What does that mean?"

"Trouble," he said, before getting out of the car. He got down on his knees and peered under the right rear end. A steady stream of dark liquid poured onto the blacktop. Reynolds cursed his luck and went into the filling station. A lanky man in blue coveralls stood with one foot up on a chair, watching the long line of standing cars.

"Excuse me . . ." Reynolds began.

"Gets worse, y'know. Later in the summer. Real bad."

"The traffic?"

"Cars all heat up till they line the road like souvenir shops." The man grinned, yellow teeth long and sharp. "There you are, that's the way to get onto the Cape weekends, one of them motorbikes."

Reynolds looked out at the road. A lone cyclist advanced steadily between the lines of automobiles. The rider looked like a cross between Marlon Brando and Jack Palance, brawny bare arms awash with tattoos. Reynolds turned back to the man with the yellow teeth.

"I'm leaking gas."

"That's not good."

"Can you do something?"

"Don't know what."

"You're a mechanic, aren't you?"

"Yup. But tanks are out of my line. What you need is a new tank, if you've got a hole in your old one."

"How do you know there's a hole in the tank?"

"It's leaking, you said."

Reynolds grunted. "Where can I buy another tank?"

"Henry Moorehead's place. If you're lucky, he'll have one that fits your car. That's a real nice car."

"Yes. Where . . .?"

"Up the road, first right turn."

Reynolds turned to leave. "Thank you."

"No point in you going, though. Henry ain't there. Not in April. Henry takes a holiday in April. Up in Maine. Got a little cabin on a lake up there, fishes and just takes it easy for a whole month each year."

"What am I going to do?"

"Don't rightly know."

"Is it dangerous?"

"Leaking fuel? I reckon it could be. A spark from the exhaust might send the whole car up, I'd say."

Reynolds went back to the Eldorado. Wanda was putting on fresh lipstick. She looked healthy and happy. Reynolds peered under the car. No sign of a leak. He went back to the filling station. "It stopped," he said to the mechanic.

"Stopped?"

"The leak, it stopped. What do you think it could be?"

"Maybe overflow, maybe."

"Overflow?"

"Gas heats up, vaporizes, liquefies, spills over. Happens a lot when the weather gets hot."

"Then the tank is all right?"

"Couldn't say for sure."

"But it might be?"

"Might at that."

Reynolds went back to the car, slid behind the wheel.

"Well?" Wanda said.

"I think it's all right."

"Are you sure?"

"I'm not sure of anything."

"If you really love me, you won't do anything to endanger my life."

He groaned and started the engine. Sounded fine, and he rolled out into the line of traffic, now slowly inching ahead. He thought about the Wheelers and decided to be nice to Wanda. "I love you," he said, squeezing her thigh.

"Hmmm."

"I'm looking forward to seeing the Wheelers. Jerry likes you a lot."

She stared straight ahead. "If you love me, you won't make me do anything I don't want to do."

Piss, he said to himself. Piss, shit, and corruption. She was going to spoil everything.

Cape Cod reaches out from mainland Massachusetts about twenty-five miles into the Atlantic Ocean, west to east, like a man's arm, sharply bent at the elbow, less so at the wrist. At no point is the Cape more than ten miles wide. The flexed arm could be taken as a continental warning to unwary sea voyagers. Or as a beckoning invitation to use the great natural harbor formed in the crook of that sandy limb.

Unlike the remainder of New England, all hills and mountains, granite and marble, and rockbound coasts, Cape Cod consists mainly of sand and gravel and silt and clay, studded here and there by gray boulders.

The Cape came into being during the Pleistocene epoch, a fragment of the Ice Age that terminated some ten thousand years ago. Indians were the first inhabitants of the area, and later the Vikings. In 1620 the Pilgrims put in to what was to become Provincetown. Though they decided to visit only, and not live on the Cape, they had a profound effect on the neighborhood.

Perhaps the bleak autumnal weather soured them

on the Cape. Or the wide mud flats across which they had to plod in order to come ashore. Or was it the immense dunes that must have appeared like ghostly mountains in the chill dawn? Whatever the cause, they moved on, putting in at Plymouth, on the mainland.

Those rugged individuals who subsequently came to the Cape learned how to work the mean land, to raise decent crops, corn being principal among them. Settlements began to take shape, the forerunners of the fifteen towns that today dot Cape Cod.

There were slaves—mostly black, some white—and only the meager material wealth of the inhabitants kept the slave population down. Whales frequently appeared off the coast, and occasionally one of the big mammals was thrown up on the beach. They were swiftly stripped and the blubber boiled for the profit of man, colony, and crown. When deep-water whaling came of age, Cape Codders took to it enthusiastically. The last whaler out of Provincetown was Captain John Cook. He went after the giant beasts until 1916.

The sea was a rough and relatively unrewarding existence for ordinary seamen, who often jumped ship. As a result, ship captains were forced farther and farther afield in search of replacements, leading ultimately to Cape Verdes and the Azores. Portuguese fishermen had plied Provincetown's waters for centuries, and their descendants now returned to put down roots. Provincetown took on the distinctive flavor of a Portuguese fishing village.

João Costa was the first of his clan to make it to the Cape. He put in long, hard hours for low wages, and when he died fifty-four years later, patriarch of a large and varied brood, he spoke no English, left no estate, and asked merely that he be buried in Portugal. The request was considered extravagant by those who remained, and they ignored it.

João's second grandson, Ernesto, who spoke both

English and Portuguese, perceived the futility of putting a lifetime into another man's service. He saved enough money to put a down payment on an old crabber, which he scraped down, calked, and painted. He was the first man in the long and uncertain history of his family ever to possess a boat of his own.

Five years later, he bought a second crabber and put his brother to work on it. When he was fifty, he sold the two crabbers and purchased an old and battered dragger. It was the beginning of a fleet of four draggers he would eventually own.

When his son, Mario, reached his majority, Ernesto turned command of the ancient dragger over to him, in return for twenty percent of the catch. Mario promptly replaced the old motor with a secondhand diesel and began dreaming of the day when he would command a fleet of his own.

Mario Costa was generally considered to be the best-looking young man in Provincetown, at least among the Portuguese population. He agreed with that assessment. He was also thought to be the smartest young man in town. He agreed with that. Mario also realized that he was doomed to spend the rest of his life fishing, a prospect that gave him little pleasure. So he made up his mind; if he had to fish, he intended to be good at it, better than anyone else. And eventually richer.

Late one afternoon, Mario was hosing down the deck, a dull job, and not worthy of an audience, when he noticed a man watching with more than casual interest. Mario concluded the man on the dock was a fairy, like so many others in P-town, and went about his business.

"Nice boat," the man said after a while.

"She's okay."

"You own it?"

"My father owns it. I am the captain." He straightened up; Mario had dealt with fags before. "You want to go for a ride? Just the two of us, and you'll pay good money, won't you? You just don't want a lot of other people hanging around."

The man had laughed at that. "You get a lot of that kind of thing?"

"Enough."

"I got something else in mind. My name is Lou Klein."

Mario waited patiently.

Lou Klein grinned, showing a lot of strong white teeth. "How'd you like to put your boat in the movies?"

Novick was gone. Back to New York to ride herd on the facile hands in his art factory. Making sure the required number of paintings was produced on schedule, dismissing those artists whose work failed to come up to his standards, those who attempted to paint better than they should.

"Do good," he said in parting to Sexton. "Be on the lookout for trends. I got a hunch pointilism is going to make a comeback."

"I'll give you the word."

"No letters," Novick cautioned. "The post office is a downer. You phone direct. Cheaper that way. I'm not there, leave a message. There's a girl on the payroll, she writes everything down."

Alone in Provincetown, Sexton settled into the small apartment behind the gallery. This was his fifth season in Novick's employ, and the gallery and apartment were like old friends met by accident, providing a reminiscent feeling of peace and familiarity.

Except for Novick, no one knew where he was or what he was up to. And he appreciated the solitude. Appreciated being apart from the world and its dangers, separated and safe from all the old pressures. He felt emotionally strong and healthy, excited by what lay immediately ahead, pleased by each new stimulus, interested suddenly in everything, as if new-born. Or reborn.

That feeling of well-being was temporary, he knew. It always dissolved, and the old, bad emotions took over, the memories. No matter how far he traveled, he was burdened by the emotional luggage of a lifetime, and he understood that eventually it would drag him down. But for now he felt just fine.

As always, the gallery and the apartment needed repair. The plumbing was a mess and it took him three days to replace rusted pipes and a broken elbow, get the water running properly. The front of the gallery was in need of a paint job, and the floor inside had to be sanded and refinished.

When the work was done, Sexton unpacked his inventory and checked it against the lists Novick had supplied. He began to hang the paintings according to a detailed blueprint: a place for every painting, every painting in its place. Novick was a man who overlooked nothing.

In his spare time, he wandered along Commercial Street renewing old acquaintances, or hiked the dunes and the beaches. Most days were gray and misty, rain falling intermittently. But occasionally the sun would appear, and Sexton would hurry off to Herring Cove to a place sheltered from the ocean winds and sun himself.

Trade at the gallery was slow this early in the season. Later it would pick up as more tourists visited P-town. But now customers came only when the weather was bad, or in the evenings. Few of them bought anything; few of them were expected to.

"It's the fat guys," Novick had said, describing his clientele. "They don't know good art from bad art, and good painting would scare them. So give 'em room, let 'em make up their own minds. What they want is something they recognize. Drives 'em crazy if they have to think when they look at a painting."

One evening a couple appeared dressed in white slacks and black turtleneck sweaters, identical soft suede jackets. They wore their hair the same way, falling gently across their temples in graceful waves, brushed back over their ears, expertly cut to a point just short of their shoulders. They might have been identical twins, Sexton thought when they materialized out of the night, the same unblemished not-so-young cheeks, the same bland expression in watery gray eyes, the same delicate features, complete with turned-up nose, courtesy of a surgeon's skillful knife. Sexton had never been sure which of them was prettier.

"Hi!" they said as one. "Remember us?"

"Jerry," she said.

"And Junie," he said.

"Wheeler," she added.

"Hello," Sexton said.

"How great to see you!" Jerry said. His handshake lacked force, a furtive touch without intimacy or meaning.

"Sexton," she murmured, and kissed him on the cheek. "You look marvelous." Her hand lingered on his chest. "Best-looking dude in town."

Sexton retreated a step without thinking about it. He wanted a drink suddenly.

Jerry produced a gold cigarette case. "Care to light up? Best Colombian . . ."

"I'll pass," Sexton said.

"Sexton," Junie said regretfully. "You never change."

"Still on the sauce?" Jerry asked.

"I'm a man with a thirst."

Junie dragged on her husband's joint. "So good, Sexton. You must let us seduce you."

Sexton displayed his teeth; it was hardly a smile.

Jerry waved his arm to take in the entire gallery. "Anything worth looking at?"

"Nothing you want."

"I dig distortion," Junie said.

"I know," Sexton answered.

She gave him her most seductive smile, set out on a quick tour of the gallery, Jerry trailing behind.

"Right on," Jerry said when they had finished. "Nothing I must buy."

Junie dipped in a girlish curtsy. "Buy me *that*, Daddy!" She pointed at Sexton.

Her husband laughed. "Set a price, Sexton?"

"Not for sale."

Junie skipped toward the door. "My loss."

"Everything's for sale," her husband replied.

"Soon," Junie said, just before she made it all the way out, "party time! Do come."

"Yes," Jerry put in. "Do."

Jerry and Junie Wheeler were part of the local landscape. They lived in a huge house, existed in a world that Sexton usually avoided. He had attended a couple of their parties, found the booze plentiful and excellent, and went only when free drinks were in order.

His summer was planned. In taking this job, he was able to earn money enough to support himself for the year ahead. The long season allowed him sufficient time in which to paint, to read, to think. He would make casual conversation with customers, with shopkeepers in town, an occasional fisherman. It was enough; he felt no need for friends, no need for intimacy of any sort.

He didn't expect the past to catch up, to come strolling into the gallery, into his life, as it now did on a cool spring evening in Provincetown.

Yet he was not unhappy at the unexpected intrusion. Surprised, startled, even a little afraid. But not sad to once again see John Patrick Michael O'Day, hero and legend of his youth, still alive and walking around.

A woman accompanied O'Day. Strikingly beautiful,

tall and full-bodied, hair worn in a single long braid. She looked vaguely familiar to Sexton, but after a second glance he concentrated on O'Day.

The director had aged since Sexton had last seen him. All of them had, of course. But being John Patrick Michael O'Day, he had done it better than most. He still held himself militarily erect, a man in command of himself and all who entered his territory. He moved easily, with that slightly upward tilt of his chin that made it appear he was inspecting everyone and every place, as if about to cast a new picture.

Though not as tall as Sexton was, O'Day was a tall man. Slender and graceful, which fit the hoofer he once was. His complexion was ruddy, his stylishly barbered hair and mustache barely highlighted with glints of silver. His hawklike nose lent interest and appeal to his lean face. He was smoking a cigarette, and Sexton assumed it was a Gitane.

Sexton held his place near the small desk at the back of the gallery, watching as O'Day and his friend looked at the pictures on the wall. They were no more than a dozen feet away when O'Day glanced in Sexton's direction.

"I know you," he said, searching for a name to go with the face, searching for a setting in which to place the face.

"On the Coast," Sexton said.

"Ah. You directed some pictures. For Columbia, I think."

"Warner's."

"Yes. Action stuff . . ."

"Westerns, a couple of cops-and-robbers."

"Yes. Good, too. You had a feel for movement. Tell me your name."

"Sexton."

"Yes, Jim Sexton." O'Day frowned. "You worked for me once."

"You've got a good memory. On *Times Hard, Times Fair.*"

"The second unit, yes. This guy is good, Vicky. Very good. You know Vicky Pierce?"

"Miss Pierce," Sexton said. He should've recognized her. Time had changed her very little, and only for the better.

O'Day was speaking. "This your gallery? Not my kind of art, but—"

"For the tourists . . ."

"All a matter of taste. You're out of the picture business. Hell, it's cluttered up with dilettantes these days. Amateur night in Dixie, all computers and accountants these days. All the fun is gone."

"I manage the gallery, that's all." Sexton grew irritated with himself; he was explaining, apologizing. For what? And why to O'Day, practically a stranger?

"We'll be shooting a picture around town," O'Day said. "Come and see us."

"I might."

"Nice meeting you, Mr. Sexton," Vicky Pierce said.

Sexton nodded in her direction. When they were gone, he sat back down at the desk, weakness flooding his limbs. He very much needed a drink. *Damn the past.*

5

If Cape Cod is a flexed arm, Race Point is the knuckle of the hand, aimed in a westerly direction, the back of the hand set against the pounding of the Atlantic. The beach, certainly one of the world's most beautiful, is smooth, wide, the sand colored a soft dun, shielded at the rear by a high line of parabolic dunes.

The summits of some Cape dunes rise up to more than eighty feet, and one dune has been measured at more than one hundred feet high. Within the curve of the dune ridge is an open sand floor. Sand blown over the crest forms a steep lee slope called the slip face. Ridges of sand run away from the shore, some dotted with pitch pine, others patched with beach grass. Still others are naked and vulnerable to the elements.

On this, the second day of shooting, Vicky Pierce stood with her back to the massive sand walls. Isolated and diminished by nature's impressive creations. She stood alone on the beach, about a quarter-mile from where O'Day hung in the air on a high boom, along with Frank Jacoby and an Arriflex camera.

From this vantage point, O'Day intended to film Vicky as she moved idly along, a tiny, solitary figure unconnected to the rest of the world. This slow shot was to set the mood for the story, establishing much of the character Vicky Pierce would portray. It would be used to open the picture, under the credits.

Walk on signal, O'Day had told her. Nothing more to do. Stroll along the deserted strand as if intent on getting nowhere. Ah, there's a shell you like! Pick it up, inspect it, take a step or two, and toss it aside. Look out to sea as if in search of something. And, finding nothing, you go on. All very simple. Easy. No sweat, right.

Wrong. She felt a rising apprehension, an anticipation of failure such as she had not known in years. A tart, penetrating awareness of personal and professional inadequacies.

Added to that, a physical distress. The wind whipped off the water, stinging her naked thighs, her arms and shoulders. In the picture, it was summertime, and accordingly, she wore only a black tank suit, not modest, not protective.

She shivered and hugged herself. Location work had never appealed to her. She was at her best in the structured and readily controlled confines of a studio. Here, too many things could go wrong, and inevitably would. Down the beach, the camera boom swung low, and O'Day and Frank Jacoby swang to the ground. She moaned at the delay and silently urged them to get on with it.

Jacoby was a stocky man with alert eyes that seemed to miss nothing, and a gray beard that made him resemble some ancient Egyptian priest. He squinted along the beach to where Vicky waited.

"This light is weird," O'Day said absently.

"I like it. The air is pure, gives us a full dose of sunlight. And the reflection off the water . . ."

O'Day lit a Gitane and traced a shallow ditch in the sand with the toe of his boot, erased it almost at once. "There's too much glare, Frank."

Jacoby glanced sidelong at the director. It was not like O'Day to involve himself in such matters. The composition of a frame, yes. The use of light for dramatic effect, yes. But never did he trespass into that area that was strictly the cinematographer's. It occurred to Jacoby that O'Day was drawn up a little tighter than usual, his voice harsher, more caustic.

"Light," Jacoby said without special emphasis, "that's my medium. The rest—camera, filters, lenses—all technical." He saw the tension in O'Day's face and went on reassuringly. "I'm using neutral density filters to compensate for the glare, Little John."

"When we do the water scenes . . ."

"Maybe I'll overexpose one stop over the meter reading."

"Yes, that should do it." O'Day swore softly. "Stay with me, Frank. This picture means more to me than it should. My guts are in knots."

"I understand."

O'Day doubted it. He doubted that anybody who had not climbed to the very peak of the mountain, stood there in charge for such a very long time, could comprehend the necessity for attaining that lofty station once again. Few men made it all the way up. Fewer remained there for any length of time. Even fewer, having been knocked off that rarefied perch, ever made it back. O'Day had vowed to join that select club. He had to.

"Let's talk business," he said, brushing at his mustache, speaking intimately, as if taking the cinematographer into his confidence. "Go for the emptiness first, the infinite stretch of sand, and no one on it. I want that sense of isolation . . ."

"Look at that sky. Empty, goes on forever."

"Yeah, good. Start with the sky and bring us down to the beach."

"Ocean in between."

"No ocean."

"The water will bridge the gap."

"We make a leap, sky to earth, and that's all there is."

"Okay."

"Okay, the camera is on the sand. It begins a deliberate search. We pick out a slight movement—Vicky. At this distance, she is unidentifiable as a human being. What the hell are we looking at? Some one-celled creature come wiggling up out of the depths? Some frightening beast unknown to us? We move in without haste, allowing her to come toward us."

"I got it."

"I want an essence here of . . . of apartness. Jesus, whatever it is, it is all alone. The camera picks up speed as it floats down to her level, begins to close in . . ."

"I'm carrying a 12-to-240 zoom."

"The audience sees her now. A woman. And she's a beauty, they can tell even at this distance. We keep closing until the audience recognizes that this is Miss America twenty years later. We can see the years through the tank suit. The heavy breasts, the roundness of her belly, the fullness of her thighs."

"I don't have to—"

"The hell you don't!" O'Day said curtly. "Show it all. She is forty years old, and it's all visible. In her body, the way she moves and holds herself, in her face. Here's a dame who's been there and back and wonders what the hell it was all about. What went wrong? The audience will identify quickly with that. What the hell, every last one of us has made the trip and asked the question."

"You're a hard man, O'Day."

"This picture—I want it cool . . . no, not cool, cold, zero degree, with a frozen look of time standing still when it begins. When it ends, it will end in a hot rush of human passion, the ice having melted to tears. Does that make sense to you, Frank?"

"It's your picture, Little John."

"Yes. In my head, it's all there, and no one, not Pike,

not Reynolds, has the same vision. Bring us up tight enough so that we can see the agony in Vicky's face, the agony and the anger, the determination to let nothing, nobody, ever touch her again. She has been badly hurt."

"I'll hold for your cut."

"Vicky will give it to us. She's to *see* the audience, recognize them as the *source* of all her miseries, strike out at them—'Let me alone!' Keep grinding until I tell you to stop."

"I like it, Little John."

"From the start, we keep 'em on edge. Never let them know what we're up to. Create anticipation, then fake them out. Jar 'em. Make 'em uncomfortable. I intend to destroy their sense of time, even place, to leave them only with the essence . . . of the people in the film, and of themselves."

Jacoby laughed softly. "None of that is in the script Reynolds wrote."

"The script won't be written until the film is done. Until we've shot it all, until I've edited it, patched it together, made something of it." He looked over to where Tom Reynolds sat slumped in a chair, staring out at the horizon. From their first meeting months before, O'Day had formed a soft dislike for the writer. The dislike had hardened during the time they had spent together discussing the script, creating new scenes, polishing dialogue.

"There's a lot of fancy talk in the script," Jacoby said.

Yes, O'Day thought. It was littered with wordy exchanges and extended speechifying, as if Reynolds were determined to instruct the world on the True and Right way to live.

"He's a college boy, that Reynolds," O'Day muttered, flicking the butt of his Gitane to the sand, burying it. "Those academic assholes have ruined more writers. What this script needs is some professional doctoring by a good old-fashioned craftsman."

"That's you, Little John. None better."

O'Day's confidence flagged briefly. "In the old days, sure. Now I don't know." He lit another Gitane. "There's nobody else to do it. Pike wouldn't bring in a collaborator. I wanted Goldman or Milius. He wouldn't go for it."

"They cost."

"Talent costs. What the hell, play the cards you're dealt. Let me know when you're ready to go. I better have a few words with Reynolds."

He went over to the writer, sat on the sand facing him, his back to the ocean. "Great view. The Cape is perfect for making a picture, fantastic visuals."

"You forget, I wrote the book."

O'Day checked his initial response. It wasn't necessary that he approve of Reynolds, only that he work with him. He needed the writer. "God made the ocean," he said.

"I didn't think a man with your experience and intellectual capacity needed God, Little John."

"A man with my experience and intellectual capacity can't do without God."

"I'm an atheist, myself."

"Everybody's got to believe in something, Tommy." O'Day put on his most agreeable smile to show he meant no harm.

"I'm not sure I understand you."

"Let's talk about the first Pierce-Crespi scene."

"I like it the way it always was."

"But you did do the changes?"

"If you recall, in the book—"

"We're making a film. What I'm after is a compression of incident, emotion, a fluid shifting sensibility."

"I feel I must go on record as protesting—"

"Your protest is acknowledged. Do you have the new pages for me?"

Reynolds nodded. "There is a precedence for the way the characters come together, the way they adhere to each other. In *Lady Chatterley*, for example . . ."

O'Day stopped listening. Reynolds was compelled to present his literary *bona fides* on all possible occasions, to squeeze them into the script, if he could. O'Day warned himself to remain alert and professionally ruthless. He accepted the pages Reynolds proffered and stood up. "Time to go to work," he said.

"If you don't need me . . . ?" Reynolds said, a plea in his voice.

"Suit yourself."

O'Day, Reynolds told himself, as he drove back in to P-town, was getting old. The sharp edge of his talent had become dull, worn down. Reynolds vowed to protect his own artistic interests.

The CooCoo Cage.

Up front, marble-topped ice-cream tables and wire chairs. Some ancient nickelodeons stood in a rank along the wall. Next to them, an honor guard of gumball machines. Suspended from the ceiling and turning slowly, a quartet of black fans, stirring lazy ripples in the otherwise still air.

Pretty girls in short skirts took orders for hamburgers, sodas, ice cream, eggs, homemade pies, and coffee. There was a contrived coziness about the CooCoo Cage, a carefully designed chic that brought people in off Commercial Street, caused them to pay more attention to each other than to the food. And rightly so; the food was that bad.

In the back, past the glass cabinets filled with loose candy for sale, past the stacks of posters and memo paper, past the carvings of seagulls and painted Cape birds, past the Mexican pottery, the boutique.

Here were old and sometimes odd clothes, once again in style. Or soon to be. Antique dresses and blouses, ancient aviator jackets, worn football sweaters, faded Levi's, belts, purses, a collection of odds and ends for decoration and practical wear.

The boutique appealed mightily to Sandy Hayden. She felt at home, comfortable, as she browsed among the old things. She hovered over a cabinet containing Indian jewelry. She moved on to a rack of sailor pants cut to size for chicks, complete with flapped fronts and the traditional thirteen buttons. Delighted with her find, Sandy held a pair to her waist and studied herself in a full-length glass. She liked what she saw—always liked what she saw in the mirror. Her breasts were large and round, the nipples in perpetual tumescence; a little too much for her height and body build, perhaps. But Sandy dug it that way. Her bottom was a tight, curved thrust, a good line. Her mouth was a sullen red pout, and her eyes were violet rounds in a white ground. Looking good, baby. . . .

"Help you?"

A salesgirl had materialized behind her. Kind of cute, with electric blond hair and faded blue eyes, a flimsy blouse stitched up back in Roaring Twenties style. A clown's smile was pasted on her small pale face.

"You think I could wear these?"

The clown's smile shifted, and so did the faded eyes. From bosom to belly to buttocks.

"You can wear anything. Want to try them?"

The salesgirl led the way to a dressing cubicle, flipped the curtain aside. Sandy stepped in and kicked off her loafers, then turned slowly. The salesgirl had not drawn the curtain back; she stood watching. *Let her look.* Sandy stepped out of her jeans and straightened up. The briefest of panties hugged her hips, hid nothing.

"You," the salesgirl said softly, "look good enough to eat."

Sandy allowed herself a long, lazy smile. "I know," she murmured, and drew the curtain.

The sailor pants fit like a second skin, and she bought them, wearing them out. "Come back and see us," the salesgirl said in promising invitation.

"You never know," Sandy said as she left.

Out front, a striped red-and-white sign with blue lettering read: CANDYLAND. The house, painted pink, edged in white, had been built around the turn of the century. A porch complete with wood turns and arches embraced three sides of the structure. Stained glass was set into all the windows on the lower floor. Halfway up Pearl Street, past Bradford, Candyland sat comfortably between an undistinguished Dutch-gambrel and a refurbished Cape Cod.

In the southeast corner of Candyland, a narrow cell with a single small window that admitted a minimum of light, a room created out of leftover space as Candyland had been rebuilt and renovated over the years. It was not much, but it had served Kiley for nearly two weeks.

At night, the chill April air turned the tiny room into a torture chamber, and the small radiator beneath the window hissed and rattled like a creature alive but gave off almost no heat. Kiley had never suffered cold gracefully. But the room was inexpensive, and Kiley was determined to make what little money he had last.

Now Kiley's funds were running short, and he was forced to think of ways to replenish his supply. A knock at the door broke his concentration, and he arranged a dark scowl on his rugged face. "Yeah?"

"Mr. Kiley, I'd like to have a few words with you, if I may."

It was Drouin, the landlord. Not only was Drouin a fag, but he was a frog to boot. If there was anything Kiley liked less than a fag, it was a French fag.

"Okay, come on in."

Drouin advanced into the tiny room in tentative steps, as if afraid he would break something. His smile was transient, his eyes darting, his hands fluttery.

At night, in his apartment in the front of Candyland, Drouin played Beethoven symphonies or Bach on his stereo. Not Kiley's kind of music at all.

During the day Drouin cleaned the rooms or worked in his garden. And every afternoon, the elements willing, Drouin sunned himself on one of the beaches until his skin was the color of worn chamois.

"Sorry to barge in on you this way, Mr. Kiley . . ."

"What do you want?"

Drouin shivered at the rasp of Kiley's voice. His eyes rolled, then settled into line. "It's just that soon . . . Easter's on the way, you see."

"Go to church."

Drouin smiled in limp recognition of what he believed to be a joke. Not very good, but Drouin possessed limited expectations. "Trade picks up around Easter, you understand. Calls are coming in, requests for reservations."

Kiley pushed himself off the bed. "You want to get rid of me?"

"Oh, my, no. Not a bit of it. Although I suppose you did forget about last week's rent. It was due on Monday."

"I pay my way."

"Of course you do, of course. I wasn't concerned. Candyland is my only source of income, you know."

"You'll get yours."

"I should hope *so.*" Drouin's brows went up and

down like broken window shades. He watched Kiley hopefully.

"Tomorrow," Kiley said toughly.

Drouin nodded, started to speak, thought better of it, and left, his mildest hopes dashed.

When he was alone, Kiley admitted to himself that his options were limited. He dared not go back to the city, to the neighborhood. By now Geek had probably returned to the streets, was talking his dumb head off, just the way Bear said he would. Sooner or later the members of Spiderman's gang would figure out what had happened to their president, and they would be very unhappy. They would want Kiley. And so would the fuzz, when the word got around. Unless Bear was able to put things straight, he might not be able to go back to the East Village for a very long time. Maybe never.

He didn't want to think about that now. Here, shaved, with his hair neatly cut, he was safe. Soon the summer crowd would come pouring into P-town, and he would become part of that crowd. He intended to do nothing to call attention to himself, to stay clean, enjoy the summer. But first he had to score. His money supply was running down, and a dude without bread was absolutely nowhere.

He went outside and mounted the Harley and rode it out onto the Mid-Cape Highway. He opened it up and felt the wind stinging his cheeks. The speed, the sense of being one with the elements, surrounded by the roar of the Harley, caused him to feel larger and stronger than he'd ever been. Than anyone had ever been. Riding his bike got him off more than any other trip. . . .

When he returned to Provincetown, it was already dark. His thoughts in order, he went back to his room and put on his Straight Arrow colors. The faded jeans were stretched tight over his round strong butt and outlined his bunched genitals. The jacket, the arms cut off at the shoulders, displayed his huge biceps, the tattoos on each of his arms. A quick glance in the mirror told him that he was looking good, ready to make his move, to connect.

Down Commercial Street, on the far side of the wharf, the Captain's Chest. At the bar, Kiley ordered a beer and a roast-beef sandwich. He ate slowly, scrutinizing the room.

At the scarred table in the back, under a yellow lamp, two men played pool, the click of balls contrapuntal to the sound of a rock group blaring out of the juke. Down the bar, a young couple were kissing, the boy groping the chick's ass. She wiggled and made some moist noises, sucking tongue. Kiley wasn't interested. Alongside the front window, the usual poker game was in progress around an oak table. Kiley finished the sandwich and ordered another beer before going over to watch the game.

The game went on every night. Five or six players, always the same faces. By now he knew their names, and they knew him, although very few words had ever been exchanged. Now one of the men raised his eyes to Kiley's.

"One open place," he said.

"Well, thanks." Kiley sat down, dragged out his bankroll. Just short of fifty dollars in bills and change. He piled it on the table.

"Seven-card," another player said.

"What's wild?" Kiley said, knowing the answer.

"Nothing. Twenty-five and fifty. Ante a half."

"I'm your boy," Kiley said.

"Fresh blood." A little man in a red-watch cap grinned. "Sucker money."

"Belongs to me," another man said.

"You guys may be too good for me," Kiley said.

The man in the red-watch cap grinned again. "Nah. You got a chance. Just a chance."

Kiley'd been studying the game for a week. He knew how each man played, how they bet. There was no way he could lose, not with these rubes. The way he figured, he'd run up his roll, giving himself a cushion until he could make a really important score. Once the summer people began to show . . .

On the first deal, Kiley drew a pair of sevens down, but couldn't help himself. He folded after the sixth card. He bet cautiously, waiting for a run of luck to start. And finally, in the second hour of play, he drew a red flush to the king, on the first five cards. He bet strong, but not too strong, sucking a couple of other players along, showing his strength following the last card, certain he had a winner.

The man in the red-watch cap showed a full house, deuces and sevens. He was laughing as he raked in the pot.

So it went. By midnight, Kiley had blown the fifty, less a single dollar for beer money. He drank the brew slowly and watched the game, his mind already made up, showing his cool. No sore loser here. When the beer was gone, he said good night and left.

He took up a position in a dark doorway halfway down the block and waited. Sometimes the bastards gave a man no choice. To walk around with empty pockets was to be without self-respect.

It was nearly two hours later before they finished the game. Through the plate-glass window, Kiley watched them settle accounts. The man in the red-watch cap was plainly the big winner, and Kiley took some satisfaction in that. He hadn't appreciated the shiteater's grin, not one little bit.

When the man in the red-watch cap left the Captain's Chest, he went straight up Masonic Place and across Bradford, moving at a pretty good clip, looking neither left nor right. Kiley cut through an alley and circled a couple of houses, getting out front. Let the bastard come to him.

On Prince Street, he took shelter in the shadows near the Catholic church, holding still, keeping his breathing shallow. He felt no nervousness, no anticipation, his legs steady, his arms strong.

The man in the red-watch cap swung into view. He was a feisty little guy, bouncing as he walked, whistling softly, as if to celebrate his luck. Kiley let him pass, then moved swiftly, slugging him under one ear. The little man went down, tried immediately to climb back to his feet. Kiley hit him twice more, which seemed appropriate to the job. Kiley went through his pockets and found the poker money. Without another look at the man in the red-watch cap, Kiley hurried back toward Candyland. Feeling good now. Like a man should feel, with a few bucks in his pocket.

Her name was Ella. So it said on the white plastic card pinned to her waitress's uniform. Ella, as in Cinderella, he wondered, saying nothing. Wanting to start nothing. Wanting to encourage nobody. She wiped the plastic-topped table with a damp cloth and arranged a place setting in front of Sexton and brought him a menu. She was contained and competent, doing her job, not more or less. Sexton preferred that people hold to their stated reasons for being; one thing at a time. Life could be confusing even at its simplest.

"Thanks," he said. "I know what I want."

She brought her pencil up to the ready position and waited. Nice-looking girl, he decided. Much too young, of course. That face, untouched by life. A still-unformed being with so much good and bad out front to meet and confront and flee. Good luck, lady.

"Some of Sam's chili with that Portuguese bread."

"Coffee?"

"Black, please."

He ate without hurrying, making a conscious effort

to separate the subtle flavorings of the chili from each other, and from the sweetness of the bread. He had embarked on a campaign to experience pleasure in whatever he was doing, to give himself over as much as possible to taste sensations. But Sam's chili, though filling, was ordinary, and he left feeling dissatisfied and wishing he had ordered something else.

Back at the gallery, he settled down with a glass of warm bourbon and a book. He had plotted a reading campaign designed to take him through to September, based on Latin-American writers—Borges, García Márquez, Cabrera Infante. He had already read and entered into his notebook comments on *One Hundred Years of Solitude*, *Hopscotch*, and *Three Trapped Tigers*. And now he discovered he was troubled by not knowing more about the literary roots of these novels and the authors. He struggled to trace the influences that shaped them, concluding finally that *Tristram Shandy* was the seminal work. He located a copy of the Penguin edition and plunged into it enthusiastically. Of such a complexity and rhythm was it that he was forced to go slowly, mulling over each chapter, often rereading, becoming convinced that here was a novel that, despite its age, was both new and innovative.

It was past midnight when he stopped reading. But sleep refused to come. He decided to go for a walk, went down to McMillan's Wharf.

Halfway out on the dock, he came upon a couple lying at the edge, making love. Their hands were quick and active, and they gave off insistent sounds punctuated with moist gruntings and moanings. If they were aware of Sexton's presence, they gave no sign, rolling energetically back and forth.

Fifty feet farther along, a circle of young people listened to a guitarist sing about wasted youth and a futile future. Sexton thought the lyric too full of self-pity and false anguish. He plowed through air thick with the sweetish odor of burning grass, out to the end of the wharf.

He peered out at the night horizon as if expecting to solve a mystery. No revelation came. Too often life had been that way for Sexton; he sought easy answers to complicated riddles, placebos, quick and painless ways. But nothing had ever been easy, and pain was a constant of his existence.

He moved his eyes across the glistening water, nowhere the same, a softly shifting seascape. That endless body was the ultimate mystery. It went nowhere, yet touched every shore, affected every life. Sexton had always been afraid of deep water. His father—that beautiful and terrible man who had so casually and accidentally conceived Sexton, and just as casually turned away from him. That hateful man who had once been the locus of his entire being. His father had heaved him into the deep end of the YMCA pool one day when Sexton was four years old. And watched the boy sink to the bottom. Only when it was clear that the boy was drowning did the father pull him out. Then chastised him for being a coward and physically incompetent.

The fear of water had been with Sexton ever since. Yet he had struggled to learn to swim to conceal his cowardice. But always he was afraid. Fear was the sole legacy his father had bestowed upon him.

A child's view of the father drifted into focus. A giant man, powerfully built, handsomer than any man had a right to be. Shining cheeks, smooth and sculptured in soft planes and gentle hollows; shadowed eyes, all-seeing; a mobile, sensual mouth; thick dark hair falling untidily. Laughing. Always laughing. *Bastard.*

Sexton made a monumental effort to consign the shattering memory, the cutting image, to a distant place. He preferred to keep past terrors a blurred landscape. Obscure. Relatively harmless.

What good did it do to remember? Why trot out all the ancient hurts and fears for another futile inspection? Nothing was changed. Nothing was made better. The guilt, the regret, the recurring nightmares—all remained, would always remain. A man simply went on doing what he had to do. Living as best he knew how. Learning a little bit each day. Staying away from the old pitfalls, and inevitably falling into new ones. Getting by.

Thinking made Sexton thirsty. A number of things made Sexton thirsty. Or at least caused him to remember the existence of bourbon, which so effectively becalmed the raging beast he carried around inside.

He had turned to go when he saw the woman standing at the far side of the wharf. She swayed slightly, as if ill or captured by private devils of her own. He considered waiting until she left so as not to disturb her, but his thirst was too great.

She came around as he drew closer, and if she was startled or afraid, none of it showed on her face. "Mr. Sexton?" she said.

He stopped and squinted through the night at her. It was Vicky Pierce.

"Are you all right, Miss Pierce? It's late for you to be out by yourself."

"You were going to walk right past without speaking," she said mildly.

"I didn't recognize you in the dark."

"May I walk with you? For safety's sake, naturally."

A layer of irritation rippled under his skin. "Suit yourself."

They were almost back to Commercial Street when she spoke again. "The nights are so still here, so tranquil."

"That will change soon." When she made no reply, he went on, as if to break through her reserve. "Your fans. Thousands of them will jam up the town. Better get your autograph hand in shape."

"I do poorly in crowds."

He made that out as a bid for sympathy and so said nothing; he had no sympathy to give.

"Little John said you were in the business," she said.

"A long time ago."

"Little John said you began as an actor."

"Little John talks a lot."

"Only in complimentary terms, where you're concerned."

He grunted. "A bad one," he said after a while. "A bad actor. Stunts were easier for me."

"Stunts can be dangerous."

"Hit-or-miss. It's not something to worry about. It's all carefully laid out. Safety factors considered, equipment checked; it's not so bad."

"I'm still impressed."

"It gets down to falling properly, absorbing impact."

"I see." She spoke wryly. "That's one trick I never learned. Emotionally, at least. Every blow, every shock, I've taken head-on. Stunts led you into directing?"

"Little John's big mouth. Mostly I did second-unit stuff. Chases, some big fight scenes, even a chariot race. Later, there were a few features. Not many."

"And so," she said, aware of the general discontent that suffused her body, the pulse that beat in her thigh, the strange lack of focus behind which she drifted, "and so you gave up the film world for the art world?"

He stared at her as if seeing her for the first time. As one might look at some strange and potentially dangerous creature. Without real comprehension.

"I drank myself out of the picture business, lady. Out of some marriages. Out of a life, you might say.

If you'll excuse me, I must get home and get myself a drink."

Watching him stride away, she understood that they were two of a kind. Both wounded creatures. Both victims, and still terribly vulnerable.

6

Making movies bored Lee Downing. The process was dull. Slow. Accomplishment virtually imperceptible. Mostly, shooting a picture involved a great deal of standing around. Technicians adjusted lights or connected cables or moved a reflector from one place to another place, two feet away. Range finders were looked through and cameras were loaded while actors rehearsed lines in subdued voices or took instruction from the director in a whisper, as if some alien spy were listening in. And out of all this, more often than not, was brought a financial dud. A critical bomb. A stinker.

He supposed *Provincetown* would be, like most pictures, a disappointment. Not that Downing was ever disappointed; he never expected anything. To him a movie was just another assignment. A job to be done. A paycheck to be collected. Nothing surprised him, and very few things troubled him, except those people who tried to keep him from doing his work. Like actors. It would be a good business if it weren't for actors. Half of them were insane, and the other half egocentric. In love with themselves. Puffed up on their own importance. Actors were always a problem.

Take Vicky Pierce. She wore trouble like a badge of honor. Trouble for Downing. That shy act didn't fool him, not for a minute. The bitch thought she was too good for him, for a mere press agent. Thought she was something special, being a star. They were all spoiled rotten, acting as if they owed nothing to anyone. Not one of the breed had any sense of responsibility. None of them cared about the ordinary working stiff like Downing. As if press agentry were some kind of disease. Hell, most of 'em would be on welfare without the ink that guys like Downing got for 'em.

Vicky Pierce. At first she had simply refused to talk to him. Always busy. Involved with more important matters. Finally she had allowed him a minute or two, and then O'Day had interrupted, claiming her time. Well, okay. Downing knew how to wait. Patience, that's what this work required. He promised himself not to be put off forever. So Downing looked for his chance, waited for a break in the shooting schedule, always on the fringe of the activity, a plastic smile pasted in place.

On this day they were shooting at the riding stables near the Holiday Inn. They had spent most of the morning trying to film a four-line scene between Pierce and Crespi, but never to the satisfaction of John Patrick Michael O'Day. Crespi insisted on changing one of his lines, and that infuriated Tom Reynolds, until O'Day was able to effect a compromise that satisfied both actor and writer. Finally, just before the lunch break, they shot the scene, and O'Day approved of what was done.

"Print it."

The company lined up for the catered lunch. Except Vicky Pierce, who headed for the small trailer that served as her dressing room.

"Miss Pierce!" Downing cried, hurrying after her.

She glanced back over her shoulder, kept going. Downing fell in step alongside. He turned on the plastic smile.

"Can I talk to you now?"

"What about?"

"I have to prepare a new biography for distribution to—"

"Go ahead."

"I'll need time—with you, I mean."

"I'm sure you can get whatever you need from one of the old studio bios."

"But, Miss Pierce—"

"I really must go now."

"There's also the schedule of interviews."

She kept going. "No interviews."

"Publicity, Miss Pierce. I've invited a lot of media people to visit during the shooting. The space will be invaluable. All the print media, some radio, even a special TV feature for CBS . . ."

At the door of the trailer, she looked at him. "I won't do any interviews."

"But, Miss Pierce . . ." She disappeared into the trailer. He turned away, berating his misfortune. He should have listened to his old man, become a bartender. The work was steady, the pay reasonable, the problems all small ones.

He went looking for O'Day and discovered him seated on a bale of hay in an empty horse stall inside the stable with Frank Jacoby. They were eating thick sandwiches and drinking beer from cans. O'Day, talking when Downing appeared, ignored the press agent.

"Wellfleet oysters, Frank. Magnificent. In the old days, they were a byword with epicures. A dish of fresh, raw, succulent Wellfleets on the half shell . . . a shot of zest into an otherwise ordinary day, Frank."

Jacoby laughed around a mouthful of whole-wheat bread, tongue, and Swiss flavored with Russian dressing. "Never ate shellfish until I was nearly thirty."

"Why not?"

"My parents were Orthodox Jews. Forbidden."

"You give up the faith, Frank?"

"It was my first wife who did it. Loved to eat. She was convinced that oysters put a charge in a man's jewels. Insisted I try them."

"And?"

"I developed a taste for oysters."

"What about the other?"

"Didn't do a thing for me. Matter of fact, neither did that wife. We split up a couple of months after."

Downing cleared his throat, flicked the plastic smile on and off hopefully.

O'Day raised an authoritative hand, and Downing fell back a step or two, waiting in the shadows. He hoped he wasn't going to throw up; the smell of horse-shit was overpowering.

"Those of us who cared, Frank, we believed the Wellfleet oyster to be a thing of the past. Exterminated, like the dinosaur or some other unappreciated species. You see, young oysters must attach themselves to something in order to grow. Otherwise, they float away, lost to connoisseurs forever. And what do baby oysters most like to be attached to?"

"What?"

O'Day drained his can of beer and opened another. "Other oysters, of course." He drank his fill while Jacoby considered that bit of information.

"Unhappily, man has injected himself into this natural and therefore beautiful process."

"Always the same problem."

"Yes. You see, the shells of harvested oysters used to be used for fertilizer and plaster. Therefore—"

"No shells for the babies to get on to."

"Precisely. Mark the end to the Wellfleet oyster."

"A sad, sad tale."

"But word has reached me through an agent long in deep cover that the Wellfleet oyster has hit the comeback trail. What brought this miracle about, nobody knows. Possibly favorable weather conditions. Possibly the infinite goodness of the gods. What matters is that they are back. We must take ourselves soon to Wellfleet and engage in an oyster-eating orgy."

Jacoby nodded gravely. "What swingers we movie folk be."

Downing stepped forward. "Little John," he said plaintively.

The director looked at him with some surprise. "Jesus, you still here! What is it, fella?"

"It's Miss Pierce . . ."

"Vicky? What about her?"

"She won't do any interviews."

"Never did. Hates being interviewed."

"I've got people coming."

"Put them onto Crespi."

"I promised I'd deliver Pierce."

"The big thing is to keep her happy, keep her acting. We've got a movie to make."

"Mr. Pike isn't going to like this. He's going to do an entire series of interviews . . ."

O'Day took a long swallow of beer. "Don't bother Vicky. Don't upset her. And don't ever again use Hillary Pike as a club to me. Now, go away. I am trying to provide myself with physical and emotional sustenance, and you give me a royal pain in the ass."

Sandy Hayden perched on the wide sill of the window of her room, hugging her knees, gazing out at the sparkling water of Provincetown harbor. She found no pleasure in the sight, eyes fixed at some point in space, paying no heed to the lone sail that drifted across the horizon or the line of trap boats coming into port.

Her body was tense with rising anger and resentment. She was able to accept personal attack, insults, active dislike; she would not tolerate being ignored. Not from *him*. He'd insisted she come up to

P-town, insisted on having her close. The promises he made! The great and fabulous things he would do for her. For her career. Put you in pictures, baby! Make you a star! All that ancient horsecrap. And she'd bought it. Bought it because she wanted it. Craved stardom, the flash, the rewards, the fame and fortune. All that glitter.

And here she waited with nothing to do. No one to talk to. Afraid to act in any way that might turn him against her. She longed to strike out, to give him some pain, to do something outrageous. Wild. Insane. Well, all right, they were playing on his terms now. Her chance would come later, and when it did . . .

She heard the knock at the door and ignored it. It came again, secretive, the sound of a man accustomed to sneaking around. There was that quality about him. As if he were about to embark on a slightly malodorous course. She placed herself in the middle of the bed, legs crossed under her, facing the door.

"I'm busy," she said firmly. "Come back another time."

She imagined the shocked expression on that pretty, pudgy face of his. He was used to getting his own way. New rules, buster. You get what you earn.

He spoke in a conspiratorial hush. "Sandy, it's me, Tommy."

"Try another day."

"Sandy, what's wrong with you? Open up! Are you alone in there?"

Her desire was to punish him, deprive him of what he so hotly craved. That, she realized, would get her absolutely nowhere. She still needed the fool.

"Door's open," she said.

He stepped inside, looked warily around. "What's going on?"

"Bastard." Show anger, resentment, but not enough to get his back up. Need was a terrible taskmaster.

"Be nice."

"Two days." She watched him shuffle closer to the bed. "I've been all alone for two whole days."

"The picture. O'Day can't make a move without me. Lots of changes going down." He lowered himself to the edge of the bed.

"I should've stayed in New York, for all the good being here is doing me."

"I'll take care of everything."

"I know what you take care of—Wanda."

He grinned a superior grin. "She *is* my wife. A man's got to fulfill his connubial obligations."

"Bastard. You come to me smelling of her and think that I'm—"

"Here, smell."

She brushed his hand away. "Suppose she finds out?"

"About us?"

Sandy nodded.

"She better not."

Sandy decided she'd pushed him enough for one day. "She never will, not from me."

This time when he reached for her she made no attempt to get away. She went down on her back, and he situated himself on top of her. His hands reached for her buttocks. It always surprised him at how much of her there was. Nothing about her was soft. Not even her breasts, so large for a girl of her height.

"You feel great," he said.

She avoided his mouth, arranged a sad expression on her triangular face. She sighed.

"What's wrong?" He massaged one breast.

"I'm worried."

"What about?"

"That it isn't going to happen. That this is all a waste of time."

"I'll take care of it, I promised you."

"When? O'Day's already started filming."

"The part is still open."

"Maybe he's got his Jenny and hasn't said anything about it to you."

"No, I'd've heard. I tried to talk to him today, but he was with Downing."

Downing, she knew, was the press agent. He sounded like an awful creep. "Maybe I'll go back to the city. An agent I know thinks he can still line me up for a touring company of that Neil Simon play."

A rush of fear chilled him. He wasn't ready to give her up, not yet. Rolling around in bed with her was still too new, too exciting, and too fulfilling. Girls like Sandy Hayden were one of the major fringe benefits of writing a movie. "I'll take care of O'Day. He listens to me."

This time when he tried to kiss her, she accepted his tongue. It was fat and heavy, rested in her mouth as if weary from the journey across her teeth.

"Hmm," she said.

"Good?"

"I missed it."

He pushed against her. "You really love it."

"Crazy about it."

"Do you ever get enough?" He began working on the buttons of the new sailor pants.

"Never from you, lover."

He swore, unable to do very well with the buttons. She sat up. "Take care of yourself, I'll do these." There was, she told herself, a great deal to be said for those thirteen buttons.

From Sandy Hayden to his wife. That was Reynolds' direct, speedy, almost compulsive route. Wanda, in bra and panties, sat on the floor polishing her toenails. She was, Reynolds reminded himself, much more subtle in her physical attractiveness than was Sandy. Her body was more delicate, smaller in its proportions, and her face had an almost aristocratic cast to it.

"The Wheelers phoned," she greeted him.

"Oh." He began to undress.

"They want us to have dinner with them."

"I'm meeting O'Day. You said you still weren't feeling so well." He wanted to get into that shower, wash away all traces of Sandy Hayden's flesh.

"I'm all right. I want to go."

He went into the bathroom and scrubbed himself vigorously. He emerged with a towel around his middle.

"You're sure you're okay?"

"I have to get out of this room or go mad."

Wanda was given to exaggeration. "This thing with O'Day, strictly business."

"The Wheelers left a number. They said they'd meet us . . ."

"It's a bar. Little John and I are meeting in a bar."

"I don't mind."

He laughed nervously. "Somebody's liable to take you for a hooker."

"What do you think I can get?" She rose slowly, posed provocatively.

"Very funny."

"What's the most you ever paid for it?"

"Me! I never paid, not once in my life."

"Would you pay for me? Say, fifty dollars."

Under the towel, he began to respond. The idea was titillating, to make it with Wanda less than half an hour after banging Sandy. What would she do if he told her? It was a crazy idea.

"Maybe fifty," he said. "If you give head."

"A one-track mind. That's all you ever want."

"I never get it."

"What if it made me sick?"

"You'd get used to it. You'd like it."

"I don't know."

"I'll make it a hundred."

"That's a lot of money . . ."

He let the towel fall. "Try it."

"My goodness, you mean it."

"Kneel down."

"Is that the way you talk to a hooker?"

"I told you, I wouldn't know."

"If I did it . . . tried it, you'd probably look down on me, think I was . . . perverted."

"I love it, I told you."

"I have to call the Wheelers."

"Do it."

"They're expecting me to call."

"They'll wait."

He backed her over to the edge of the bed, sat her down.

"I don't even know what to do."

"Get closer. That's fine, just right."

"You really like that?"

"Don't stop."

"You'll warn me before you come . . . ?"

"Yes. Now . . ."

"Like that?"

"Yes."

"Well . . ."

"Wanda!"

"What?"

"Don't talk."

The Harbormaster was the kind of drinking place O'Day was fond of. No tourist hangout, this. No watering stop for the rich and the fancy. No pickup joint for the horny singles.

The Harbormaster was plain. Without much artificial light to display its flaws and the flaws of its visitors. It smelled of beer drunk and of beer spilled, and it was clear to even a casual observer that here neatness counted not at all.

You wanted a drink, you went after it. Up to a long,

scarred bar tended by a flush-faced brutish fellow with the thickest wrists O'Day had ever seen. A few old fishermen sat around sipping red wine, puffing their pipes, lying mightily to each other about their exploits in the good old days.

A man with the looks of the outdoors in his leathery cheeks argued about money with a woman at the table near the kitchen. The cook, a lank of a man with hair to his shoulders, slouched over the bar and studied a racing form. An erect old man wearing a captain's hat drank sherry at a table near the entrance and dealt solitaire.

O'Day felt at home. His back to the wall in the deepest, darkest corner of the place, he drank draft beer out of a chilled glass mug and sucked a Gitane. Across from him, Lou Klein and Frank Jacoby.

"Producers," O'Day said. "Creative pisspots."

"Pike giving you a hard time, Little John?" Jacoby asked.

"Nervous in the service. The man's never had a winner. Doesn't know what it takes or how to make it happen, but he can't keep his hands out."

"It's his package," Klein said.

"The man brought us all together," Jacoby added.

"Some mixture. An over-the-hill director—"

"Come on, Little John!"

"An aging star, a fairy leading man, a lousy novel, and a worse script. That Reynolds, what a pretentious boob he is."

Jacoby jerked his thumb toward the entrance of the bar. "The boob has arrived, complete with his lady. Not bad, either."

"Too good for him," O'Day said. He smoothed his mustache, killed off the beer, puffed the Gitane. He made a commanding gesture, and Reynolds led Wanda over to the bar, settled down to wait. "Responds well to silent direction," O'Day said. "It's words that get him into trouble. The writer's disease."

"All writers, Little John?" Klein said.

"It goes with the territory. Pike says he wants more juice in the picture."

"Juice?"

"Action. Pike wants the picture juiced up."

Jacoby groaned. "It's a love story.'

"Pike is an incipient bookkeeper, suffering from hardening of the economic arteries. Producers. They'll ruin a project and then blame the director. The bastards wasted Orson's talents. They kept Losey on the outside looking in. They . . . Damn, what's the use? Bring me another beer!"

The barman responded at once.

Klein said, "I got a boat, Little John."

"Terrific. What we don't have is a director for the second unit. Pike's offered me a handful of fourth-raters. He's got to keep trying. What about the house?"

"I found us a beach house. Set back on a hill, with a great view of the harbor. Decks all around. If you don't like it . . ."

"We'll need three days in the house, but schedule one extra, just in case."

"You got it."

"I'd like to talk about the love scenes," Jacoby said.

"Never mind scenes," O'Day corrected. "Let's talk about attitudes. Relationships. Tender is the way we go. Gentle, exploratory. The woman has been around, used and abused. She bears scars, gentlemen. She is frightened of being hurt some more. The boy is twenty years younger than she is. Believe me, that shakes any dame. She needs him, wants him, is terrified of losing him. She also knows it can't last. She's alone in the middle of an emotional ocean clinging to an unsteady human life raft. She's doomed and knows it, but she hangs in there, gutting it out. When can we have the house?"

"In the morning, if you want it."

"I want it."

"Anything else, Little John?"

"Just one thing. Let's not keep Vicky on edge, waiting around. She's not loose, and likely not to be. Help her out whenever possible."

"You got it, Little John."

"Frank, that's a long sequence. I'd like to keep it fluid, go without a single cut if possible."

"I've got it worked out. We'll need rehearsing time."

"Crespi's no problem. He crammed in stage experience. But Vicky . . . let's be careful."

Jacoby clucked sympathetically. "Some reaction shots will help, just in case. A cover shot."

"Yes."

"Pike'll scream," Klein said. "The budget's on the way out now."

"Screw 'em," O'Day said. "Maybe I'd better warn you guys, I am going to make one hell of a movie, with your help."

Klein and Jacoby were talking rapidly and laughing when they left, excited and making plans.

O'Day glanced over at the bar. Reynolds seemed ready to leap off his stool. O'Day nodded, and the writer hurried across the room.

"You always leave your wife alone at the bar?" O'Day asked. Some flashy nervous element in Reynolds aroused O'Day's combative side. Perhaps it was the smug, overweening conceit of the man. To O'Day he seemed to have been stripped bare of all moral concerns in the pursuit of self-interest. Whatever it was, to be in Reynolds' presence caused O'Day to feel mean and caustically aggressive. "She's a good-looking dame," he said. "She was mine, sumbitch, I'd never leave her by herself."

"I'm keeping an eye on her." Reynolds hung the words out toughly, like the Duke issuing a challenge, showing his manhood. With a guy like O'Day, it was vital that a man establish his credentials. "We're expecting friends," he tacked on, by way of explanation.

Let it go, O'Day instructed himself. Life was looser nowadays. Men didn't live by the old standards. Especially where women were concerned. In the time of his youth, O'Day and his pals respected women. Oh, sure, they crawled into that bushy nest every chance they got. But wives, mothers, sisters, sweethearts, friends—you protected them, made sure no one took advantage. Respect provided an almost total ethical construction by which a man lived. Moral guideposts.

"We're going into the beach house in the morning," he said to Reynolds.

The writer blinked his soft brown eyes, eyes that reminded O'Day of a retriever he'd once owned. That dog hadn't been worth a goddamn.

"Good," Reynolds said. "First time together for Crespi and Pierce. Gonna be magic."

O'Day snubbed out his Gitane, inspected his nicotine-stained fingers, and warned himself to quit the weed. Chest pains, sweating, and the changes in his cardiogram. No heart attack that time, but watch out. Doctors were all so reasonable, as if life was an expensive piece of laboratory equipment into which you fed certain data and inevitably took out correct answers.

"What you need," he said to Reynolds, "is a little insanity."

"I'll get a bagful at the market next time I go."

Flaky writers were the best, O'Day had long ago decided. They rummaged around in their madness, coming up with fragments of their lives, splinters of pain and despair. Pain and despair made good movies.

"Do the new pages tonight." O'Day said it casually, lighting another Gitane, watching Reynolds. He was not a man who handled the unexpected well.

"That scene, it's the strongest scene in the novel.

Hillary loved it, told me so himself. Anatole Broyard said in his review in the *Times* that—"

"Pike ain't here, and Broyard can't make a picture. The scene gives me emotional cramps. It needs work."

"I won't do it."

O'Day knew better. Reynolds might someday stand up for his own artistic beliefs, his own work. But not today. Not yet. "Wanna beer?"

Reynolds shook his head, the pudgy face blotched with resentment and repressed rage. His heavy lips were drawn up in a tight bloodless line.

"Too much talk," O'Day said. "Too many words, ideas. Let's give it an injection of real emotion, get the actors out of that verbal wind tunnel."

"The beauty of the scene is—"

"Okay. Crespi is the aggressor, no more. She makes the opening moves."

"But Little John . . ."

"This boy has to locate his balls. If he ever had them, he's misplaced them. Vicky's going to help him search."

At the bar, Jerry Wheeler took a stool next to Wanda Reynolds. He kissed her on the cheek and squeezed her arm affectionately. Then it was Junie's turn. Another kiss, another caress, this time of thigh.

"Your friends," O'Day said.

A chorus of laughter went up, and Jerry's hand fell onto Wanda's arm and stayed there. Reynolds began to feel uneasy.

"Wanda will be all right."

O'Day wasn't convinced. "The point is, the boy is about eighteen. Maybe a year older."

"In my novel, he's twenty-five, been around."

"Make it nineteen, we'll compromise. Obviously Vicky is much older. I want the contrasts made clear, blatant. She's older, worldly and experienced. That way, we've got built-in drama, shock value, and audience concern." O'Day leaned back, fixing the writer with his deep pale eyes. "Without shoving it down their throats, let people begin to suspect that our leading man is gay . . . or is he?"

"Gay! For Chrissakes, Little John, he is supposed to be a *stud.* His pecker is at attention from dawn till dusk."

"Put him at half-mast, pal."

"I think we ought to talk about it."

"Sure, and then we'll do it my way anyway."

"I didn't know you were an incipient fascist."

O'Day pointed the Gitane at Reynolds. "This is no democracy, boy. I pull the strings, exercise the power. We talk, exchange ideas, argue it out, and do it the way I want it done. So, in the picture we have a dude who has gotten it off with a woman only one time. Maybe once. And if he did, he still isn't sure he made it all the way in the dame. This boy is scared of what he is, of what he ain't, of what he might be. Fags always move in on him as if they know something he doesn't know. 'What the hell am I?' he keeps asking himself. All of a sudden, this fantastic lady—Vicky Pierce—lush and lovely, comes on strong. She makes it clear she is very much available."

"Something about it disturbs me."

"What?"

"I can't put my finger on it . . ."

"When your finger finds the place, let me know. The boy sweats blood. Should he, shouldn't he, can he? Essential questions when you're young. At least, the kind of young I used to be."

"I still don't like it."

"She makes the moves. But slow. Slower. Tenderly. That first time together, cut back on the talk. Let their faces do it. Their hands. Their bodies. I've put you on the trail, Tommy boy, can you find your way from now on?"

"I don't know about this."

"I know."

"I'm inclined to make a strenuous objection."

"Never make a fight you can't win. Lost causes are for the losers of this planet. You, I know, want to be a winner. Do it my way and you'll become famous, rich, and popular with the ladies."

Reynolds remembered Sandy Hayden and shrugged away any idea of continuing to oppose O'Day. He couldn't afford to antagonize the director. Not now. He arranged an agreeable smile on his mouth.

"You're the boss."

"You're on your way to the highest hill in Beverly, kiddo."

Reynolds kept the smile in place. "The role of Jenny—it isn't cast yet?"

"I'm going after Joey Heatherton. She's working clubs."

"Oh. I've found a girl, she'd be great for the part. Perfect."

"Perfect?"

"She studied with Strasberg or Berghof, one of those."

"When I am King of the Universe, first thing will be acting teachers up against the wall. What other faults has she got?"

"Great-looking girl. Same type as Heatherton."

O'Day directed his attention to where Wanda sat at the bar. She was slender and well-formed, and her face gave off a sultry promise that he suspected was lost to her husband. Mrs. Reynolds required special stroking, the kind of stimulation that would make her put aside the cool, competent cloak she wore. She had a wide, full mouth, and it was O'Day's belief that no woman with a wide, full mouth could be less than terrific.

"Nice-looking woman, your wife."

"Yes, Wanda's okay."

"You don't want to screw it up just because some ambitious pussy is throwing some your way."

"Oh, it's not like that, Little John."

"It's always like that. Send her around."

"Well, thanks. I appreciate it. Her name is Sandy Hayden."

"I'll remember. Now, go home and do the rewrites."

"Yes, yes, I will. You can depend on me, Little John."

O'Day knew better.

It was nearly two in the morning when Reynolds finished the scene. He read it over and was immensely pleased by what he had accomplished. It was better than good. Warm, romantic, every word advancing the action, revealing something more of the characters. It was better than O'Day deserved.

The sound of the key in the door drew his attention. Wanda came into the room. She kicked off her shoes and began to undress, crooning softly.

"I think you're drunk."

"High," she corrected. "Great grass, courtesy of Jerry and Junie."

"Why so late? You didn't have to stay out all night."

"You said you had work to do."

She disappeared into the bathroom, and he heard the splash of her urine in the bowl. The sound always excited him. A little weirdness never hurt, he told himself. She returned wearing a short nightgown.

"They ball, Tommy."

"How can you be sure?" A premonition of disaster seeped up under his skin, and he wanted to scratch it away.

"You said so yourself."

"I said it wouldn't surprise me if they did."

"They do." She sat on the bed, knees up.

"That Jerry, he was all over you."

"He's cute." She eyed him with mild surprise. "You're jealous! You said balling turned you on."

"The *idea* of it."

"You said you wished I'd make it with another man, tell you all about it."

"Fantasy is one thing, reality something else."

She lay back on the pillow, her eyes fluttering shut. She made an effort to savor her feelings at the moment, to analyze and understand them. Part terror and part anticipation, a rising hope that something better and more fulfilling lay just ahead. She recognized a change that had taken place. A dramatic alteration in her attitude, a change that had been a long time coming. The future was a threat and a promise, all at once, and therefore sweetly desirable.

Behind her lidded eyes, she tried to visualize Tommy. No image floated into view, no clear memory of what he looked like. Her husband was a stranger to her. Even more startling, she began to wonder just how well she knew herself.

So much was missing in their lives, in their marriage. Elements long absent, to which she could not give a name. How often she and Tommy spoke about love, about being in love. Tommy would emphasize his need for her, his desire, insisting that she was more exciting than any other woman he had ever known. But love and sex appeared to her as separate items in their life together, never in touch, never blending. Perhaps there was no such thing as love, simply an invention to legitimize the animal drives that people surrendered to. She didn't believe in love. Not anymore. She didn't believe in anything. Except getting as much out of each day as she could.

For some reason she couldn't fathom, she recalled their wedding night. A comedy of errors, misunderstandings, no different than the rest of her relationship with Tommy Reynolds.

"I'm sorry," he had said when she came back out of the bathroom.

"Did you have to . . . all over my belly, that way?"

"I said I was sorry. You were too tight."

"You talk about all the women you've had. Don't you know how to do it right?"

"Our first night, I was too excited. I lost control. Don't worry, it'll be all right next time. You'll have to help more, that's all."

"Help!" The idea had startled her. She had expected him to play an almost totally active role in bed. She wasn't used to doing very much, her experience limited to being stroked and caressed by men, and only occasionally had she even put her hands on anyone. "What can I do? I'm a virgin. We should've done it before we got married."

"You should've said something."

"You said you wanted your wife to be a virgin on your wedding night."

"That was a long time ago."

"Boy, have I been dumb."

"It's going to be all right. I know what I'm doing."

"You can't prove it by me," she had replied that first time, wanting to hurt him.

Now her eyes fluttered open, and she located herself in the hotel room in P-town with Tommy, her husband, perched no more than a yard away on the edge of the big double bed. "It's all talk, isn't it?"

"What is?"

"Sex, for most people."

"Meaning what?"

"Meaning that sex is all the Wheelers ever talk about. According to Junie, Jerry has the world's biggest machine—that's what she calls it, a machine."

"Ah, size is nothing. All that crap about size, kid stuff."

"Don't be defensive. I don't think I could get a bigger one inside me."

"But you'd like to try?"

"I didn't say that. Oh, Tommy, you are the one always pushing us to swing. You keep saying you want to swap with another couple. You're the one—"

"Okay, I said it. I'm not so sure now. What about you?"

She chewed her lip. "Aren't you a little bit curious, Tommy?"

"Curious? I guess so. It's only natural. How do you think you'd feel watching me get it on with someone else?"

"Like Junie?"

"Whoever."

"I don't know. Strange."

"Would it excite you?"

"I don't know. Maybe. I guess it would. Would it excite you, to see me with another man?"

"I'm not sure I like Jerry. There's something shifty about him, nasty. I don't trust him."

"What if they were to invite us?"

"To ball?"

"Yes."

"What do you think?"

"It scares me, Tommy. Suppose I feel different after? I mean, I might feel terrible, full of guilt and shame. I could get turned off sex completely."

"Or you could go wild."

"I'd like to be freer in bed. More open. To be able to please you better."

"You think that's where they're at?"

"I think so." She sat up. "If Jerry says something to you, if he invites us . . ."

"What do you want me to say?"

"You decide."

"Either way?"

"Yes."

"If I say so, you'll do it?"

"If you really want to."

"I'm not sure I want to, but if I do . . ."

"Then I'll do it."

"You make it with Jerry? While I watch."

"Yes."

"And you'd watch me put it to Junie?"

"Whatever you want to do."

"It would make me crazy. Just wild, I'd fly." He guided her hand to his erect penis. "If we were doing it . . ."

"Right now?"

"And this was his . . ."

"Jerry's?"

"You know what you'd have to do, what he'd want."

"Yes."

"Imagine it that way. And do it."

"Now?"

"Yes."

She wet her lips thoroughly before she bent over him. She was, he remarked to himself, surprisingly good for a novice.

Theo Sudakis writes on assignment for International Features, Inc. His reports about films and film personalities are published in nine languages in Europe and North and South America. Theo Sudakis works out of his office in Rome, traveling extensively to meet with his subjects. This copyrighted article is reprinted here with the kind permission of Mr. Sudakis.

MOVIES AND LIFE: ART AND EXISTENCE, ONE AND THE SAME

by Theo Sudakis

BEVERLY HILLS (I. F.) You don't expect to see Hillary Pike striding along out in the bright California sunlight. What strikes you first is the absence of color in Pike. His cheeks are drained of tint, his eyes like those of a lazy lizard blinking against the glare; he is plucked clean of hair, smooth, slim, fitted into a stylish white suit, white loafers, a white shirt, open at the collar to reveal a pale, decadent expanse of chest. Pike does not belong out-of-doors.

Inside, it's another matter. The man quivers with ambition. He vibrates with a lust for accomplishment. He swells with the need to wield power, to display his authority, to reveal his genius.

"My father was a rat," he declares in a hushed voice that tickles my fear glands. I had asked him to tell me something about his beginnings, his early life, seeking those private, even secret, tidbits of information that reveal so much about a man's psyche. "A man of great intellect—an inventor, a poet, a lover of beautiful women, a soldier of fortune. He deserted my mother and me when I was six, and I've never thought about him since. Except to hate him virulently. Any chance he'll read this? . . . But then, for all I know, he may be dead. Rumor has it so. Let's get out of the sun."

We settle into the cool, shaded confines of the Polo Lounge in the Beverly Hills Hotel, watering place of entrepreneurs, and other hustlers of varying persuasions. The drinks are perfect. The conditioned air is perfect. The perfect place for Hillary Pike. He seems to take on shadings of his background, and though his color doesn't improve indoors, that deathly clown-white complexion becomes less apparent.

"So you hate your father?" I try to get us back on the Oedipal trail.

"My mother made me what I am today." He smiles, and not a tooth shows. He giggles, and only breathy exhalations are heard. He laughs with delight, a silent crimson cavern in that pale visage.

"You loved your mother?"

"Fabulous woman."

"As brilliant as your father was?"

"Not a brain in her head."

"But loving, considerate, kind."

"If she'd been my wife, I'd have deserted, too."

"Yet you said . . . ?"

"Had to get out from under that burden. Had to learn to work. Learn to create. Learn to manipulate. Couldn't have accomplished a thing without Mommy and Daddy." Again that silent laugh. Here, clearly, is a man at the top of his game. But what is the game?

Movie producer, yes. Rich movie producer of *Provincetown*, on its way to becoming one of the biggest grossers of all time. Coming up fast on *The Godfather*, on *Jaws*, you name it. Golden Palm at Cannes (they say Pike's parties were the greatest, wildest, most tasteless ever given). The New York film critics bestowed their approval on *Provincetown*, and it looks like a good bet to cop seven (count 'em, seven) Oscars when award time rolls round. And he wants to talk about Mommy.

"Yes," he says, waxing nostalgic. "My mother couldn't balance her checkbook. Never fried an egg she didn't burn. Never met a man who couldn't get into her pants, first shot out of the bag. Hard lady to live with."

"Yet . . . ?"

"Said to me on her deathbed, frail and clicking her dentures like castanets, said, 'Son . . . I have only one regret.' I got up real close, not wanting to miss a thing. 'Never knew,' the dear old lady said, 'what it was fags did to each other. Guess I'll never find out now. . . .' "

"And she died?"

"No, not for weeks after that. Strong as an ox, that woman."

"Did you ever tell her . . . ?"

"What fags do? What kind of a son talks to his mother about such things? There was some part of mother in *Provincetown.* Yes, I believe there was. You may quote me. That's what drew me to the novel in the first place, made the picture a labor of love."

"Is it true you've already done fifty million domestic?"

He ran a delicate hand over that white shining globular dome that was his head. The lizard's eyes blink, stare, make a poor reporter shudder.

"Money is not the thing. Hardly the driving force behind a man who wants, no, make that 'needs,' yes, needs to bring to life his creative offspring. For me, the process is all."

"All?"

"Making a picture is where it's at. I care about film. Make that 'cinema.' About all that goes into it. No other art form conveys so much. The meshing of diverse creative talents. High risk, high tension. It's almost like owning your own professional football team, putting it all together. Man is truly alive only when he exists on the outermost edge of his sensibilities. To make something unique, even special, out of nothing . . ."

"The novel was a best-seller."

Words flick out across his bloodless lips like a serpent's tongue. "I read the book in manuscript form. There was some doubt in the publishing community that it was worth publishing. I saw its merit, you might say. I involved myself in publication, convincing editors, publishers, et cetera, et cetera. I talked endlessly to my contacts at the paperback houses, insisted on the correct deal. Many a night was spent with the author and the editor revising page after page, inserting, deleting, altering for the good of the work. . . ."

"You did all that?"

"Love alone can bring a man to the brink of greatness. Art alone provides a link with the future. Creation alone makes man immortal."

I scribble notes. Hillary Pike checks what I've written. "I can repeat it, if you like."

"No, that's fine."

"You're sure?"

"I've got it straight. What about O'Day?"

"I wouldn't want to be misquoted."

"It's down, word for word."

"Let me read it through."

"If you insist."

"You don't think it makes me sound too . . . poetic?"

"Perfect. It's you."

"Perhaps. A labor of love," he starts out again.

"Tell me about John O'Day?"

Hillary Pike grumbles. It is a thin, white sound, much like his skin, with faint blue undertones. "Some said no. That O'Day was over the hill. I fought for him, sensed his touch was right for what I wanted. The gift—"

"O'Day's directorial gifts are large."

"No, no, not his, mine. The gift of magic, I call it. Did you get that? Shall I repeat it?"

"Not necessary. What about the trouble?"

"Trouble? There was no trouble."

"I've heard there were many problems, difficulties. Crespi . . ."

"A man gets sick. It's his God-given right to get sick. I'd never hold a man to a contract who gets sick. I'm too human for that. As for poor Vicky . . ."

"What really happened?"

"An honest-to-God tragedy. Such a magnificent talent. Also terrifically good-looking, as everybody who goes to the movie can see for himself or herself. Even at her age, nobody like her. Not even our beautiful and talented and very sensual little Sandy Hayden, who has got it all. You must be struck by the lightning of good fortune to discover a Sandy Hayden."

"Those nude scenes . . . ?"

"Please . . ."

"You don't want to discuss it?"

"I prefer . . . Sex in pictures, so controversial."

"What part did you play in bringing about the final nude scene?"

"Sex in movies these days. Shameful, really."

"A great deal of the sex, implied and explicit, in the picture was not in the book."

"We improved a great deal on the book, I'd say."

"Not everybody feels that way. Some people, critics . . ."

"Who cares about critics? John Simon, who reads a guy like that? Or what's-her-name in *The New Yorker*?"

"Kael."

"The other one—you think people pay attention? They don't, believe me. Anyway, horses for courses, as they say." He gives that silent laugh.

"Different strokes for different folks. They say that, too."

"I like it. Mind if I use it sometime? With full credit, of course."

"What about the violence?"

"What about the violence! Life is tranquil, without dangers? Nobody gets hurt or killed or robbed? It should only be so."

"Tom Reynolds has claimed that his book was mutilated, his scenario castrated. His agent tells me there may be a lawsuit."

"Reynolds—I made him what he is today. A millionaire. Famous. A winner of prizes. Did he ever have it so good? He's doing one for young Zanuck. Or is it Bob Evans? What's the difference? Sue! I dare him. Let him prove I did something bad to him, all that money in his hands. Shame, is all I've got to say."

"How did you come to alter the relationship in the book so effectively? Originally the man was older, aggressive, the woman young and—"

"You've gotta have a feeling for it. When I cast Crespi—"

"I thought O'Day—"

"No, no, whatever gave you such an idea? I cast Crespi. Brooding, sensitive, fey."

"But all that happened on the Cape?"

"We were lucky. There was talk of changing the concept. Putting a muscle man into the part. I fought like the devil against that. Would have ruined my concept of the picture."

"And so you cast—?"

"Sometimes you get lucky."

"Luck plays a big role in your life?"

"Luck and a modest gift from above. A producer has to produce, to coin a phrase. You understand what I'm saying to you?"

"Yes, yes."

7

O'Day woke weary and reluctant to get out of bed. His limbs were cumbersome, heavy, and a pulse beat ominously in his thighs. Eliminate tension, he warned himself. Remove the causes before it's too late. He'd been blessed with good health, with a strong body, but time was making itself known to his flesh, and some of the old arrogance was gone; the feeling that illness and death came only to other people no longer existed. Men his age could go quickly. Torey McMartin, for example. No better screenwriter ever put word to paper than Torey; dead at fifty-eight of a heart attack. And Sam Mendelsohn, a fine character actor; a stroke took Sam on his forty-fifth birthday. Choose life, O'Day warned himself, and remembered an old joke:

"I have only two problems," the patient told his psychiatrist.

"What are they?"

"My fears and my anxieties."

In his private moments, O'Day was frequently displeased with himself. Sixty years of living had brought forth . . . an artistic mouse. Nothing much of worth. He viewed himself dimly, a shell of a man. Without wisdom or courage or much strength. All those gifts that had once seemed so impressive, inexhaustible and overlarge, had been worn down, dissipated, lost to a flurry of passing days that seemed remarkably alike to him. Any talent he had left was for making do, feinting and faking, getting by. The old drive was gone; he'd lost a step or two, and the new kids were running him out of the playground.

Shape events—that was the big thing once upon a time. Move people around. Writers, actors, technicians. Make a piece of film here. Another piece there. Until at last there was enough for him to cut and paste into a full-length picture. Making movies was what he did. Directing was what he did. He'd put his act together early, given it a certain manly style, and people liked what he offered. He had a damned good run. But . . .

His power had never been absolute. Commands could be issued but results seldom guaranteed. Actors blew lines. Or got drunk. Or came down with a dose. On location, light failed. Equipment broke down. Money ran out. Mistakes were made. Executives stuffed into plaid sports jackets cut with their own self-importance insisted he employ this pretty little girl. Or that agreeable young lad. And always they refused him final cut, ruining some of his best work, keeping him from making it better. Until he'd been around long enough, made enough money for them, grown famous enough, to demand full rights as a director. There, in the cutting room, O'Day discovered his ultimate gifts. The ultimate power.

All that was behind him, and now every day was an effort. This morning, that quiet scene between Vicky and Joe Crespi—it would not go well. It would not go easily. He wanted intimacy from the actors, and neither of them was yet comfortable enough in the roles to give him that. So he would demand take after take, and the crew would make jokes behind his back.

He sat up and put his feet on the floor, reassured by the solid contact. He reached for a Gitane. And, dammit all to hell, Pike was flying up. This afternoon, to put his wormy-white thumb into the pie. Sumbitch. . . .

A good morning. The sky was clear, and the sun shed a penetrating glow of fine heat, rapidly growing hotter. Sexton went out on the deck and examined the day. He gazed across the beach and across the smooth expanse of harbor water to where the schooner *Blue Water* sailed majestically out to sea, her nearly three thousand square feet of canvas fat with the wind.

The captain of the *Blue Water* was Henry McClintock, a bantam of a man, aggressive and smart, a tricky chess player. He and Sexton sometimes played the game and drank good whiskey together. A retired skipper of luxury liners, Captain McClintock had purchased and refurbished the *Blue Water* in order to haul tourists around the harbor on sightseeing trips. When the right whales were running, McClintock scheduled special trips out to sea for a look at the massive beasts.

Sexton knew that McClintock was testing his vessel for the upcoming season, making certain the diesel engines were in harmony, that the electronic gear was in working order—the direction finder, the depth sounder, the long-range radiotelephone. Tourists liked the idea of putting out aboard an ancient windjammer; they thought it romantic to hear the creak of her timbers and listen to the slap of water against the wooden hull, the whine of the wind in the rigging. But very few of them wanted to be at the mercy of the elements, insisting they be protected by modern safety devices. The *Blue Water*, like so much of P-town, Sexton told himself, owned the appearance of the old and perhaps better days. But like P-town itself, it was just a carnival con game, dressed up in New England propriety. A commercial hustle. And that, he supposed, was part of P-town's charm. The hustle itself.

Sexton went back into the apartment and put on swimming trunks before driving out to Race Point. A hundred yards up the beach, a handful of people were making a breakfast out of corn and fish cooked in foil over an open fire. They were drinking beer out of cans, and he could hear their voices on the wind, loud outbursts of laughter.

Sexton went in the other direction until he could no longer hear them. He spread his blanket on the sand and took off his sweater and put his back against the slope of the dune, allowed his eye to range across the huge and empty sky. He tried to read the book he had brought, but the sun warmed his body comfortably, and he soon became drowsy. He closed his eyes and let his limbs go slack. Soon he was asleep. The crump of thunderheads woke him. The sky was dark gray and swirling angrily, the air cold and penetrating. Carrying his belongings, he climbed over the dune toward the parking area.

By the time he reached the battered beige Beetle, a thin rain had begun slanting down. Once inside the car, he fortified himself with a long pull on the bottle. A man who didn't drink, he reassured himself, was a fool. A man who couldn't drink was a boor.

He laughed aloud at his own pretensions, and started the engine. The Beetle rattled and clacked and rumbled unhappily, but as always, it started. There were more than 150,000 hard miles on the little car, and Sexton felt a bond with its faltering but still-dependable engine. He had come late to an appreciation for people and objects that survived under stress. He put the Beetle in gear and rolled toward the exit.

Out of the rain, a figure came running toward him, waving frantically. He came down on the brake and rolled down the window and waited patiently.

"Hey!" came the cry. "My car won't start." It was a girl, drenched, hair plastered along her cheeks.

"You look awful," Sexton said pleasantly.

"Funny man. Can you give me a hand?"

Sexton glanced past her to where an old blue Mustang stood, looking not much better than its owner. "What's wrong with it?"

"I have no intimate knowledge of automobiles, that's why I need help."

"I'm no mechanic. Get in, I'll drive you back to town."

She came around the other side of the Beetle and settled into the passenger's seat. She stared determinedly ahead, water streaming down her face.

He offered her his handkerchief. She rejected it with a shake of her head. "Take me back, please."

He put the Beetle back in gear. "Listen, lady, I never laid a glove on that car. Would you like a drink? Cure your nastiness." He meant it as a joke.

She didn't laugh. She didn't even smile.

"Just trying to be friendly," he said. A quick look told him the girl was young, late teens probably. There was a faintly Oriental cast to her face, her skin tawny, her cheekbones prominent. Her eyes were very large, very dark, and very angry.

"You've seen enough," she said, not turning. "Keep your eyes on the road."

He reached for the bottle.

"That stuff is poison," she said scornfully.

He pulled the cork and drank.

"For crying out loud, you'll kill us both."

"Might do you some good, lady. You have a foul temper."

She faced front and didn't speak again until after she had gotten out at the gas station. "You don't even remember me," she said.

"Should I?"

She was muttering as she walked away. "I don't know what I see in you, Sexton."

Sandy Hayden appeared at the door to Lee Downing's hotel room at the appointed hour. She took a deep breath, arranged a cheerful expression on her face, and knocked. Downing opened almost at once.

"Say," he said, checking out her breasts first thing, "looking great! Come on in."

One look told her a lot. Downing rated only a bedroom, nothing fancy. Suites were for movie stars, directors, producers, not publicity people.

He came up behind her, placed his hands on her waist, standing very close. "Nice, very nice."

She swung around, looked up into his face. He shifted closer, and she felt him up against her. He was ready, for all the good it was going to do him. He tried to kiss her, and she stepped back.

"What's wrong?" he said.

"You said you were going to help me."

"I said I *might* help you."

"You can get me to Hillary Pike."

"He's upstairs now, with O'Day. You didn't do so well with O'Day, I take it."

"Don't be too sure."

"Then why are you here?" His laughter mocked her.

She ignored it; she needed him, and when she needed someone, Sandy could ignore a great deal. "Are you going to help me? O'Day wasn't very encouraging."

"Does Reynolds' wife know about you?"

"I think I'll go now."

He held up his hands. "Take it slow. I like you, I want to help. But I'm a guy who . . . well, I like to get what's coming to me."

"What do you imagine is coming to you?"

He took a single step forward. "You look good to me, very good."

"I turn you on?"

"Feel me."

"Uhuh. I'm here to meet Mr. Pike."

He frowned. "You think he'll go for you?"

"Let's talk about Pike."

"Pike. I imagine he likes a blow-job as much as the next man."

"Does it make you feel good to talk to me this way, Lee?"

"You'd fuck a dog. I've known a thousand like you."

"Only if he's pretty."

"What?"

"I'd fuck a pretty dog." She laughed.

After a moment, he joined in. "You're a cunt."

"And you love it."

"Yes." He put his hand on her breasts, and she held still until he tried to kiss her again.

"No. First get me to Pike."

"I can't guarantee he'll hire you."

"Just get me to him."

"And then?"

"After Pike, you get yours."

Pike claimed the largest table in the Drydock with the same moral certitude Cortes displayed in taking Mexico from the Aztecs. He sat there, slim and white and straight, behind a Bloody Mary, watching the dancers gyrate on the tiny space cleared of tables for that purpose. His serpent's eyes darted from bust to buttock with voracious intensity, as if seeking the most vulnerable target at which to strike. He licked his lips with the tip of his tongue.

The waitress, a picture of Alice Cooper spread across her yellow T-shirt, appeared and blocked his view. He lifted his gaze in some annoyance.

"You're not drinking," she said, as if offended.

"You're worried about me?"

"We like to keep our customers happy."

"Whattaya got in mind?"

She sucked air into her lungs, and her immense breasts came into clear outline under Alice Cooper, the nipples tumescent. Pike looked them over.

"I'm an actress, you know."

"No kidding."

"Maybe you can work me into your picture."

"You know who I am?"

"Everybody knows who you are, Mr. Pike."

"You ever get to Hollywood, look me up. I could use a chick like you."

O'Day came into the Drydock, and Pike waved to him. "Business before pleasure," he said, dismissing the waitress with a flick of his pale, tapered fingers.

O'Day sat down. "Very healthy girl."

"A dyke."

"How do you know?"

"I can always tell. There's something about them. She wants to make it with me."

"You're loaded with sex appeal, Hillary."

"She says she's an actress."

"Ah."

"You ever make it with a dyke, Little John?"

O'Day blinked against the dimness, willing his eyes to come into focus. Outside, the sun was bright, and he had managed to perceive a vitality and good health in the world, the rich promise of tomorrow. Here, inside the Drydock, this was a night world, no matter the time of day. In fact, the Drydock was a discotheque, and day or night the throb of a heavy rock beat reverberated off the bloodred walls. O'Day felt pressure on his eardrums, and an unpleasant musky scent drifted into his nostrils. Pike might have chosen a more agreeable place for them to talk.

"Not lately," he said in answer to the question. Making pictures had always been his great love. Women had always played a minor role in his life. He had never married, never actually lived with a woman. Once, when he was nearly forty years old, he had spent a great deal of time with one woman, Livvie Rhoden. She had been petite, pretty, vivacious. But both of them had known it was a temporary arrangement, and looking back now, it seemed that they had merely drifted apart. The visits less frequent, the phone calls seldom, until there was nothing. Just a faint memory.

"Fantastic action," Pike said, lips barely moving. "Dykes don't dig it with men, so when they do get it on, there is all that hostility. Hate is a terrific emotion, very stimulating. Dykes bang at a cock like they want to rip it off."

"Delightful prospect."

Pike bared his teeth; it was not a smile. "Great stuff, this scene. Work it into the picture, Little John."

"We don't need it."

Pike's eyes jerked back to the dance floor. "This is wild action." He clicked his teeth in skittering approval. "Look at 'em go."

The dancers—all female—came in all shapes and sizes and colors. In the flashing red and blue lights, they twisted and humped, engraving surrealistic configurations on O'Day's retina. He blinked.

"You certainly can pick 'em, Hillary."

"Give the world a hard-on, this stuff—men, women, queers of all persuasions."

"Make it with the waitress, Hillary. You'll feel better."

"I want the picture to be a winner."

"Let me make it my way."

"Got to jazz it up."

"We are filming a simple love story. Tender, gentle, moving. A tale of personal exploration and hope that engages two otherwise lost people."

"You're too fucking romantic, Little John."

"We agreed, at the start, to do it my way."

"Nothing stays the same. I'm not getting any happier about things. The opening shots—they stink, Little John."

"Thanks."

"I'm getting heartburn from the dailies."

"Give it time."

"I like action. Pictures where something happens."

"Faith, Hillary."

"That Crespi. All fag, a three-dollar bill."

"We're back to that."

"Who needs a queer leading man?"

"Crespi's perfect. Looks right. Acts right."

"I think we should get rid of him. I can't stand fags."

"This is a love story, Hillary. We agreed long ago. The camera picks up Crespi's sensitivity. He is very good."

"No balls. Who's gonna believe Pierce gives him nooky when he's got no balls? Get a guy in there with balls."

"We stay with Crespi, Hillary."

"Nothing's moving, Little John. I want action, a few fights."

"You want violence, get Peckinpah."

"Ah, he wasn't available, Hillary."

O'Day swallowed his anger and his pride. No confrontation at this early stage. Commitments were still too tenuous. Film could be easily reshot and O'Day replaced.

"I like the story as is," he said.

"What I have in mind is this," Pike said, shifting closer to the table. He brushed a fleck of dust off his white sleeve. "A yacht pulls into the harbor . . ."

"What yacht?"

"It belongs to this rich dude. Unknown to him, one of the crew is smuggling a load of coke into the country. The smuggler drops the stuff off into the ocean—

plastic bag, a floating marker, like that. A fisherman comes along, grabs it off. Vicky is connected to this rich guy, and—"

"Hillary, slow down. There's no yacht. No smuggler. No fisherman. Not in our script."

"Make it up as you go along."

"That's crazy."

"The yacht, it's on the way up the coast. Be here in a couple of days. I bought it," he ended defiantly.

"You're going to ruin the picture, Hillary."

"No," Pike said, his voice threatening, soft, his head swaying. "No. I want this picture. I need it. It matters to me. I want it better, not worse. You got to understand."

A vague, ill-defined discomfort came alive in O'Day's chest. Gas, he told himself, wanting it to be true. He breathed deeply, aware of his pulsebeat, reminding himself that much younger men had heart attacks, dead before they had finished their lives according to plan.

"Let's stay with the original concept, Hillary." He tried not to plead.

Pike faced the dance floor again. A wildly swinging bottom of immense proportions drew his attention. Huge cushions of flesh, jiggling crazily. Great soft mounds, separated by a deep-shadowed crevice. Jesus, she was naked under her pink shorts. Pike's tongue flicked across his dry lips.

"I want action."

"We haven't cast for it."

"Drop Crespi. Find a guy with muscles and balls. An unknown, maybe. You make him a star, Little John. You can do it, you've done it before. What an ass. . . ."

O'Day spoke in a low, flat voice. "No."

Pike sighed. "Jesus, I'd like some of that." He brought his eyes around to the director. "Let's not fight, Little John. We want the same thing, a terrific picture. I am going to become an important producer.

You need a hit to put you back on top. I wouldn't want you to blow your last chance."

"Crespi stays." O'Day felt his heart beating much too rapidly.

"Sure, whatever you say. By the way, Lee Downing's come up with a chick he thinks is right for the part of Jenny. Maybe I'll hire her, with your approval, naturally."

"Can she act?"

"You got Crespi. He can do all the serious acting. I want to get some sex into this flick. Something to turn people on. Okay with you, Little John?"

O'Day lit another Gitane. "Whatever you say, Hillary." If Pike heard, he gave no sign. He was watching the girls on the dance floor.

Ernesto Costa and Victor Fereira spent an hour or two every afternoon in Lili's Doughnut Shop. They drank coffee and played checkers and spoke about fishing, politics, and other related matters. Between moves, the two men listened to Flora Purim on the jukebox as she wailed an accelerated version of "Andei."

Ernesto, a big man with muscular shoulders and a wide, thick chest, tapped out the beat with broad fingers. Victor was smaller in all his proportions, a swarthy man with a birdlike set to his narrow face. When either of them spoke, it was in the overloud voice of a man used to being out-of-doors, as if yelling into the wind.

"The goddamn Russians," Ernesto said, returning to one of his favorite topics of conversation. "Somebody's gotta do something soon."

"King me," Victor said.

Ernesto did so. "They're a menace, I tell you. Every fisherman in New England knows it's the god's honest gospel truth."

"Rotten Communists," Victor said.

Ernesto moved a checker. "They're a threat. Ruining fishing. A man can't catch enough to make a living. The country better smarten up."

"The government better do something."

"The government!" Ernesto snorted. He hated only the Russians more than he did the United States government. "What's the government care! We're finished, us fishermen. Fishing's finished."

"There's only the tourists left."

"I hate their guts."

"They spend money, admit it."

"Tourists and dope smugglers, that's what Provincetown is all about."

"The whole country. The dope catchers do pretty good. Civil Service, with good pensions."

"I hate all bureaucrats."

"King me."

"Thirty years I been playing checkers with you."

"That long, Ernesto?"

"You always win."

"I been pretty lucky, I guess."

"I found something out."

"What's that, Ernesto?"

"You cheat."

"Please king me, Ernesto."

Ernesto obliged his friend, made a move. "The Russians, they suck up everything that swims." Mario entered the doughnut shop. Ernesto gave no sign he recognized his son. "One day, you know what? There's no more fish is what. People gonna wanna know how come. Who they gonna blame?"

Mario drew a chair up and sat down. "You're winning again, Victor."

"I been pretty lucky lately."

"He cheats."

Mario raised his brows. "That right, Victor?"

"Don't listen to your father, Mario. He don't mean it."

"Nobody listens to me, that's why the country's in such a mess. You kids," he said to Mario. "To you it's a joke. When there's no more fish, we'll see who is doing the laughing then. The Russians, that's who."

"Listen to your father, Mario. He knows."

"Nobody's laughing, Pop. Victor, you get another king with that move."

"That's right. King me, Ernesto."

"Mario, when you play you talk. Otherwise shut up."

Lili brought a mug of hot coffee. "You want a doughnut?"

"Lili, you make the worst doughnuts on the Cape."

"Fresh kid. Good catch today?"

"No such thing anymore," Ernesto said. "Nineteen and fifty-seven, there was over a billion pounds caught off New England. A billion. Now it's maybe half that much. Yellowtail flounder, used to be it brought maybe six cents in New Bedford. Eighty-five cents today. Very bad."

"Too much overfishing," Mario said.

Victor executed a triple jump. "I win."

"You cheat, it's gotta be you cheat."

"Just luck, Ernesto."

"The Russians," Ernesto said. "*They* overfish."

"Us too, Pop. Cod, haddock, yellowtail. None of it's gonna be abundant again."

"Get rid of the Russians, it'll all be the same."

Lili, a short woman, wrinked and brown, laughed mockingly. "Ernesto Costa, the final authority."

"Go away, woman."

On the jukebox, the exuberant "Guarare."

"Hey!" Mario cried. "Come on, Lili, do the salsa with me."

She made a face, avoided his grasp. "I do the conga. Sometimes."

"You're getting old, woman," Ernesto said.

"Me! You're crazy. Looka this bunch. Maybe I'll rent a dragger, put you all to work. Here's a full crew at one table."

"Hey, Pop, break out the oilskins."

Ernesto patted his massive round belly. "No more for me. Tomorrow I'm gonna go out and dig up a bucket of clams. Come along, Lili."

"So you can give me a short count."

"Never cheated a woman in my life."

"Not this woman. I'd cheat you first."

She strutted back to her place behind the counter.

"Some woman," Victor said.

"Little bit scrawny." Ernesto avoided looking at Mario. "How was the fishing today?"

"Okay."

"When you gonna be in the movies, Mario?" Victor said.

"Not me, the boat, Victor."

"You better-looking than those actors I see on TV."

"He's a fisherman, not an actor."

"The money's good, Pop, just for renting."

"You're a fisherman."

"How good?" Victor said.

"Five times what you can make on your best day, Victor."

"To hell with their money. A fisherman, he fishes."

"They want me to get another boat, Pop."

"They haven't even used one. What for?"

"I don't know. They're all a little crazy, those movie people. They're gonna shoot some extra scenes at sea. Mr. Klein says they got some kind of a fancy yacht coming up."

"My boats are for fishing. Go to Leitão. Those crooks will cheat you."

"Another game, Ernesto?"

"Don't be so stubborn, Pop. I may be able to get them up, maybe ten times a day's pay."

"Ten times." Victor was impressed. "Your move, Ernesto."

"I'm only your father, Mario. Since when do American sons listen to their fathers?"

"Think about the money, Pop."

"Money's not everything."

"It's a lot," Victor said.

Odd fragments festered in Sexton's mind like the changing patterns in a kaleidoscope. At night, in bed, sipping his last bourbon, he would struggle to assemble all the colored parts, to make it whole and in that way put it finally to rest. His imagination provided no rest. No visual comfort. Until he admitted ruefully to himself that there was but one way out: he had to paint the picture.

Size and scope were essential elements of his vision. He required room and space on which to render what he felt. Knew. Saw. He recognized that he was on the verge of some great personal discovery, as if a long exploratory journey was about to end. Or begin.

Canvas wasn't right. Not this time. What, then? On the south wall of the gallery, a painting of waves breaking over a rocky shore, spuming white foam. One of Novick's standards. Technically correct, the effort was no better and no worse than a thousand others produced in the Greenwich Village Art Factory. With one salient exception. It measured a delicious, enticing, massive four feet by eight feet. A fine, hard Masonite board.

Perfect for Sexton's plans. He executed a savage dance step in celebration of his intended banditry, then carted the Masonite back to his apartment and the waiting easel. Working fast, he covered the seascape with broad strokes of thick white paint until it was totally obliterated. Novick, he thought happily, would suffer an artistic stroke when he discovered what Sexton was up to.

He applied a second coat to the Masonite the following day, and waited impatiently for it to dry. The huge white expanse sat in silent challenge, a ghostly landscape daring Sexton to fill it up.

At last he went to work. Ten minutes of stroking and daubing made him irritable and resentful, and he tossed his brushes aside. In a creative frenzy, he laid paint on the board, using his fingers, his knuckles, the heel of his hand. Dissatisfied with a portion of the work, Sexton snatched up an old rag and wiped it into a blurred mass. The result startled and pleased him, and he began to use the rag in a more controlled manner. His excitement increased, and he worked faster.

Alien figures faded into view. Like space travelers come to rest, a burning light emanating from their improper forms. A glowing globe that was neither light nor dark, yet seemed constantly in motion. A precise architectural lintel going from white to gray to black. A slant of shadow and light without beginning or end.

Sexton painted nonstop for nearly forty-eight hours. Then he slept for twelve hours. He woke full of new energy and went back to work.

Two more days passed before he stood back to examine the fruits of his wild efforts. He saw a bleak landscape jammed up with shapeless shapes and with colors that were mere reminiscent glooms of color, hardly worthy of the name.

What had he done? Sexton refused to provide an answer. Better not to know. There was nothing to know—except that some mysterious, magical, perfect portion of himself had erupted onto the Masonite. There it was. The sum of all he was or ever would be, set nowhere in time or space, and therefore now and forever.

Bullshit!

He shut off his brain and went back to work, until he had filled in the remainder of the board. Done at last. But not quite. Something was missing. A lost part that must be found to pull it all together. He swore at himself for being incomplete and inadequate to the task, then dug into dark corners of himself for what he needed.

A shuffling footstep in the gallery summoned him back to Novick's world. He considered ignoring the intruder, who was by definition a waster of time, a raper of talent, a fat tourist from Wichita in an alligator shirt and two-tone shoes. But Sexton had stolen Novick's massive showpiece and accepted Novick's pay, so he wiped his hands and went out to do his work.

Vicky Pierce was there to greet him. Hardly expected, but surprisingly welcome. She came around to face him, as if to peer into the eye of the camera.

"I'm disturbing you," she began, took a step toward the door.

"No," he lied. "It's a sunshiny day. You're supposed to be engraving your talent on acetate for posterity."

"And the great American movie-going public."

"You'll become immortal, win an Oscar."

"I've stood in wet cement in front of Grauman's Chinese. There is no greater honor."

"All that razzle-dazzle—sometimes I forget I used to be part of it."

"Most of it is gone. The computers, human and otherwise, have taken over. I liked it better the old way. At least the pirates who ran the studios were real people."

"People are going out of style. Machines are in. They break down, you don't have to put them on pension. Just screw in a new part and throw the switch on."

She stood without speaking, as if waiting for him

to go on, an expectant expression lifting her upper lip, exposing a line of shining teeth of incredible perfection, save for one slight chip. That chip turned Sexton on. "You are one fine-looking lady," he said.

No change in that expression. "An artist's opinion?"

"A man's opinion."

"And a fine-looking man."

Those sea-green eyes of hers never wavered, and though she didn't move, he felt her getting close. Too close. He broke into an anxious sweat and remembered that he hadn't had a drink in almost a week, since he'd begun the painting.

"Come with me, I've got something to show you."

He led her back into the apartment, to a place in front of the easel, then pulled back out of her line of sight. Fear rose up in him like a corrupt flood, and he was afraid he was about to make a fool of himself. Her opinion—Why?—mattered. Another egomaniacal actress. A burned-out star. He would sell her some of Novick's crap and send her on her way, everybody satisfied. To hell with what she thought.

She looked at the painting for a long time. She exhaled. In pity? In regret? In pain at what she was suffering? She moved to another point, closer, inspecting details, isolating elements, looking for . . . what?

Finish, damn you!

She stepped back and took all of it in at once. She glanced at Sexton, returned quickly to the picture. Then she put her back to it as if to seal it off forever.

"Never hang it, Sexton."

"That bad, huh?" He gave her one of his awful smiles.

Her tone was dull. "It belongs to no time. To no movement. It stands alone, vulnerable. You've created a savage bomb, Sexton. You're a dangerous man."

He tried to lighten the moment. "Art students will riot in the streets of Paris—that what you mean?"

"Yes." She was serious, intense, worried. "They'll gang up on you, the flashy neon types of the art world—students, critics, collectors, the keepers of the museums. None of them will tolerate this, Sexton."

"What the hell are you talking about?"

"You are a great painter, Sexton."

He didn't want to hear that. Greatness imposed a terrible burden on an ordinary man. Caused him to regret what he had failed to do. And what he had done.

"I'm just slogging along, lady. Now and then I put a little paint down to keep my hand in. There's nothing to it."

"They'll come after you. They'll get you." She shook her head in wonder and despair. "Don't you know how good you are?"

He chose his words carefully. "This . . . this painting. I understand that I've broken through to something deep in myself. It's new for me, different. I haven't assimilated it yet. Maybe I'll go on with it. Maybe not. In any case, nobody cares. Nobody's interested. Nobody buys." He ended heavily, as if to cut her off from saying any more.

"I'll buy it."

"No," he said too quickly. Then, more gently: "I'll give it to you, if you really want it."

She shook her head in refusal. "What I do want is some lunch. Buy a lady a sandwich, Sexton?"

"Do better than that. What do you say to a picnic? I put together a fantastic picnic."

"Why," she said softly, "are you still standing there, when you should be in the kitchen?"

Lee Downing drove the rented Continental. Big, expensive cars filled him with an inflated sense of his own importance and triggered all his old ambitions. Downing had always hungered for the trappings of wealth and power. Especially power. He dreamed, even at this middle stage of his life, of some magical event that would hurl him to the top of the heap, give him the rewards he so rightly deserved, make him Lord of the World.

But for now he was only a unit flack, and he was careful to drive carefully lest he upset his passengers, all of them his superiors if not his betters. Next to him, Lou Klein, and next to him, Tom Reynolds. In the roomy back seat, Frank Jacoby and O'Day flanked Hillary Pike.

Downing peered at the producer in the rearview mirror. "Be there in a couple of minutes, Hillary."

"Watch out where you're driving," Pike shot back. In the dim interior of the Continental, Pike seemed more washed out than usual. "Shoot around the yacht," Pike said. "It should be here in a day or so. Use the hell out of it. Wait'll you see it, pure class. Cost me a lot."

"Sounds like a beauty," Downing said. "It ought to get us into the boating magazines. I'm working on it now."

"Look at the road," Pike said. "What about the fishing boats?"

"Two draggers," Lou Klein answered.

"I've sent for another Arriflex," Jacoby said. "A hand camera. Power packs, belts. We're ready to go."

"Good, good. Reynolds, you stay on top of the re-writes. What I want—"

The writer shifted around in his seat. "Hillary, I've been meaning to talk to you about that."

"There's nothing to talk about. Changes have to be made."

"I don't see the necessity for it, Hillary. Certain basic elements exist in the story and are unalterable. Theme indicates—"

"Cut the crap," Pike grumped. "You know my con-cept, follow it."

"There are areas of fundamental disagreement, Hillary. Your concept and mine are diametrically opposed."

"We agreed on a story line."

"I didn't agree. After all, it's my novel, my script."

"My movie, dummy."

O'Day stared out the window, finding a perverse pleasure in the exchange.

"I don't have to take this," Reynolds said without conviction.

Pike massaged his hairless scalp. "Writers come cheap. There's an army of them in Hollywood, all with shiny new typewriters, ready and waiting. Do what you're told, and you'll be okay. Explain to him what I want, Little John."

O'Day pulled at his mustache. "Check out your TV set, Reynolds. Hillary wants what they show on the box. A little ersatz sex and a lot of blood and guts. Right, Hillary?"

"Are you bad-mouthing me, O'Day?"

"True is true."

"You were on your butt when I dug you up, Little John. Remember that."

"True is true. You made me what I am today."

Pike decided to let it alone. He had more important matters on his mind. "Instead of bad-mouthing me, Little John, you should be out getting the casting right."

"Oh!"

"Like the young chick's part. I found a stupendous girl for the part. Perfect in every way. Looks like I have to take care of all the details." He surveyed the men in the car as if expecting a denial. None was forthcoming. "A real beauty, fresh, unknown, and a gold mine of talent." When no one spoke, he went on. "Little John, I want you and Reynolds to work on building up the part. Sandy Hayden, she's going places, gonna be another Monroe or maybe a Lana Turner."

"Sandy Hayden?" Reynolds said weakly.

"Yeah. Wait'll you see the face on this kid, the shape. And don't any of you guys claim later you discovered her. She's all mine."

O'Day leaned back, eyes closed, smiling softly.

Reynolds, frozen in place, wanted to cry out in protest, in anguish. Sandy belonged to him. He had brought her to P-town. He was to be her entry into pictures. She would be obligated to him. How had this happened? What had he done wrong?

"Keep the dailies coming," Pike instructed, just prior to climbing aboard the rented helicopter that was to carry him back to New York. "We could have a good thing going here."

"Sandy Hayden," Downing said to Reynolds as they rode back to town. "Isn't that the chick you—?"

"Shut up," Reynolds said. He glanced around, as if anticipating a challenge. When no one spoke, he went on. "I'm not going to take Pike's shit. I don't have to." No one responded. "I will not allow my work to be castrated by a bunch of artistic whores, incompetents, has-beens. Integrity has no price, and—"

O'Day leaned forward and tapped him lightly on the shoulder. Reynolds turned around. "Tommy, be still or I will punch you right between the eyes."

They made the rest of the drive in silence.

On Head of the Meadow beach, Sexton erected a windbreak out of driftwood and an old Mexican blanket he carried in the Beetle. They settled down in its shelter, a warm sunny island cut off from the rest of humanity. They ate chunks of salami and cheese with Portuguese bread and watched screeching gulls circle and dive for fish.

"Poor fish," Vicky commiserated.

"Gulls have to eat, too." He drank bourbon from the bottle he had brought along, offered it to her.

"No, thanks. I drink more than I should. Gin, mainly. Bad for the figure."

"The trick is to drink exactly the right amount. Too little leaves you frustrated and thirsty. Too much puts you out of control. There's not a damned thing wrong with your figure."

"Thank you. How do you know when you've had enough?"

"Practice. How's the flick coming?"

"I'm just a mannequin. They turn me on in the morning, shut me off at night. Talk to Little John if you want artistic opinions. A thousand dollars for your painting."

"Rich movie star. You can't corrupt me. O'Day is a first-rate director."

"A lot of time has passed. He may not be what he once was."

"Few of us are."

"You strike me as a man just coming into his own."

"Late off the mark."

"Better late than never."

"You've got a way with words."

She laughed. "Don't be nasty. It must have been nastiness that got you thrown out of the picture business."

"Nastiness, booze, and a penchant for punching out recalcitrant actors."

"So that's how it was. How'd you get into the business?"

"Acting, to stunt work, to setting up the gags, to directing. A straight line, but a weak one. What about you?"

She looked into his face for some hint of mockery, but she saw only a softening of that ordinarily rocky visage. "Haven't you heard the stories about me?"

"Stories about kings and queens—those are the best stories."

"There were men," she said simply. "Lots of them. Some husbands, a dozen or so studio-approved lovers, plus a company of one-shots."

"So you slept around. You're not the first."

She felt suddenly, inexplicably angry at him. "Oh, damn you, Sexton. Go to hell!"

He laughed at her discomfort, a harsh sound without amusement or kindness. "Get off it, lady. Guilt and sin are no longer in fashion."

"That's your final word on the subject, is it?"

"Don't you keep up with the times? Let it all hang out. Do your own thing. If it makes you feel good, it is good. There is no right and wrong anymore."

"Who says so?"

"All the pluperfect arbiters of contemporary life—the very chic, the innocent young, the exceedingly clever among us."

"I guess," she said after a moment, "I'll never measure up."

"Smartest thing you ever said." He offered her the bottle again, and she took a short pull, handed it back.

"Smooth," she said, hamming it up.

He grinned. "I have been married to actresses," he said. "Number One left me for a more . . . tranquil life. My drinking and fighting gave her an emotional itch. Number Two also left me."

"Also for the quieter life?"

"Nah. For a part in the Australian company of *The Moon Is Blue* or some other theatrical classic. I think she teamed up with a sheep farmer. Then, there was Number Three."

"Another professional?"

"A professional pain in the ass. When last heard of, she'd been busted for hooking in Kansas City during the Republican convention. Number Three always did have a certain conservative aspect to her makeup."

"Seems like we've both played the failure game."

"So that's what we have in common."

"Smart-ass," she said, grinning when she said it.

Harm's Way was ripe ground for Kiley. The quarry were all set up for him, waiting, anxious for him to sniff them out, move in for the kill. Shadows and rotating lights provided the privacy the patrons of Harm's Way found desirable. The dim, irregular lighting wiped years off faces scarred by time, brought men back to a youthful beauty in an atmosphere that prized youth and beauty above all other characteristics.

Gay bars were all alike, Kiley believed. In the Village. Up on the East Side. Here in P-town. The young and pretty fags stood around waiting for someone to make them an offer. The older ones, weary and frightened of being alone, searched for a face kindly and receptive. And all of them waited breathlessly for someone like Kiley to appear. One look, and they knew he was the real article, a true man, what they profoundly lusted for and could never possess.

Kiley moved up to the bar of Harm's Way as if he belonged. Big, powerful, bursting with sexual energy. He accepted the stares, the visual pleas, the long, mournful inspections, and ordered a beer. He came in full Straight Arrow regalia, displaying his tattooed arms, aware of how tautly his faded jeans stretched over his hard, round ass. Let the faggots look. There were only a couple of bucks left in his pockets, and he had to score soon. He killed the beer and called for another.

"Wouldn't," a refined voice whispered at Kiley's ear, "you prefer something somewhat stronger?"

His name was Harold. He was almost as tall as Kiley, but running to gray and thickening around his middle. His watery eyes were never still. He was, he said while they drank Chivas Regal, a married man.

Not happily, he explained, but passably. He had three children whom he loved and a wife who was a decent sort and more than pretty. Evidently it wasn't enough.

"You're a fag," Kiley said finally.

"Aren't we all?" Harold thought he was being funny.

"Not me."

"Oh, I'm sure of it. I'm not interested in some gay child with no hair on his balls. Your balls are hairy and huge, aren't they?"

Kiley stared at him without speaking.

Harold grew uneasy. "I've offended you. I'm sorry. Please don't be angry with me."

Kiley poured the rest of his drink down the front of Harold's Hawaiian print shirt. Harold shuddered. "Animal," he hissed. Then: "Can we go away together? I have a very nice room, actually."

"I can't."

"You can't!" Harold almost lost his temper. "Why not? Why are you here? What do you mean, you can't?"

"I'm busted. I have to find a job."

Harold was relieved. He giggled. "Oh, that can wait, dear man, till later. Perhaps I can help you out, a small loan."

"How small?"

"Twenty-five dollars should do."

"Fifty."

"How can I be sure you're worth that much?"

"Shove it," Kiley said.

"Just spoofing, lover, a joke. Shall we go?"

In Harold's room, he sat down on the edge of the bed. One hand came to rest on the massive buckle of Kiley's belt. A finger touched his zipper, tracked slowly downward. "Bull," Harold said.

"Better believe it." Kiley drew off his jeans and turned to face Harold.

"Oh, God!"

"Take it, faggot. Take as much as you can."

Watching, as if from a great distance, Kiley got a hold on Harold's hair, yanked roughly. "I want you to know, while you're blowing me, it's a chick I'm thinking about. The wildest-looking chick in the world. I am . . . no . . . queer. . . ."

Harold lay on his back on the bed, snoring. Kiley rolled off the other side of the bed and dressed. He searched the pockets of Harold's trousers, came up with a handful of bills. Pleased with his find, and carrying his boots, he silently left.

Back in his own room, he counted the money. Twenty-two one-dollar bills. Twenty-two bucks! The dirty little fag had shafted him.

8

Twenty minutes out of P-town, they ran into rough seas, as Mario Costa had said they would. In the wheelhouse, he laughed a little.

"Look at 'em," he said to his crewman, Paulo. "Seafaring men."

A rasping cackle broke out of Paulo, a wizened little man with hollow cheeks and bright eyes. "It's easy work, Mario."

"Wasting time. The old man is right, I'm a fisherman. That's what I should be doing, fishing. Take the wheel."

He snatched his pea jacket off the wall and went up to where Vicky Pierce was huddled amidships, and draped the jacket across her shoulders. "This oughta help."

She gave him a wan, grateful smile.

"You needed this?" Mario said. "You love boats and the ocean, right?"

She made a face. "I keep wanting to upchuck, but nothing comes."

"Give it time."

"Mario, I'm overwhelmed by your sympathy. You do this every day?"

"Weather permitting. Except Fridays. Day off Friday. Go back in the wheelhouse, you want to, it's a little warmer out of the wind."

She nodded but made no move, clutching the jacket to her chin. Being here was insane. Letting Little John talk her into making the picture was insane. She wished she were back in the farmhouse in Connecticut, by herself on the long porch, sipping gin and lime, watching the river flow, not thinking, waiting for the pain to finally end.

Mario made his way to where O'Day and Frank Jacoby stood poised in the bow, as if carved figureheads.

"This is some ocean you got here," Jacoby said. He seemed to be enjoying himself, his cheeks glowing pink, his spadelike beard glittering with moisture. "How's the diving around here?"

"Diving?"

"Sure. I scuba every chance I get. Must be interesting down there. We get a chance, I'll take you down, Mario."

"No, thanks. I do all my swimming in a pool, my head above the surface. See those clouds?" On the horizon, coming their way, a bank of dark thunderheads. "We're in for some weather."

"They coming our way?" O'Day said.

"The wind always comes in off the sea." He seemed surprised at the director's ignorance.

"I envy you," Jacoby said. "You got a terrific life here."

Mario checked Jacoby out to see if he was being serious. "It's okay." A fisherman might complain about his work, his way of life, but only among his own kind. To outsiders, they invariably turned optimistic, if not cheerful. "Nobody tells you what to do out here." Ernesto, Mario thought wryly, would not have agreed.

The dragger bucked in the choppy sea and veered to starboard. Jacoby glanced over at the second dragger, churning alongside. Much too close.

O'Day indicated the second boat. "We'll have a camera on each boat, Mario. I'll want to be able to position each one as we go along. How do we do that?"

"I can work out some signals with Vincento. Hand signals."

"Good. What about sea traffic? I don't want the area cluttered up with a lot of sightseeing boats."

"I'll put us where it's quiet, Mr. O'Day. Just tell me what you have in mind—maybe you want me to read your script . . ."

Everybody wanted to be part of the act, O'Day thought. "Let you know when I know. My writer's working on the material now."

"And the other boat?"

"The yacht, you mean? It's immense."

"Everybody needs a toy," Jacoby said.

"I gotta get Mr. Pike to tell me how he does it." Mario spoke earnestly, looking from Jacoby to O'Day as if for an answer.

Jacoby responded. "Same way you do."

Mario frowned. "You mean this dragger! It's a working tool. I don't even own the damn thing."

O'Day tried to light a Gitane and failed.

"Turn into the wind," Mario said. "Cup your hands like so. There, you got it."

O'Day dragged on the French cigarette. It was damp, already a victim of the sea. "Pike owns the yacht," he said. "That's the difference between him and the rest of the world."

"What do you mean," Mario said to Jacoby, "the same as me?"

"Okay, the man who does own it, he writes off depreciation . . ."

"Sure."

"Repairs . . ."

"It's legal."

"The yacht is a working tool for Pike," O'Day offered. "He buys it with production money and orders me to work it into the picture. So the yacht gets into the act."

Mario's face lit up. "And when the picture is done, Pike buys the yacht from the company! Is that it?"

"For a song," O'Day said. "Used goods."

"The production company takes the difference in price as a normal business loss."

Mario whistled into the wind. "And if Pike wants, he can sell it, probably at a hefty profit."

Jacoby gave the fisherman a slow, insinuating wink. "You are one shrewd Portugee."

"I like it," Mario exulted. "I bet that Pike has lots of tricks like that. Wonder if he'd let me in on some of them?"

"Keep your distance," Jacoby said. "Men like Pike have guys like us for breakfast."

"All producers are sharks," O'Day said. "The nature of the beast."

"Speaking of sharks," Jacoby said. "Is that going to be a problem?"

"Agh, once in a while you see a little mako, maybe. But none of that great-white crap they put in the movie. Porpoise, some right whales. Nothing to sweat about. Those clouds are coming fast. I better turn her around, head in."

"You're the captain," O'Day said.

"Nice boy," Jacoby said after Mario's retreating back.

"Yeah," O'Day said, stepping gingerly over a coiled hawser. He went back to where Vicky sat alone and shivering. "You shouldn't've come."

"Had to get my feet wet, so to speak."

"You'll be okay. It'll be calmer when we shoot. Lou Klein is out hunting for stunt doubles, Vicky, so . . ."

"I'm a good swimmer. At least, I was."

"We'll see. I'm taking no chances with my star."

She avoided looking at him. "By the way, whatever

happened to that sweet little love story you were going to make, Little John?"

That evening Sexton and Vicky Pierce drove down the Cape to the inn at Duck Creek for a lobster dinner. They spoke little until midway through the meal, when she took his hand in hers.

"It's a man's hand," she said, releasing him after a brief interval. "They're strong, your hands, but you've got paint under your fingernails."

"Sorry if you're offended."

"Nothing about you offends me, Sexton. You should know that by now." She picked at the lobster. "I have a thing about hands."

"Your hands are very nice."

"I have always been careful about my hands, more than any other part of my body. My mother, you see, had horrible hands. Gnarled, blotched, the joints and knuckles swollen."

"Arthritis?"

"Poverty. That's the truly fatal disease. It murders the spirit and the body. I made a vow to myself, when I was a girl, not ever to be poor."

"And so you became a movie queen."

"My mother was forty when she had a massive coronary. She died spitting blood, in pain, but laughing. She was glad to get out of the hellhole she had lived in. Forty is not a very long time to live."

"So you went out and became a movie star?"

Was he taunting her? The burnished face told her nothing. She put the lobster fork aside, no longer interested in food. She emptied her glass of the excellent Pouilly Fumé and waited for him to refill it. He did, with quick impatient skill.

"What I did was to go to work as a receptionist at Gladding, Cooper, and Mathewson, advertising. A Mr. Simpson hired me. Mr. Simpson was the personnel manager, and he made it very evident that I owed him a favor, for he had done me one. Jobs at G.C.&M. were very much in demand, you understand. Mr. Simpson explained about favors to me one night in his private office on his very expensive leather couch. The leather was very cold against my back."

"Bastard."

"Oh, I don't know. Mr. Simpson was not much different from a lot of other men I've encountered. Not that I liked him. I didn't. But I did like what he did to me, what he taught me to do. There's something to be said for being used, Sexton, when the use is as pleasant as that turned out to be. Ah, Sexton, I've shocked you."

"No. I gave up being shocked when I was seventeen."

"What happened when you were seventeen, Sexton?"

His eyes stared out at her from the shadowed sockets without blinking, and in the dim light his craggy face took on the blank, bare look of a death mask. "That's when I killed a man for the first time."

For the first time. The words lodged back in her skull, a cutting memory never to be displaced. She drank some more wine and noticed that her hand had begun to tremble.

He almost smiled. "It was in Korea."

"War," she said with relief. "That's different."

His eyes never left hers. She felt helpless, afraid of what he would say next. "He was my company commander. He was a poltroon, as they used to say. A base coward. Rotten all the way through, mistreating people, bullying. I made up my mind to kill him."

"You were judge and jury . . ."

"And executioner. I planned it, and I did it. With his own gun. A nickel-plated thirty-eight that he wore on his hip like Wyatt Earp."

"No one suspected you?"

"No one."

"Sexton. You frighten me."

"My controls are better these days."

"You frighten me a lot."

"The army awarded him a medal posthumously. As if he'd committed some heroic act, getting himself killed. The army enjoys doing silly little things, like kids playing at war."

"How . . . ?"

His finely carved features displayed a kind of grim passivity. He looked in that split-second like some piece of sculpture designed by a master artist to survive for a thousand years, shiningly beautiful and perfect in every way.

She shivered.

"I won't hurt you," he said quietly.

"I could never kill."

"We all do it, one way or another. Intentionally or not. When I was eleven years old, I thumbed my way around the country. Living out of garbage cans, hustling beer and sandwiches for gamblers, doing odd jobs, stealing when I had to. Then I met Mike Berger. I was fifteen then, and I got into a fight with an older boy. I beat him, fair and square. But fair and square isn't how life is lived. Three of his pals jumped me, stomped me into the dirt. They'd've killed me, if Mike hadn't come along.

"He nursed me back to health and got me to reading good books and helped me screw my head on straight. Mike gave me my first paints."

"He sounds nice."

"Too nice. He got himself mugged one night. He gave the dude all the cash he had—eight dollars and change. And then this hero pushed a six-inch blade into Mike's heart. Four or five people saw it happen, but none of them did a thing to help."

"Poor Mike."

"Dumb Mike. He didn't know enough to run, and he was unable to fight."

"You decided not to let that happen to you."

"You got it, lady."

"You became a tough guy."

"A fighter, a killer when necessary."

She became aware that she'd been holding her breath. Slowly she exhaled, longing to embrace him. "And I became a whore."

"Simpson? That's not whoring."

"There were others. Gifts at first, money later."

"That's whoring."

"Sexton, you have no pity."

"No pity. No guilt. Nobody forced me to kill, nobody forced you to fuck."

"You are a bastard."

"I'll get the check," he said in reply.

Outside, he guided her toward the beige Beetle. "I don't want to go back yet," she said.

"Get in," he said.

She obeyed, and he rolled out of the parking area. "Men have always led me around," she said without complaint. "A man gave me a dose, and that put me out of the whoring business. Another man put me into modeling, and that led to pictures. Seems like somebody has always put me through my paces. 'Yes, Victoria, you may take one giant step.' "

He drove into Wellfleet, parked behind the town hall. In an old-fashioned candy store he bought her some black licorice whips and penny candies. They headed back to the Beetle without urgency.

"Thanks for the dinner, Sexton," she said.

"If I came down too heavy . . . well, it's my way."

"You wined me and dined me. You let me talk about myself. You made me feel good, and you made me feel bad. You bought me some sweet things. What more could a girl want?"

"It's a good question," he said.

At the door of her suite, she invited him in for a nightcap. "You drink bourbon, I've got some."

He said it was too late.

"I don't sleep much, so you won't be putting me out. I'd welcome the company."

He warned himself that it was a mistake, and ignored his own warning. He'd spent a lifetime acting stupidly, he told himself. "Well, one drink."

They sat side-by-side on the couch, carefully apart, and reminisced about how it had been when the big movie studios were alive and well. "I miss it," she admitted. "The excitement, the conflict, the feeling that you belonged to a company, a family, almost. It was a home. I felt safe."

"I never think about it."

"Never?"

"Hardly ever."

"Little John needs someone to take over the second unit."

"No, thanks."

"You'd be back in the business."

"And you think that's what I want!"

"Isn't it?"

"I've had it with pictures. Making fantasies with people whose lives are fantasies for people who want to live fantasies. Not for me."

"It was an idea."

"Not a very good one."

"Whatever you say, Sexton." She waited for him to say something, and when he didn't, she turned to face him squarely. "You're afraid you can't do it anymore." She issued the words as if they signaled the discovery of some long-concealed and celebrated treasure.

He bared his teeth in what she hoped was a smile. "I'm afraid I might do it too damned well."

"I don't understand."

"I was good, better than good. Directing came easy to me. Oh, there was tension, but what the hell, a drink or two took care of that. Nobody paid any attention, and I was on my way up the American ladder of success. Nothing in the way. Until life stepped in and dealt me the rawest deal of all."

"Failure."

"Success. I am talking about Making It. Columbia came across with a contract offer. Big pictures. Big budgets. Big *everything*. No more cowboys and Indians on the back lot. No more ten-day shooting schedules. Here was the real thing. Turned me into a scared pissant."

"Why?"

"Why! You know what success does to a man? Puts the monkey of responsibility on his back. Demands that he come across bigger and better, that he top himself every time. Make a picture that earns a million, they want you to double up next time. Come across, Mac, we're all watching. Screw that noise. I wasn't going to let success ruin my life."

"You turned down the offer?"

"I headed for the hills. Ran for the desert. Guaranteed my own failure."

"Where did you go?"

"Across the border, into Baja, away from the rockets' red glare. Ended up in some forsaken Mexican village with more flies than people. The tequila was cheap, and I stayed on until my funds ran low. After that, I developed a taste for pulque, the stuff they make out of cactus. Not bad, once you get used to it."

"You came back."

"Back to bourbon and painting pictures that nobody wants."

"I do."

"And managing Novick's art supermarket. From nowhere to noplace, and you would have me give all that up? No way."

"We're alike, Sexton, scared people."

"You did your act. I ran."

"You're not running now."

"Lady, pay attention to the lessons of history . . ."

"History," she murmured, leaning his way, "sucks, as they say."

"Those who ignore the lessons—"

"You might kiss me first, Sexton. It's only polite."

"No harm in just one small kiss."

"Sexton," she said into his mouth, "don't count."

Don't think, he cautioned himself, fitting himself against her softly molded body. Don't look into the future; it may not arrive. All that mattered was now, and that had turned into a moist warm mouth and a fine woman's body anxious to take and to give.

There was much shifting and turning and caressing until clothes began to fall away. The tempo increased, a raw thrust toward completion. He wanted to please, to fulfill his part of this unspoken bargain, to give pleasure.

She trembled and grew moist and made small cries, and he wondered if it would, after all, work for them. He clung nobly to her and kissed her everywhere . . . .

"So sweet," he heard her voice say, her damp thighs tightening against his cheeks. She rocked and gasped and pulled at his thick hair until she boiled over in a painful spasm. She fell back at last. "So long for me without. So good, so very good. Now, let me be good for you."

He stood up and located his glass, emptied it. He was rawboned, with ridges of muscle striped across his shoulders, his middle. His thighs bulged powerfully, and his arms were veined and strong. A long ugly twist of scar ran down one side.

"I love the way you look," she said.

He began to put his clothes on.

"Maybe it's the booze," she said. "You drank too much. We'll sleep, and in the morning—"

"Stop kidding yourself. I go through the motions, but there's nothing left. The feeling is gone."

"Let me try."

"Give it up, lady. Nobody wins with a busted flush."

"It's the first time—"

"And the last. It was a mistake from the start. I can't get it up anymore."

"This is an awful scene," she said, trying to laugh. "I could never play these lines."

He made himself smile. "We can still be friends," he said, full of self-mockery. "Goddamn movies. Confuses a person. Sometimes you can't tell where the flicks leave off and life begins. Or is it the other way?"

"Take the job, Sexton. It'll do good things for you."

"Will it fix a broken pecker?"

"It's worth a try."

"Well, sweetheart"—he spoke in Bogart's voice—"I wouldn't think so."

It was, she remarked to herself when he was gone, a lousy imitation.

The weather held. Sunny days, long, and growing hotter. People began to shed their clothes whenever possible. More and more flesh was visible along Commercial Street as strollers appeared in shorts and T-shirts and halters. Women in bikinis appeared in the shops and the restaurants and the discos. Tanned young men were everywhere, eyeing the girls hungrily. Or each other.

The beaches were more crowded these days. Sun worshipers bunched together around the lifeguard stations on Race Point and worked determinedly at getting the best tan on the Cape. The thick, warm scent of tanning flesh rose up like heat waves, and young women requested men they'd never met to oil their backs; it was always done with long, heavy, lingering strokes. Some people lay facedown on the hot sand and from time to time moved as if trying to become part of the beach itself, or to elicit some erotic response from the hot sand. Volleyball games took place. And men played touch football as if it were the Super Bowl. Women watched and waited patiently, certain that as the sun went lower and the air turned cooler, their time would come. Once in a while, a couple would leave the beach together, making no announcement of their departure, indicating no time of return. No one asked where they were bound or what they intended to do. No one had to.

Summer had come to Provincetown, and flesh cried out to hot flesh along the entire strand. Satisfaction was in order.

Wanda Reynolds lay in bed and wished she had not come to Cape Cod. It simply wasn't any fun. Not for her, anyway. Tommy left her alone most of the time, and she had visited all of the shops on Commercial Street, had already bought a number of items. What was she supposed to do now?

Had she remained in New York, she could meet a friend for lunch at Serendipity or the Ginger Man or go shopping at Bloomie's or Bergdorf's. Or take in a movie in the middle of the day. Here she was left alone, and that, to Wanda, was a most devastating fate. Her own company left her gloomy and dissatisfied.

She imagined that Tommy would one day become a very successful and famous writer of movies. That would mean they'd be very rich and live in a large house in Beverly Hills, probably. She expected such good things to come her way. After all, she was a very beautiful girl, very desirable, and she had a right to the best that life could offer.

But she was getting impatient. Life with Tom Reynolds was less than she wanted it to be. For one thing, they didn't have much to talk about anymore. Nothing serious or meaningful. Just Tommy's work, or a review he had read in the Sunday *Times*, or something like that.

Tommy bored her. His conversation bored her. His ideas bored her. His preoccupation with work bored her. His clumsy endeavors in bed bored her. Not that she ever let him know. She had been brought up to believe a woman's function was to please and support her husband in all ways. But she did envy Tommy the fun he seemed to have in bed. He seemed to enjoy her body much more than she did his. Perhaps that was the way nature intended it. Lately, after making love, Wanda had begun to feel that there was something missing, as if her pocket had just been picked.

She wondered if it was the same for other women, wished she had someone she could talk to. And other men—were they the same in bed as Tommy was? Did they expect their wives to do the things Tommy wanted done? Her curiosity had grown a great deal lately, and she discovered that she was no longer disgusted by the idea of putting his penis into her mouth. Not that she had gone all the way that way, of course. What would he think of her if she did a thing like that? Especially after only two years of marriage. Still, she couldn't help but imagine.

And the other things he spoke about when he grew excited. Talking about other people, about doing it with another couple, or about having her do it with another man, and reporting back to Tommy about her adventures. Just the thought of such activities sent a shiver along her spine. Wanda yearned for adventure. For new excitement to enter her life. She wanted romance. Thrills. Personal rewards. But she understood that such fantasizing was silly, childish, futile. She was a married woman, fully committed to her husband, his career, his way of life. Still—

The telephone interrupted her ruminations. She recognized Jerry Wheeler's syrupy voice.

"Hey, love," he began. "The sun has finally come out. Junie and I are headed for the beach. You and Tommy like to come along?"

She experienced immediate disappointment. "Tommy's not here. He's doing research about those fishing boats for that stupid movie. Oh, I wish I could go."

"Well, why not? Four is fine, three is glee. Pick you up in twenty minutes."

They drove out to Brush Hollow, a beach set down between Wellfleet and Truro, in Jerry's black Jaguar, agleam with chrome. Wanda oiled herself thoroughly with Bain de Soleil and flattened out on her back, face raised to the sun.

"Always wear a bikini," Jerry said. "You have a superb body."

Wanda decided that Jerry made everything sound slightly dirty, as if it should be whispered about behind closed doors. He seemed to wear a perpetual leer.

"Look at that!" Junie said presently.

Wanda didn't stir.

"Twins," Jerry said. "Pick and Pat."

"Laurel and Hardy."

"Stop and go."

"Don't stop," Junie giggled. "Go, go, go."

Behind closed eyes, Wanda tried to shut out their words. The increasing warmth of the sun made her drowsy and contented. She wanted only to lie still.

"The blond is monstrous," Junie said.

"Twice the size of the other."

"But when it counts, who can say?"

"Wanda," Jerry said. His hand fell on her thigh, squeezing gently. "You must see this."

"Later, Jerry."

"Time's running out," Junie said.

Wanda sighed and sat up, squinted against the glare.

Jerry gestured, and she followed his direction. Two young men were advancing toward them along the beach. Both were young, tight-bodied, and quite naked. She blinked and looked again.

"Oh!"

"Heavy, heavy," Jerry said.

"They're naked!"

"Of course they are, my dear. Otherwise you wouldn't be able to see their beautiful cocks."

"There must be a law." Wanda grew flushed and wanted to look away, but didn't.

"Take your choice," Junie said.

Jerry squeezed Wanda's thigh again. "Which one do you like best?"

Wanda had never before seen a man naked in public. Nor had she ever seen more than one man naked at a time. Before Tommy, she had never actually *looked* at a naked man. Not *there.* Not for long, anyway. Boys she had known had sometimes opened their trousers, exposed themselves, asked her to do things to them. She had always dragged her eyes away and refused their requests. Almost always. Even with Tommy, she had avoided any close visual contact with his penis.

"I prefer the littler one," Junie said.

Jerry spoke with some pride. "My wife insists that size has nothing to do with it."

"It's all in knowing how to use what you've got," Junie said. "I prefer stubby dicks, the kind that can split a girl open."

"And you, Wanda?"

Wanda was unable to make a response. Her throat was coated with dry dust and her tongue swollen. The two naked men passed by, and she found herself staring at their tight, tanned buttocks. They were beautiful.

"How does Tommy measure up?" Junie asked.

Wanda cleared her throat. "What kind of a place is this?"

"Jerry, when he's hard, is a monument to nature. Comes a little too fast for my taste, but what the hell. We all make do."

"Thanks a lot, sweet. She gets it from me every morning and every night, Wanda, without fail. And that is after twelve years of marriage. My wife is just your normal everyday nymphomaniac."

"And you love it, my dear."

"She's right."

"Let's face it, any day without three or four orgasms is a wasted day. Don't you agree, Wanda?"

Wanda, who had never been able to produce an orgasm, except with her own hand, said nothing. As far as she could tell, most of the other people on the beach were also naked. She forced her eyes away.

"Why," Jerry said mildly, "don't we join the party? Shall we strip down, ladies?"

Junie took off the top of her bikini. "What a lovely idea! Wanda?"

"I couldn't."

"Suit yourself," Jerry said, rising. He took off his patterned briefs.

Wanda clamped her eyes shut, fell back on her towel, holding herself stiffly, determined not to look. She had seen enough. More than enough to last her all her life. A mournful moan issued from her mouth.

"Something wrong, love?" Junie said.

"What am I going to tell Tommy about all this?"

Jerry, very close to her, said in a mocking voice, "Everything. Every blessed thing."

Sandy Hayden arrived at the top of the Pilgrim Monument first. In the time left to her, she took in the view in slow stages, filing each segment away in her memory. Storing up memories was something Sandy had consciously trained herself to do. One day she would be old; that was inevitable. She might be sick. She might be poor and lonely. All possibilities. It was important when you were alone and old to have good memories, to prove to yourself that you had enjoyed a good life. Or at least as good as ambition, energy, and a terrific figure could provide.

Downing made it up to the top a couple of minutes later. He was sucking air in noisy gulps, as if afraid he'd be cheated of his rightful share. He was sweating profusely. Sandy discovered a perverse pleasure in his distress.

"You're in rotten shape, Lee," she remarked cheerfully.

"Fuck you."

She eyed him speculatively. "Think you can handle it?"

He mopped his face. "Letting you talk me into this, I must be nuts. I hate heights."

"Exercise, and don't smoke. Lose a few pounds. You've still got time to make a comeback." She turned back to the view.

"You're twenty," he got out. "I'm past forty."

"You indulge yourself."

He came up behind her, hands on her waist. "Indulge this." He pushed himself against her.

She freed herself. "Look across the bay. You can see Plymouth."

"You owe me," he muttered. His heart had slowed, and his breathing returned to normal. For a moment back there . . . well, men his age were always getting coronaries. You read about it in *The Hollywood Reporter* all the time.

"Those tall buildings, can that be Boston? I've got the part. I've got Hillary Pike. I no longer need you, Lee."

"A sweet kid, that's what you are."

"Admire the view, Lee. This is my first time on the Cape. I don't want to miss anything."

"Come back to my room, you won't miss a thing."

"Never met a dude yet didn't think he was God's gift in the hay. Talk, talk."

He grabbed her arm, spun her around. "I did you a favor."

A swift movement brought her closer to him, and she drove her elbow into the pit of his stomach. He grunted and fell away.

"For Crissakes!"

"Don't get rough."

"You owe me."

"You're repeating yourself."

"You admitted it—I got you to Pike." He jerked the plastic smile back into place. "All right, what else do you want?"

She assessed him deliberately. "It seems to me you have a very weak bargaining position."

"Maybe you underestimate me."

"Maybe. Tell me all about it."

"The industry is loaded with chicks like you. Willing to screw your way along. Only, it doesn't always work."

"Tell that to Hillary."

"Okay, this time it got you a small part in a crummy little picture by a guy who never did anything noticeable before. Don't you understand about Hillary? He's scratching just to get by."

"O'Day . . ."

"Little John is out of the past. He operates strictly on memory. And this is Pierce's last gasp. You think this is a stepping-stone to becoming a star? Forget it —you're jerking off."

"I'm still listening, Lee."

"You want to be a star, right?"

"Right."

"Let me tell you something, stars don't just happen. They get *made*. Representation, the right agent, manager, people with connections. The right kind of publicity."

"And you could get me that kind of publicity?"

"If it's worth my while."

"We could sign a contract. When I hit it, you hit it, too."

"Sounds okay. You'd still have to come up with the kind of agent who'd work for you. Somebody like Bibi Kaplan."

"Never heard of her."

"She's young, ambitious, and about as hot as anybody right now."

"And a friend of yours?"

"We play penny poker every Friday night. Bibi and I, we're both big winners."

"Do you think she'd represent me?"

"I could discuss it with her."

"Would you, Lee? I'd be ever so grateful. Once she agrees to take me on."

"No. Beginning now. This minute."

"How do I know you'll follow through, Lee? I'm not very experienced in these matters."

He looked her over, grinning, and reached for her hand. "Let's go."

She exhaled. "I do need a good agent. I do need a good publicity man, someone I can depend on. A friend. Are you going to be my friend, Lee?"

The plastic smile shifted, and shifted again. "Forever. Or at least for as long as we need each other."

When screenwriter Tom Reynolds and journalist Linc Whitfield met in Cannes during the recent film festival, they spent a good portion of three days and three nights in conversation about a variety of subjects pertaining to the cinema as an art and as an entertainment. The results of those talks later appeared in the magazine Cinema Today and Tomorrow. *The complete interview appears here.*

TOM REYNOLDS:
NOVELIST AND SCREENWRITER
by Lincoln Whitfield, Jr.

CANNES: The weather in the south of France turned chilly, gray and dismal, but the festival at Cannes went on without interruption, a garish celebration of film, sex, and commerce. Commerce edged out the other two for first place, with sex a flashy third.

Cannes vibrates with sexuality at festival time. It makes the air heavy, like the forerunner of a summer storm. It flavors your afternoon coffee. It accompanies your breakfast like the morning paper. It's bought and it's sold with the fervor and haggling of a North African *souk.* It is offered up by the young and terribly ambitious to the jaded and very successful.

Said Tom Reynolds, turning away a shapely starlet whose intentions are neither subtle nor unique, "Getting laid is no trick when you're young and have had some success. I need something from a woman to cling to after orgasm."

Some facts about this Tom Reynolds: he is around thirty, give or take a year or two. He's rather handsome in a softly rounded way, with the kind of skin that, if you press hard against it, will remain indented for some time. Or so it seems.

His scenario based on his novel *Provincetown* has been acclaimed by critics throughout the Western world. The New York film critics selected *Provincetown* as the best picture of the year, John Michael Patrick O'Day the best director, and Tom Reynolds got the award for his screenplay.

At the moment, Reynolds is finishing a script for Richard Zanuck and David Brown, and two weeks ago he sold an original idea to Paramount and will do the script in return for, rumor has it, $350,000. Not bad for a young fellow who had never done a film script until two years ago.

Tom Reynolds and I began our talk on the beach one afternoon, looking out at the Mediterranean, watching the expensive flotilla of yachts that seem drawn to Cannes the way flies are to dung.

We continued over dinner at Les Moulin des Mougins, the superb restaurant which, local lore instructs us, was the favorite of Picasso.

After dining, we put ourselves onto the Croisette, that lovely thoroughfare bordered on the one side by palatial hotels and cafés and on the other by the beach and the Med. Past walls plastered with posters for monster films and soft-porn pictures we go to the Grande Salle of the Palais des Festivals to see Antonioni's latest film. Afterward, we drink fine red wine—French, naturally—in the bar of the Carlton Hotel amidst tourists, tycoons, and the omnipresent hookers who peddle their asses in a variety of languages.

In the days that followed, we continued our conversation in the relative sanctity of the old-world Grand Hotel du Cap, near Antibes, comparatively safe from interruption, except from fly-by-night film producers hoping to sign Reynolds to one thing or another. Here is what we talked about—my questions, Tom Reynolds' answers:

Q. All of us connected with the cinema are film freaks and have been so for a long time. Can you remember when it was that you first became obsessed with films and what triggered . . . ?

A: No. That is to say, my adolescence was occupied with other matters. My parents, especially my mother . . . very cultured people. I was a fairly balanced youth. Athletics—tennis, that is—books, the theater. I would say my formative years were defined by literature.

Q: That's very good. Your mother?

A: A poet in her own right. An essayist, really into the rights of women before it became fashionable. She also was a superb teacher.

Q: About your father?

A: A university professor, a writer also. History, political science, quite erudite, though a man remote when it comes to being in touch with his own feelings.

Q: Yet you turned to fiction, novels, eventually film. Would it be correct to state that movies, to use the common term, were an adult aberration on your part? Nothing derogatory intended.

A: I suppose that's so. I've come to film late, but with considerable passion and sincerity. *P-town* was my first script—sold, that is, and produced.

Q: You've written other scripts?

A: Experimental scenarios, some of which are quite good, and that is an objective opinion.

Q: Yes. I would imagine that to have a director of O'Day's stature on your first effort must have provided an immense help. Very supportive.

A: Little John is established—

Q: Thirty-odd films . . .

A: Experienced, no doubt about that. The track record is there.

Q: A giant . . .

A: Let's take nothing away from him. But there was that fallow period prior to *P-town.* He'd been out of it for a long time. Nothing stays the same.

Q: You feel that the art of making film passed him by?

A: Not what I said. Not what I meant. Questions exist, however, there were doubts, areas of disagreement. . . .

Q: Conflict?

A: Purely professional conflict. And rightly so.

Q: Inevitable between a writer and a director.

A: Yes.

Q: Can you give an example?

A: O'Day comes out of another time. His cinematic persona was formed mainly in the big-studio era. Film isn't made that way any longer.

Q: A rich time. Colorful. Goldwynisms and all that.

A: They produced crap, and you know it. Directors today—Truffaut, Altman, Wertmüller . . .

Q: Masters all.

A: Yes.

Q: Then you are saying . . . ?

A: Just this . . .

Q: O'Day has always dominated—

A: I am not a man to be intimidated by reputation or anything. The point is, I wrote the book. I wrote the screenplay. No one else.

Q: Absolutely. I understand your point. Would you say that O'Day gave anything at all to the final script? After all—

A: You expect me to provide a number?

Q: Ten percent? Twenty? The director—

A: If the final version is flawed, I take no credit for it. I was not in the cutting room at the end.

Q: All right. But O'Day—

A: Let me put it this way, in all modesty. I invented the characters, the events; imagined, shaped, polished, put it all down. The relationships are my creation. The dialogue.

Q: And your colleagues have recognized your contributions. All the awards, prizes, accolades . . .

A: Nice but not necessary.

Q: There is the money.

A: I write for personal satisfaction.

Q: How did it come about that you were employed to do the screenplay?

A: There were discussions. Many long ones between Hillary and myself . . .

Q: Hillary Pike, the producer?

A: Yes, Hillary. Let's face it, the novel was already a success. Soon to be, that is. People were turned on to it, to the situations, the characters. Jenny, for example . . .

Q: Sandy Hayden was magnificent.

A: I had to fight to get O'Day to cast her.

Q: You discovered her.

A: A friend from an earlier period.

Q: I've read the book and the script a number of times. I've looked at the picture. There are certain dramatic differences between the book and the script, and again between the script and the film as being distributed.

A: Different mediums require different treatments. A novel should be read. A screenplay . . .

Q: A cinematic blueprint.

A: Exactly.

Q: There was little violence in the novel.

A: I cannot quibble with that. Violence is an essential thread in the complex fabric of American life. In that regard, the picture is true to life.

Q: You are saying violence is central to our contemporary mode of life? You believe that?

A: Don't you?

Q: It exists.

A: Then it is.

Q: I'm not sure I understand.

A: Artists, the movies, didn't invent war. Or murder. Or violence. Violence solves many problems for human beings. It answers many questions.

Q: It terminates many lives.

A: So it is, so it has always been.

Q: And you believe always will be?

A: I have no doubt.

Q: Then you'd prefer to work with . . . ?

A: I'd prefer that life was sweet and gentle, and people would be loving to each other.

Q: About Vicky Pierce.

A: What about her?

Q: I felt, I feel, she is, after all, a legend in the film world. Larger than life, you might say. Coming back that way, all that happened . . . doesn't her presence in the picture tip the balance?

A: I wouldn't say so.

Q: You wouldn't?

A: No.

Q: How do you account for . . . ?

A: A very great lady.

Q: Vicky . . .

A: A plus factor. Her presence expands each scene she's in. Her character, her personality, multiplies the value a writer injects into a script. To have her was pure good fortune. She was in retirement, you know.

Q: O'Day got her to come back, I'm told.

A: She read the novel, the script, wanted very much to play Laura.

Q: I didn't know that.

A: Oh, yes. My feelings for Vicky, Miss Pierce . . . [At this point, Reynolds' eyes grew moist, and for an interval he was unable to go on. Making a great effort, he signaled we were to continue the talks.]

Q: Back to the function of the screenwriter. What is that function, would you say?

A: To tell a story. Story is what it's all about.

Q: Your technique—tell us something about that.

A: I'd rather not get into that. Technique is a little like the armature a sculptor employs, necessary but unseen.

Q: Still . . .

A: Never spoil another dude's hustle. [He laughed a pleasant laugh.]

Q: Are you implying that technique is a trick?

A: There are ways and means to achieve ends. Technique gets a writer to the end, that's all.

Q: I see.

A: People direct their attention to the wrong areas.

Q: Still . . .

A: Sure.

Q: I guess so.

A: Sure. Look, what's important?

Q: Important?

A: To get your characters—your main characters, anyway—together. At the right time and the right place. Anticipate the audience, that's the trick. Get characters into action before the audience expects it to happen.

Q: I've never heard it put that way.

A: Of course. Film is a storytelling medium. After that, a visual medium.

Q: Some people would disagree.

A: Yes. Well, let me tell you. O'Day, he was always

coming down with some image or other. He sees it that way. Okay. I don't have to. I mean, he was repeatedly coming around saying he had this shot or that shot he wanted in the picture. Write a place for it. Well, man, we all know that's the wrong way to go about it.

Q: Would you blame—?

A: Absolutely. The difficulty with the sea shots. All that trouble. The logic just wasn't there, not integral, you see.

Q: I've always believed—

A: That's the wrong way, wrong as hell.

Q: Film is a series of still pictures . . .

A: Put in motion.

Q: Very important.

A: Don't make too much of it. Story—first of all, you've got to have something to say. Worth saying.

Q: No one will argue with that.

A: What the hell, that's where it's ultimately at. Take loneliness . . .

Q: Thematically?

A: Vicky Pierce in *P-town*, you see.

Q: Beautiful. I wanted to discuss that with you.

A: Loneliness. Okay, so you mess around until you come up with the right metaphor.

Q: The resort town was your metaphor for loneliness?

A: Ever been there?

Q: Once. I—

A: Off-season or on . . . lots of people, but no human contact. Nobody touching emotionally, you dig what I'm telling you? Okay, so here we are—we've got a theme, a metaphor . . .

Q: And then?

A: You must come up with a story.

Q: Plot?

A: Call it that. It's the easiest part. I mean, if it gets sticky and you have to do it, you can always lift a plot from—

Q: Plagiarize.

A: Face it, everything's been done before. . . .

9

"I liked it," Dodd declared in a high-pitched, mechanical voice. He was a shriveled, hunched man with tiny hands and feet. He sat in a chair that was too large, too high for him, and his legs swung idly, feet nowhere near the floor.

Not at all Hillary Pike's idea of what a successful businessman should look like. Pike was a believer in people looking right, running to type. The Franklin Jay Dodds of the world jarred the symmetry of things, put life out of whack. Pike preferred that all pieces of the human puzzle fit neatly into place.

"How nice," Pike said without enthusiasm.

There sat Dodd, dwarfed, deformed, ugly. Possessed of some tens of millions of American bucks. And intent on accumulating even more. Dodd had two professed interests in life—money and women. He liked his money in hard currency, his women in large, great, shimmering mounds of flesh.

"I'm sure it'll make money," Dodd added.

Hillary Pike's pale cheeks grew paler, if possible. On the far edge of translucence. Taking on that sickly blue cast. Bile formed in his stomach, pushed up into his throat by a slight eruption of nervous gas. Less than anything else, Pike had need for a money man with critical pretensions. Pike wanted Dodd's dough and nothing else. It never seemed to work that way; his world overflowed with experts on moviemaking.

"Don't be so sure," Pike said, and was immediately sorry. Too much haggling, hustling, grinding out production money had dulled his instincts. Put his nerves on edge. A man needed relief even from work he loved. Maybe he'd fly back up to P-town; Sandy Hayden had the world's greatest mouth.

Dodd twitched and squirmed, his bony bottom forming a depression in the big chair. "I only invest in order to make money."

"Don't worry," Zeke Bechtol said, laying accountant's oil on troubled fiscal waters.

"I must worry. I need to make money."

"This is a good deal."

"I like to make money."

"Nothing is a sure thing," Pike said.

Bechtol tossed a warning glance his way. "What Mr. Pike means is, you never can tell."

Pike reached for some unsalted peanuts sitting in a can on the low round coffee table. Three glasses of now lukewarm Vichy water was the only other refreshment offered by Dodd. He was not a man given to frivolities, not where business was concerned.

Dodd watched Pike chew the peanuts. His features twisted up as if being scourged by some profound inner agony. "Is it possible," he squeaked, "that I could lose money?"

Pike grew impatient. They were wasting time. The midget was a kook, a weirdo, a freak. Pike didn't want him around. "Nothing is guaranteed," he said gruffly.

"But the script is so good," Dodd said. "The picture is bound to be."

"A script is a selling tool," Bechtol said patiently. "A beginning. Nobody can be sure how it will turn out—on film, that is. That's all Mr. Pike meant."

"It makes me nervous not to make a profit on an investment."

Pike had had enough. He stood up. "You wouldn't be happy with us, Mr. Dodd. Forget about it."

Dodd almost tumbled out of the chair. "Now, wait. Wait. What do you mean? I haven't decided anything, not yet. Bechtol, you came to me. You begged me to read the script, to invest. Now this! What does it mean? How do you do business, Mr. Pike? This is no way to do business. You're upsetting me. Very much."

"Sit down, Hillary," Bechtol said.

Pike sat.

"There," Dodd said. After a moment, his breathing returned to normal. "As I said, I like to make money."

"There's more than one way to skin a cat," Pike said.

Dodd began getting jittery again. "What's he mean, Bechtol? What's that about cats?"

"An expression, Mr. Dodd. What Mr. Pike is saying is that it is possible to turn a profit by losing money."

"That bothers me," Dodd complained. "It really does. I have never made my peace with that kind of thinking. Frankly, gentlemen, it sounds slightly perverted. Obscene. Un-American."

Pike leaned forward, the long delicate fingers forming a steeple, the hooded eyes wary. His voice came out in a shaded whisper. "Understand this, Mr. Dodd. I want to be rich. Rich and successful and famous. Making pictures is all that matters to me. I take nourishment from the business, the action, the excitement, the kind of people I work with. But, man, we must make a profit. We must put in what the public wants to see. So we go where the action is."

Dodd fastened his eyes on Bechtol, determined to ignore the producer and his decidedly unorthodox views. "I was extremely impressed with the romantic possibilities of the story."

"There's been changes," Pike said.

"What? Why? I mean, what for? Does Mr. O'Day agree with these changes?"

"Mr. O'Day is in accord with all changes. After all, he is the director."

"Yes," Dodd said, little relieved. He watched Pike work on a handful of peanuts. The man's appetite was insatiable. "And Miss Pierce. A little slender for my taste, but still . . ."

"She's put on weight," Pike said.

"Has she!"

"How do you feel about violence?" Pike asked.

Dodd pulled back in the big chair. "What do you mean?"

"The changes," Bechtol reminded him in a mild, businesslike voice.

Dodd allowed himself to look at Pike again. "You are changing that gentle tale of love and devotion into some kind of cops-and-robbers story? That's terrible."

"Blood and guts," Pike said.

Dodd made a face.

"The real thing. Sex and violence, that's what sells."

A shrewd assessing light came into Dodd's squinched-up eyes. "Changes," he muttered balefully. "Changes cost money. The more a picture costs, the less likely it is to show a profit."

"Exactly," Bechtol said.

"It's not clear to me," Dodd said excitedly. "Not clear at all."

Pike leaned back in his chair. He was beginning to feel tired.

"What you need," Bechtol went on, "is a tax loss."

Dodd leaned precariously forward until Pike was certain he would fall out of the chair. For him, it would be a long way down to the floor. Pike hoped he'd hurt himself. Seriously.

"I'd love to meet Miss Pierce," he said, smacking his thin lips. "A tax loss? How?"

"Maybe," Pike said, "the picture will never even get to completion."

Dodd pouted. "No completion, no release. No release, no box-office receipts. No box-office receipts, no income. No income, no write-off."

"I'll complete," Pike said sourly.

"Will you release?"

"I'll release."

Dodd ventured another try. "Who will release?"

Pike decided the midget was smarter than he looked. "Universal, probably."

"Probably?" Dodd echoed vaguely.

"There will be income," Bechtol said. "Not enough to offset expenses, possibly. That would mean . . ."

"A tax loss," Dodd said.

"At last," Pike said.

Dodd stole a glance at the pale man. "I don't know."

"What? What don't you know?"

"Did you see *Seven Beauties*?"

"Wertmüller's flick? I saw it."

"I was just wondering," Dodd offered timidly. "In your picture, couldn't you put in at least one nice fat girl? . . ."

A Trumpy cruiser just short of ninety feet, she rode low and firm in the choppy sea, circling slowly, awaiting O'Day's instructions. The Trumpy had surprised them, O'Day most of all. He had anticipated something much flashier from Pike, some sleek aluminum job built for a Greek millionaire, complete with private seaplane and tiled swimming pool.

The Trumpy was old, built in 1935, given a major overhaul thirty years later. Her power plant consisted of twin GM 6-71 diesels and a 20-KW generator. She had radar, automatic pilot, VHF, all the necessities for embarking on a long sea voyage. The Trumpy had cruised the islands of the South Pacific, crossed the Atlantic four times, spent two full years in the Mediterranean.

O'Day, on one of the draggers, turned to Frank Jacoby, who had been fussing over his camera. "Ready to go?"

"Ready," Jacoby responded, making some last-second adjustments on the fluid head tripod.

"Okay, the yacht's coming back."

Plumes of white spray shot across the bow of the Trumpy as she swung around, headed back in their direction. The crew had ducked out of sight, leaving one man in view—Kiley. He stood on the aft deck as if claiming it for himself, legs solidly planted, a powerful, threatening figure.

O'Day didn't like him. Was repelled by the man at first glance. Ever since Lou Klein had discovered him storming over P-town's dunes on his Harley. Ever since Klein had brought him around for O'Day to inspect and pass judgment on. But the antipathy he felt hadn't kept O'Day from hiring the biker. Kiley, tough and unafraid, possessed of all the necessary physical skills, would be useful in doubling for Crespi in some of the more dangerous scenes, as well as performing a minor role as a member of a smuggling gang.

On the Trumpy, Kiley felt a rush of good feelings. A high akin to biking down an empty highway at full throttle, without helmet or leather. Neon flashes went off behind his eyes, and there was an excited roar in his ears. Why not? It was all there, out front, plain as day. A crazy treasure chest of riches and rewards, fame and fortune, all his for the taking. Fate had finally come down on his side, given him that one good break. Tapped him for the movies. At last he was going to get what he deserved.

O'Day was the main man. The king. President of

the club. The one to suck up to. Kiley intended to get close to the director, make known his good qualities to the man. O'Day was Bigtime Charlie in the flesh. He'd been there. Done it all. Made his name. Now he was getting old, and he'd want to leave something behind to signal his visit. A memorial to his achievements. Kiley intended to be that marker.

Also Jacoby. The Jew was a top cameraman. He would make other pictures, and it would be smart to have him as a pal. Be cool, Kiley warned himself. Go slow, go smart. Don't blow the big chance.

Crespi was the problem. Doubling for him, doing his stunts, working against him once or twice while the cameras ground away. Crespi was a pretty little queen, soft and tawny, like some kind of a scared rabbit. No different from some of those freaked-out dudes you found along the upper East Side. Next to Kiley, Crespi would look just like what he was, a nervous little fag. But when Kiley did stunts for the actor, he'd make him look good. Great, he amended. He'd make Crespi look great.

O'Day's voice drifted across the water. Kiley snapped back to the present. "On the yacht! Kiley! Can you hear me?"

Kiley lifted a hand in acknowledgment.

"Okay, Kiley, here we go. When I signal, go into your act."

Kiley, wearing clothes that were duplicates of the clothes Crespi would wear, his hair styled to look like the actor's, tried not to appear too big, too strong, too unlike Crespi. The cameras were pointed at him, angled in such a way as to keep his face out of the pictures, making it seem to viewers that he was in fact Joe Crespi.

"All right!" O'Day shouted. "Let's do the scene. Cameras, Frank!"

"Rolling."

"Kiley, you're on!"

Kiley inched closer to the yacht's railing, peering into the sea as instructed. He made a pointing gesture, and according to O'Day's coaching, cried, "Hey! Look out! Somebody's gone overboard!" Later, he knew, Crespi's honeyed voice would replace his on the soundtrack.

He ripped off his shirt and kicked off his shoes, climbed up to the top rail. Puffed up with pride at being the focus of so much attention, he posed there for a beat or two longer than was necessary, before launching himself in a powerful dive.

He surfaced, looked around, struck out toward the nearest dragger, under the recording eyes of the two cameras. He was twenty feet away when he heard O'Day call, "Cut!"

Kiley hauled himself on board and dried off. He spotted O'Day in conversation with Vicky Pierce and joined them.

"How'd I do, Mr. O'Day?"

O'Day looked up with some surprise. "Okay, fine. Get back to you in a minute . . . Kiley." He returned his attention to Vicky Pierce. "Let me get a stunt girl."

"I can do it, Little John."

"That water's cold."

"That's a fact," Kiley put in happily. "And pretty rough."

O'Day tried to light a Gitane in the wind. The match went out. "I'll get a double."

"No."

He struck another match, but the Gitane failed to catch fire. "Damn. There's something wrong. I shouldn't be doing the second-unit stuff. Where's the man Pike promised me? Everything's going too slow. I'm no good at this."

"I'll do my best for you," Vicky said. "What about Sexton?"

O'Day looked at her without comprehension.

"He could do the stunts. You said yourself he used to be good."

"I'll talk to him."

"Don't mention me when you do."

"Okay. All right, let's do it if we're going to. Kiley! There you are. Listen, man, what were you thinking up on that railing? This is not a beauty contest. There's a dame down in the water in trouble. Don't pose up there, get after her. Jesus, man, you were up there long enough for me to count the hairs on your chest."

"I'll do better this time, Mr. O'Day." But he was talking to the director's retreating back. A bulge of resentment swelled up in Kiley's throat, but he said nothing. He knew what he wanted, what he had to do to get it; this was no time for mistakes.

A small boat carried Kiley back to the yacht, where he dressed himself again and took up his position in the stern. He signaled that he was ready.

"Let's go," O'Day said, "before we lose this good light."

"Stand by," Jacoby said to his crew.

"Vicky!"

"I'm ready."

O'Day sighed and nodded. "Okay, into the water."

Vicky shivered and shook under a pile of blankets. Three cups of steaming tea and two shots of gin had done little to help. Over her pajamas she wore a heavy sweater, and she hugged herself desperately, but the chill of the Atlantic Ocean still gripped her.

She lay in the bed and willed sleep to come. It did no good. She willed her mind to remain empty, her muscles to relax, her nerves to come to rest. Nothing happened.

Someone was knocking at the door. The idea of confronting another human being was terrifying, and yet she was constitutionally incapable of resisting the summons. She put on a robe and opened the door. Lee Downing stood there, his face a plastic mask of assumed pleasantries.

"Hope I'm not disturbing you," he began, as if by rote.

"I'm not feeling very well."

"This won't take long."

She wanted to send him away. To close the door in his face. To rage against this intrusion. Instead she invited him in.

She went back to the bed and got under the covers, still wearing the bathrobe. He looked down at her with professional curiosity. She looked awful. If they were going to get some good publicity out of her, she'd have to shape up. Take better care of herself. He spotted the bottle of gin on the night table. He'd heard she took a nip now and then.

"Maybe you ought to see a doctor." Say the right words, win her over. "I'll call somebody."

"Just tell me why you're here."

"Don't you like me, Miss Pierce? Gee, I sure like you. I really like you."

"What is it?"

"Letita Belmont arrived a couple of hours ago."

"That awful woman."

"She wants to interview you."

"No."

"She asked specially for you."

"No."

"She's important, Miss Pierce."

"No, I said. Please go away."

"Syndicated in about four hundred papers."

"Let me alone, I don't feel well."

"She admires you a lot."

"I don't do interviews."

"And TV. Letita's got an audience of maybe thirty

million for her TV shows. Means a lot, that many people."

"Later. Talk to me in a few days."

"I've got to work out a schedule, you see."

"Tomorrow. We'll discuss it tomorrow."

"She's only staying for a couple of days."

"I can't think now."

"I promised her Vicky Pierce. Letita's a fan, very simpatico."

"I can't."

"Mr. Pike told me you would be cooperative."

"I'm an actress. I have only a limited amount of energy, time. No, please."

"I'll have to ask him about that, why he said you'd work with me, I mean. I must have misunderstood him."

"Joe will talk to her."

"She doesn't want Crespi. She wants you. Letita says you're one of the giants of our industry. The last of the great stars. She said that."

"You're not a nice man."

"We all have our work. Letita can only help a person's career. That's my professional opinion, as a press agent."

She closed her eyes.

"You all right, Miss Pierce?"

"I have never been all right."

"Maybe I should call that doctor."

"I never will be all right."

"Do you think you could talk to Letita tonight?"

"That's madness. Can't you see the condition I'm in?"

"This is a flying visit for Letita, in and out, so to speak."

"Tomorrow."

"I knew I could count on you. Tonight would be much better. The schedule."

"Tomorrow, I said."

"Sure, whatever you say. We could do it right here in your suite. Have dinner sent up. Why not do that? Easy on everybody. I'll order. You want something special, just say so. Make it easy all around. Say about nine o'clock? Be a sport, Miss Pierce."

"Just go away."

"Then you'll do it? Tonight?"

"Tonight."

"Boy," he said, "you're a first-class person, Miss Pierce."

Ernesto Costa spooned *sopa de abobora* into his mouth, pausing only now and then to stuff a chunk of sweet bread after the thick yellowish liquid.

"I still don't like it," he said.

Mario raised his hands helplessly, let them fall. "Pop, making movies is not like anything else I ever saw. You go out to fish, or Antonio fixes the plumbing, or Joaquim puts up a new house somewhere, all of you know what you're doing. These movie people, they make it up as they go along. One day one thing, one day something else."

"Sounds like a craziness to me."

"They pay good."

"You should be out fishing."

"I want my own boat, Pop."

"I got my own boat, and I didn't have anything to do with movie people."

"It takes a lot of money, these days. You know that."

"You don't know what it means to work hard for something. Everything's gotta come easy. Listen, I made up a *velha*. You want some?"

"I'm not hungry."

"My leftovers not good enough for you."

"Pop, come on."

"Come on where? Big-shot movie star, my son."

"Pop, I'm just running the boats is all."

"Listen, I'm a pretty good cook since Mama passed away, Blessed be her soul. You never were a good eater. How long's that crap gonna go on?"

"The picture? I don't know. Now they're talking about a couple more weeks."

"Insanity. Meanwhile, you're paying rent to those robbers at Leitão. Two draggers . . ."

"I'm making a fortune, Pop, even with the rent. More in a day than I could fishing for a week."

"Fishing is your work. Those picture people, they won't be around forever. A fisherman should fish. But you'll do what you want. Kids never listen to their fathers."

"Was it different when you were my age, Pop?"

Ernesto lifted a hand in mock threat. "Fresh kid, get outta here."

Long after his son had left, Ernesto sat staring at the door, trying to remember what it was like to be young and hungry and full of plans for the future.

O'Day hoarded his rage as if it might be in short supply. He parceled it out in miserly portions so as to keep himself vigorous and sensitive to the rising possibility of imminent disaster.

Nothing was going the way it should; he was wasting his time, the worst of all personal crimes. Time was the dearest commodity, lapsed seconds irretrievably threatening his vitality, his hopes, his life.

In anger, he marched down to the harbor and put himself down on the sand, back to the rotting pilings of a long-abandoned pier, laboring to isolate his difficulties and so attend them one by one. The strategy failed, his brain cluttered with a jumble of thoughts and fluttering emotions.

"Balls!" he bayed at the low moon in the sky.

Behind him, a voice answered, "If I had them, I'd be king, said the queen."

O'Day glanced over his shoulder. "Go away, Sexton."

Sexton sat next to O'Day. He uncorked the bottle he was carrying and drank. "Bourbon," he said.

O'Day took the bottle. "Our country, right or wrong," he toasted.

Sexton reclaimed the bottle. "My mother, drunk or sober."

"What a sentimental man you are, Sexton," O'Day said caustically.

"You're a romantic, Little John, sitting on the sand, howling at the moon."

"Better'n being a quitter."

"You saying I'm a quitter?"

"Well . . ."

"I'll take my bottle now."

"You're sore."

"No, I'm not sore."

"The hell you ain't. I know when a man's sore. One word, and you get your back up. You always were that way, Sexton."

"What the hell do you know about how I was?"

"No secrets anywhere. You drink too much, anybody ever tell you?"

"Lots of times. It's all in knowing when to stop."

"It's all in knowing when to start."

"You don't make sense."

"I make lots of sense, always have."

"Start what? Drinking?"

"Start back, that's what. Come to work for me."

"You offering me a job?"

"Yes, goddammit."

"I already have a job."

"You were good once, Sexton, you'd be good again."

"Bet your sweet ass I'd be, if I wanted to be." Down the beach, Sexton saw movement. Two young men coming in their direction. They walked casually, too casually, glancing sidelong at the men seated on the sand.

"How you doing, fellas?" Sexton said, as they came abreast.

"Hi," one of the young men said, and they went on.

Sexton put his eyes out toward the water. It shimmered in the moonlight, dark, ominously thick and slow. "I'm a painter now," he said.

"Vicky told me about your painting. Sounds like one of my nightmares."

"It's big, Little John. You got a bad wall you want to cover up? You can have it cheap."

"The bottle, you're hogging the bottle." Sexton handed it over. "Damn picture's gonna drive me up the wall. Got to have a man for the second unit. What it needs, I can't provide."

"Talk to your producer."

"First it was all low budget, cheap and fast. Then Pike wants changes. Action, fights, rewrites. He brings in a yacht and scraps some good footage. Money is suddenly not a problem. What the hell's he up to?"

"Problems, problems . . ."

"He'd like to get rid of Crespi, wants me to put somebody with muscles into the part."

"It's his picture."

"No, goddammit! It's mine. I can make it something that counts. That's good." He fingered his mustache and knuckled his eyes, finished off his cigarette. "I hired a stunt guy, but he's getting away from me. He roughed Vicky up today, copped a feel or something, I'm not sure. Maybe I haven't got what it takes anymore."

"No way, old man. You got it, you'll die with it."

"You could help, Sexton."

"Vicky talks too much."

"You do the stunts, stage them right. Handle the second unit."

"No more gags for me."

"Maybe I *should* dump Crespi."

"He's a pretty good actor."

"We were out in one of those fishing boats. Crespi puked his guts out the whole time. Sure, he's good, but if he's always sick?"

"Fire him, and make the producer happy."

"Fuck you, Sexton."

"Nice way to talk while you guzzle my booze."

O'Day tilted his head back and drank.

"Hand it over." Sexton took a short pull, enough to wet his throat. He felt it trickling into his stomach.

"Those kids are coming back," O'Day said.

"I noticed."

"Four of them this time."

"I noticed. How fast can you run?"

"At my age, walking's hard."

"Figures." Sexton corked the bottle and made a place for it in the sand. He stood up.

"Maybe," O'Day said, struggling to his feet, "they're just out for a little stroll."

"Maybe." When they were twenty feet away, Sexton said, "You're back again, boys."

They kept advancing. "Out for the air," one of them said.

"The beach is free," another said.

The biggest of the four, swollen with his own strength and courage, got out in front, moving stiffly, like a dog picking a fight. Sexton watched him without reaction. He felt pleased to be involved again in what he knew he did well, something where victory and defeat were so clearly defined. The big youth was plainly stupid, Sexton remarked to himself, putting himself on the line this way. Sexton plucked at his memory for the most efficient way to deal with the situation.

"Go away, fellas," Sexton said.

They kept on without haste, as if they'd been through it all before. Good size to all of them, with power shoulders and heavy arms, faces sullen in the night, focused on why they had come. A few strides away, they went into a separating maneuver, putting Sexton and O'Day at the center of a circle, closing in.

"Fellas," Sexton said. "You wouldn't do us any harm, would you?"

The one out in front lowered his chin as if preparing to charge. "Gonna wipe you out, man."

Nothing more to say, Sexton decided. Talking only postponed the inevitable. Best thing was to get it on without waiting, get it over as fast as possible.

Like Nate Archibald going to the basket, Sexton got off on that long quick first stride, coming up low and close to Big Boy. He planted his fist on Big Boy's chin, maintaining his drive, swinging his elbow against Big Boy's cheek. Still charging, Sexton drove his shoulder under Big Boy's jaw. Big Boy went over on his back, breathing noisily, blood dribbling from his mouth and his nose.

"Jesus Christ," one of the others said.

Sexton, arms spread wide, hands upturned, faced them. "There you are, fellas. You know what I can do. I'll give you a break, take you all on at once. Ready. Set. Let's go."

The trio went into a clumsy retreat.

"Take your friend when you go," Sexton said.

They ventured back after a whispered consultation and hoisted Big Boy erect, dragging him up the beach toward Commercial Street. At a safe distance, one of them turned and shouted, "Stinking fairies!"

O'Day, a quaver in his voice, said, "They think we're queer."

"We are a little strange." Sexton located the bottle and took a drink. "Figured we'd be easy pickings. Wanna kill it?" He extended the bottle.

O'Day drank, dropped the empty bottle to the sand. "You liked it," he muttered. "Sumbitch, if you didn't really like it."

"Come on, old man, I'll see you get home all right."

10

Kiley bellied up to the bar, the way he'd seen it done in some of those old westerns. A sidelong glance left, another right. Then order some whiskey. A man rides slowly and alone into town, giving off emanations of menace, sudden and total destruction. Way to go.

All the punks were looking him over. Sucking up gut. Pumping up nerve enough to throw down on Kiley. Shee-it, wouldn't even let a man drink in peace and tranquility. Keep a tight asshole, men.

"Kiley, isn't it?"

He laid a bleak, heavy stare on the intruder. The face was familiar. He struggled to put a name to it.

"Lee Downing," the intruder offered.

"Oh, yeah. You're the publicity guy."

"Buy you a drink?"

Kiley gave Downing his bony profile to look at. "Why not?"

"How do you like movie work?"

"There's a lot of standing around."

"You put your finger right on it. Too much waiting."

"I dig action."

"I know what you mean."

The hell you do, Kiley thought. He rolled his shoulders, vaguely threatening.

Downing said, "You remind me of a cocked pistol, ready to go off."

Kiley liked the image. He imagined himself as a smoking gun, a death machine. Look out, world! Kiley's here.

"You do good stunts," Downing said.

"You think so?" Kiley was encouraged to hear that. Downing was, after all, a pro in pictures. He would know.

"You never did it before, did you?"

Kiley grew defensive. "I ride a Harley, charged and supercharged. You know what it means to get your legs around a hot thousand-cc engine? I've been out there up around a hundred and forty miles per. I have done free falls. You are looking at a man at home on land, on sea, or in air."

"I see what you mean. Hiring you was a good move."

"You think so?"

"Oh, yes. I heard O'Day tell Jacoby. Said you were a man, and Crespi just a boy."

"Crespi . . ." There was disgust and despair in Kiley's voice.

"Know what you mean, man. Lots of movie stars are that way, southpaws. Or at least switch-hitters. Crespi comes across fuzzy to me, like he was never formed right."

"Something's missing."

"You're on target. Pike would like to can Crespi."

"How do you know?" Kiley felt his hopes rise, mind sifting though everything Downing was saying.

"I heard him say so."

"You actually heard him?"

"That's it."

"He's still in the picture."

"O'Day is stubborn."

"He wants Crespi? You just said—"

"Little John is not happy, I kid you not."

Kiley stared at the glass in his big hands. "Means zero to me."

"You never know. Jacoby said O'Day ought to fire Crespi and replace him. With you, Jacoby said."

"Jacoby said that?"

"Then he laughed."

"Why? Why'd he laugh? What's funny?"

"O'Day wasn't laughing."

"He's a man, he understands."

"Maybe something will happen."

" 'Maybe' doesn't add up to shit."

"I guess that's right. After all, it's not like you're an actor."

"Nothing to it."

"A lot of people work real hard at it. Study. Do stock, all kinds of things. They never get anywhere."

"I could pull it off, if I set my mind to it."

"I bet you could."

"Said I could, didn't I?"

"I'd like to see you get the chance."

"Too bad you're not the man who hires and fires."

"Maybe I can help."

"How?"

"Downing's the name, publicity's the game. You mind getting your name in the papers?"

While waiting for Wanda to finish her shower, Reynolds stretched out on the bed and read the new pages he'd written. There was no way O'Day could fail to appreciate what he'd done; the dialogue was taut, the action heavy, and some of his camera directions innovative.

Wanda came out of the bathroom, wearing nothing. She smelled of soap and too-sweet perfume, dusted lightly with baby powder, primly perfect in her nakedness. Even the pale pubic bush, kept neatly trimmed with a pair of blunt steel scissors. She lowered herself onto the other end of the bed in what, for another woman, might have been a provocative pose. Wanda merely seemed girlish, healthy. Sterile.

"You are the cleanest chick I've ever known," Reynolds said.

"I'm glad you think so." She lowered her chin in coquettish modesty.

He hadn't meant it as a compliment. "When I was at Yale, I had an affair with an older woman. Her name was Margaret. She always smelled."

Wanda made a face.

He grinned at her distress. "From sweat or piss, sometimes from her husband. He'd screw her, and she'd come to me right afterward."

"Without bathing?"

"Drove me up the wall. I disgust you, don't I, Wanda?"

She decided not to give him the satisfaction of a response. Instead she stood up, slowly turning, displaying her front and her back.

"I went with Jerry and Junie today to a nude beach."

For the first time, he realized that her breasts and her buttocks were colored a delicate pink. He sat up in disbelief.

She gave him her sweetest, most innocent smile. "Jerry is a fabulous fellow. He's quite wealthy, you know. He runs a check-cashing service."

"A loan shark," he said, with inexplicable anger.

Her smile held. "He also owns laundromats, twenty-five of them. I never considered that anybody actually owned laundromats. And coin machines. The kind that sell candy and cigarettes. Jerry says it's a good business."

"You took your bikini off in public?" Reynolds' brain was muddled, shifting cumbersomely from thought to thought, his reaction time slowed down.

"All of us got naked. Jerry also sells frozen yoghurt. The profits are immense, he says. I admire a man who knows how to get what he wants."

"You let Jerry see you naked?"

Wanda gave her best girlish laugh. "The whole world could have seen me, if it looked. I was naked on a public beach."

"My God!"

"Front and back. Junie, too. What a delicious body she has. No wonder Jerry married her. They met at an orgy, you know."

"She told you that?"

"Yes. She was doing it with her mouth to every man who would let her, she said. Trying to find out how many she could do. Like trying to set a record, you see. She decided Jerry's was the best. Or at least the biggest. That's what she said. What a way to meet your husband."

"I don't believe it."

"I do."

"All three of you were naked?"

"All three of us."

"Oh, God . . ."

"I even talked to a couple of guys, strangers. Both of them were kind of cute."

His confusion mounted. Suddenly he didn't know her, didn't recognize her actions as belonging to the woman he was married to. All this was unreal somehow, out of character for Wanda. She had always possessed cool and remote sexual and social manners, and now he was glimpsing a new aspect that made him afraid.

"How?" he heard himself saying. "How did you feel?"

"In the beginning," she said, "I was very nervous. It felt . . . peculiar."

"The men you spoke to, did they look at you?"

"One did, at my titties and my pussy. The other one wanted to, I could tell. But he didn't."

"Oh, God."

"You're angry."

"Don't be ridiculous. I'm not some stiff-necked square like my father. I . . ."

"You are so angry, I can tell."

"Well, what in hell do you expect? My wife tells me she's been showing her snatch off to a bunch of strangers. How many did you screw?"

"You know better than that. I don't understand you, Tommy. All along you've been trying to get me to—"

"Ah, you did it for me! All for me!"

"You know what I mean."

"And you know what I said. Together. As a team, a couple. Nothing separate. That way, we both enjoy everything. Did Jerry try anything?"

"Just a little talk. Compliments."

"He liked what he saw?"

"Said my ass was a winner." She giggled. "You ought to see him. He *is* very big."

"Soft."

"Hard."

"He got it up! There on the beach?"

"Sitting opposite Junie and me, his knees raised." The tip of her pink tongue appeared in the corner of her mouth. "Tommy, it turned me on."

"Oh, that's beautiful."

"I couldn't help it."

"Look at me. Here. Is he that big?"

"Tommy . . . he's bigger."

"Shit."

"But I like you the way you are. Yours is prettier, more sensitive."

"What the hell does that mean?"

"You're an artist, creative."

"You want to do it, ball the Wheelers?"

"I've been thinking about it all evening. Do you think I could become . . . sexy and wild?"

"Try."

She took him in hand. "They're going to give a party

for the entire company of the picture. They want us to come. Afterward, Jerry said . . ."

"The four of us?"

"That's what he said."

"Oh, Jesus."

"You want to?"

"Do you?"

"I think so. Yes. You'll have to tell me exactly what to do."

"You'll know."

"I want you to tell me. To command me."

"Yes."

"I'll do it, whatever you say."

"And afterward . . . ?"

"When we're by ourselves?"

"Yes, then."

"I'll talk to you. Tell you everything. How I felt. What I liked. What I was thinking."

"Yes. Yes."

In the morning, early, O'Day took them out to shoot Joe Crespi in the water. These were close shots that would subsequently be intercut with earlier versions of Kiley rescuing Vicky Pierce, giving the impression that it was Crespi doing the job.

The sea was rougher than O'Day liked, and by the time they had reached the filming area, Crespi had twice thrown up. Now he sat weakly against the wheelhouse, cloaked in a blanket, his eyes closed.

"Poor Joe," Vicky said.

"He's useless," O'Day responded harshly.

"He's sick. This is not his kind of work."

"He's here, he gets paid, he's got to come through."

O'Day moved down the deck to where the actor sat. He spoke his name.

Crespi raised his pale, strained face. "Time to go to work?"

"You look lousy," O'Day said. He was careful to keep

his voice objective, to show no weakness to the other man. He was committed to Crespi, and fought against admitting, even to himself, that Pike might be right. Crespi was all wrong for the part as it was shaping up. "I can shoot around you today," O'Day conceded.

"No. I want to do it."

"We'll try again tomorrow."

"It won't make any difference. I won't change. Let's shoot the scene." He struggled to his feet, and his hand closed on O'Day's arm. There was very little strength in the fingers. "I have always been afraid of the water. I was never very physical, even as a boy, not an athlete. I am a good actor, Little John. I will do whatever you ask of me. I will. Please don't stop me. It wouldn't be right, not fair."

O'Day made up his mind. "Okay, we'll try it." He went back to where the camera crew waited. "He's ready to give it a shot," he said to Jacoby.

"Can he cut it?"

"We're going to find out soon enough."

At five minutes past eleven, Joe Crespi slid into the heaving sea, following Vicky Pierce. O'Day positioned them and called for action. They shot the scene.

"Awful," O'Day said when it was over.

"He looks a little uncertain." Jacoby was trying to be kind.

"He looks," O'Day answered thinly, "as if *he* needs to be rescued. Pike is right about dumping him. Let's do it one more time."

They did it three times, each take as bad as the first one. Then Crespi's right leg cramped, and they had to pull him out of the water. Back on deck, he suffered an attack of the dry heaves.

O'Day called for a lunch break.

At three o'clock Crespi felt well enough to go back into the water. By five, they had shot nine takes, none of them very good. O'Day was clear about one thing:

Joe Crespi was not the stuff movie action heroes were made of. But the slender actor had guts, and O'Day admired that and told him so.

"I'll be all right tomorrow," Crespi vowed.

O'Day didn't believe it, not for a minute; Crespi would never be all right.

11

Kiley couldn't clear it out of his head. The image kept shifting back, lingering in hazy outline like some childhood memory.

He tried to imagine what it would be like for him to be an actor. A matinee idol! Top of the line, not some ordinary cat whose name meant nothing. Paul Newman. Steve McQueen. Christ Almighty! Compared to him, they were little boys. He was all man, big and powerful, all muscle and brass balls.

A blast. Downing had given him the word. O'Day thought Kiley could do it. O'Day recognized that Kiley was a member of a select breed. O'Day dug Kiley. That was the director's number-one ego trip, turning unknowns into stars. He'd done it a dozen times, Downing had said.

Here's the body, man. Let's get it on.

But that conversation had taken place five days before, and nothing had happened since. Crespi, that quivering mass of human jelly, was still on the payroll. Still fumbling his way through scene after scene. Still screwing up the shooting schedule. As useless as tits on a boar. By all rights, he should've been fired long ago.

Well, fuck them all. Kiley was a free spirit. A gypsy. Superstud on a superbike. Going and coming as he desired. Unencumbered. Nothing stood in his way. *Nobody* . . . All that movie crud, who needed that?

Large and awesome in his Straight Arrow colors, Kiley marched along Commercial Street. People took notice, man. Women turned on. Men drew back afraid. Kids froze in place, blinded by his shining perfection. Take a good look—at a real man.

Up a narrow street past a line of small frame houses, set down to face the harbor, as if to welcome seafarers after a long and arduous journey. Prettily painted havens for clean and honest people too frightened to get out in the real world and live.

Kiley roared out his rage. "*Fuck you!*"

There was silence. And then a plaintive male voice came floating back. "Please . . ."

Kiley broke into a run. Going as fast as he could. He sucked air harshly and felt his heart pumping blood. He put on his famous finishing kick. Look at 'im go! Beautiful. He made it across the finish line, immersed in crowd noise. Olympic Gold Medal winner!

He kept going, aware that he needed something. Had to satisfy the undefined craving that lined his mouth and throat. He swelled with need until he remembered where he could go, where all his hungers could be satisfied. He went faster.

Sandy Hayden wanted desperately to go to the party. She had always loved parties. As a child, to miss a party, to fail to be invited, was to experience total disaster. The end of the world. She loved the anticipation. The noise, the bustle of people laughing and talking, crowding up against each other. She loved the smell of liquor and cigarettes, the suggestion of sexuality that filled the air. The possibility of something new occurring with someone new. Some unknown kick.

Damn Tommy.

God knows she'd been invited often enough. The Wheelers had sent her a formal invitation engraved on fine stock. As a member of the *Provincetown* company, she was entitled to go.

Vicky Pierce had gone out of her way to introduce herself to Sandy, to try to make her feel at home, to offer any help that might be required. Was she for real? And reminding her about the party, as if the invitation was hers to give.

Frank Jacoby had said he hoped she'd come. And that stunt man, Kiley—what a disgusting animal he was. And Lee Downing, of course.

All of them were after a piece of her. Wanted to get into her pants. Jacoby . . . In return for a couple of closeups, she might just give him a good night or two.

Tommy, you prick.

O'Day. She needed him. Had to come up with a way to win him over to her side. She'd flashed her boobs in his direction, wiggled her ass. But nothing. Maybe she was being too subtle. With O'Day behind her, there was no telling how far she might travel. Right to the peak of the mountain. The director was everything on a picture. The brains, the true creator, the ultimate power. John Patrick Michael O'Day could turn little Sandra Elizabeth Theresa Isabel Handuski into a shining star.

Reynolds, you pitiful bastard.

Tommy had insisted that she not go. "Can't you see the problem it will create?" he had pointed out in that so very reasonable manner of his, all head and no heart. "Wanda is going to be there."

"I won't go near either of you."

"Stay away."

"Why!" she wailed. "I'm a prisoner in this room."

She considered telling him to shove it, going anyway. After all, Pike had hired her. Pike would keep her from getting fired, despite anything Reynolds might say. Unless Tommy told Pike about them. She wondered if he guessed about her and Downing? She ordered herself to calm down, to consider the situation in terms of the long haul. Her career was all that mattered. Reynolds was on his way to becoming a big, important movie writer. She didn't want him for an enemy. So she'd agreed not to go to the party, and here she sat alone and frustrated, embittered over the lousy hand dealt her by fate.

"Fuck, fuck, fuck!" she railed at the walls of her room. She beat the mattress and later did violent exercises. None of it helped very much. Until Downing called.

"I'm on my way to the Wheelers," he announced. "Pick you up in ten minutes."

He was just making sure he had a bed to crawl into later on. Well, fuck *him*.

"I'm not going."

He was smarter than she thought. "Reynolds, huh? He's playing it cool."

"His wife is going to be there."

"So are a number of media people I've invited up. You should meet them. A couple of good spreads, and you're on your way."

She hesitated, weighing possible gain against loss.

"Don't worry about Reynolds. I got you to Pike, didn't I? Trust me."

Not for a minute. She put a smile into her voice. "Make it twenty minutes. I need time to get dressed. You want me to look my best."

"In that case, don't put too much on."

Sexton sat in a straight-backed chair in front of the huge painting and stared at it, sipping bourbon from a water tumbler. He surveyed the work with increasing despair and regret, convinced that his reach far exceeded his artistic grasp. Like everything he had ever done, this too was a failure. The original concept was large and imposing; but his ability to execute it was incomplete, his talent small and insignificant.

O'Day had called it a nightmare. So it was. A nightmare circus. That was what he would call it. *Nightmare Circus*. Those weird alien figures, the ghostly gray tone of the picture, those strangely voluptuous lines. He was fed up with it all.

He turned away. In a few days, when the paint was dry, he would varnish it to a high luster, fix it forever in place. Unless he destroyed the monster first.

He got into the shower, the water very hot. He soaped his body repeatedly, scrubbing his skin until it glowed pink. He located the water tumbler on the sink and drank the rest of the bourbon in two long swallows. Then, as he moved to return it to its place, he felt the glass slipping out of his soapy grasp. The tumbler shattered on the tile floor of the shower.

He crouched down and studied the scatter of glass. He ran a finger across the cutting edge of one sizable shard. He pressed harder, and a globule of blood appeared on his fingertip.

He drew the point of the shard across the inside of his left wrist. A raw streak signaled the path followed by the glass. He placed the shard back to his wrist, steadily intensifying the pressure.

The pain was bearable as he drew the glass from one side to the other. Blood seeped into view, flowing in watery rivulets along his forearm.

Sexton separated his wrist from the glass and stepped carefully out of the shower. He washed the shallow cut in the sink and stanched the flow. After removing the shattered glass from the shower stall, he shaved himself. Carefully.

He donned clean blue jeans, a faded old work shirt

and a pair of huaraches bought years ago during his Mexican sojourn. They had grown dark and worn in his service.

He decided to wait before taking another drink. The booze at the Wheelers' would be excellent, in good supply, and free of charge.

12

Once a beach cottage of no particular distinction, the Wheeler house had grown and spread over the sand hills like an architectural plague. Early on, guest cottages had been erected, connected by covered walkways; and later, the walkways were enclosed.

An entertainment wing was put on, and a garage for three cars. The garage subsequently became a paneled game room complete with pool table, slot machines, pinball games, a poker table, color television, a wet bar, and a brick fireplace painted white. A studio was built, a greenhouse, and porches and decks, breezeways and balconies, room after room, a glacial construction creeping toward the outer edges of the Cape as if intent on covering all the available land.

There was a strange, ramshackle orderliness to it all, a beachcomber's necessities inflated into a millionaire's playpen. Reclaimed, renovated, refurbished. Renewed each spring by a platoon of efficient servants who descended upon the house to dust and sweep and shine and repair, lest the Wheelers be confronted with even the slightest dislocation or discomfort.

On the first Friday in April, Jerry and Junie had arrived on the Cape. They flew into the P-town airport in a Lear jet owned by one of the corporate entities that Jerry commanded. Or influenced. Or directed.

Whichever was more suitable. Minutes after their arrival, they were solidly and comfortably ensconced in the house, as if never away, to stay until the first chill and empty days of autumn.

The house was ideal for a party. Part of the plan, Junie liked to claim. Great numbers of people were readily accommodated, and the variety of spaces permitted different activities to proceed simultaneously. Parties were important to Jerry and Junie. They gave a party every week or so during the season. Each one seemed bigger, better, noisier than the one before. Part of the social strategy.

Hand-in-hand, the Wheelers cruised the bars and shops and restaurants on Commercial Street, recruiting participants. Fascinating strangers who might offer new experiences, tastes, delights.

"A cast party for the *Provincetown* company!" they announced.

"Come early," Jerry said.

"Come anytime," Junie amended.

"Just come."

"Please."

The party burst into life. A few guests drifted onto the scene without impact. Introductions were made, drinks offered and accepted. All very civilized. Until at one certain point the socially explosive combustibles gave off a spark, flared, exploded into action.

Talk turned to shouts. Laughter segued into loud guffaws. There was the amplified squawk of a stereo blasting out the Stones in all their throbbing glory. Alice. Bette.

The air thickened with the scent of burned tobacco and the sweetish smell of good grass. A serving man in a white jacket and white gloves offered a bowl of Steuben cut glass filled with white powder and sniffing spoons. Some of the guests snorted their fill of the coke through rolled-up hundred-dollar bills or solid-gold straws.

Bars had been established in strategic corners throughout the house. Each was manned by sober black men in scarlet waistcoats who poured liquor with style and in large dosages.

Even before Sexton put in an appearance, some of the guests had started performing in odd and memorable ways. Two men threw fists in defense of the sanctity of their respective marriage beds; both were badly beaten. One of the wives was distraught at the condition of her husband, the other over a budding love affair so bloodily and crudely interrupted.

A social historian saw the fisticuffs as clear additional evidence—if such was needed—that marriage was an institution putrefied and dormant.

A woman with recently inflated silicone breasts displayed them and danced on a glass-topped coffee table.

An executive of an oil company offered a thousand dollars in cash to the sixteen-year-old daughter of an executive of an automobile company if she would allow him access to her anus. She kneed him in the crotch with considerable velocity and joy, causing him to vomit all over the floor.

At ten o'clock, a male model, his face the product of a surgeon's knife, sat down on the floor and began to cry. He wailed that he wanted his old nose back.

A recently divorced woman from Tiffin, Ohio, sat opposite the model on the floor and stroked his new nose, telling him that it was beautiful.

The social historian pointed out that the family had become a social dinosaur, fading into the mists of history.

The sales manager for a breakfast-food company declared loudly that he was a radical revolutionary ready to blow up all the institutions of the capitalist West.

The glass-topped coffee table shattered under the pounding of the woman with the silicone breasts. Blood spurted in a precise crimson arc out of one of her wounds, and she tried to stem the leak with her other hand.

A famous and wealthy physician, concerned about the rising cost of malpractice insurance, left the party at once.

The divorced woman told the model that she considered fucking a stranger to be a friendly thing to do, and he agreed with her. They wiped away each other's tears.

A six-foot-two-inch lesbian with a classic face and a statuesque body put it to the sixteen-year-old daughter of the automobile-company executive this way: "Would you care to try my dildoe for openers?" The girl gave her the middle finger and went looking for some real fun.

The wife of one of the beaten husbands returned to the party without her mate. She was unable to locate her intended lover. She began to drink, and later passed out, and someone stole her purse and nearly three hundred dollars.

The social historian saw this as free enterprise in its purest form.

The radical revolutionary announced that all academics were mealymouthed shit-eaters.

A lady schoolteacher from Boston poured her drink over his head.

The social historian declared that violence was the last act of desperate humanity.

Sexton's arrival caused no stir. He slipped into the heaving mass of bodies, glad to be anonymous, glad to have come, thirsty and reasonably cheerful. He took up a place behind one of the larger bars and filled a tall glass with a little ice and lots of bourbon. Then he began mixing drinks for other people. The barman hardly noticed his presence, accustomed as he was to the eccentric habits of his employer's guests.

Faces came and went, and Sexton delivered a drink to each of them, marking each with a pull at his own glass. Life grew sweeter, and an enlarged sense of fellowship encased him in its transparent skin. People looked much better as the evening wore on.

Until some inner alarm sounded. His eyes jerked this way and that in suspicion and hostility. Everywhere, people were gulping liquor, guzzling as if the supply were about to run out, swinish drinkers who threatened Sexton's own alcoholic well-being.

In defense, he put a fifth of bourbon under his arm and went hunting for a secure hiding place. Only when the bottle was secreted away was he able to resume his own drinking in earnest. He toasted his perspicacity and cunning. In the face of doom, a wise man prepared for the worst.

Joe Crespi was uneasy. But then, he'd always been out of joint with his surroundings. In all his thirty years, he could recall no single occasion when he'd felt comfortable and good in a crowd. People in groups filled him with social despair. He felt unattractive, unwanted, always the outsider.

Even as a boy he'd never made friends easily. He was never good at games, never athletic, never able to join in readily in the rough escapades that other boys seemed to revel in. Soon the word went out; Joe Crespi was a sissy, a weakling, a coward. His father, a muscular specimen who wore his manhood like a patriotic symbol, was outraged when he heard the way in which his son was characterized, and reacted predictably: he beat the boy hard and often. Changing nothing, of course.

Crespi discovered that he felt good only when he was alone or in the company of one other man. Someone much like himself. Sensitive, gentle, enjoying relaxed and extended discussions of poetry and literature, of music and theater. The men he liked had no need to challenge the world or its ways.

Acting provided an escape for Crespi as well as a means of earning a living. From the beginning, he was good at it. He enjoyed the pretense, making believe he was someone else, putting himself into some imagined life and circumstance, if only for the hours he spent on stage.

Soon he was being generously paid for doing what he would have done for nothing. His success allowed him to create a safe and private world away from the theater—and later film—where he was able to be himself, to function naturally.

He yearned to become a better actor, to achieve the highest levels of performance. When O'Day had come along with this role, this picture, Crespi had accepted immediately. The part would surely stretch his talent, polish and perfect his craftsmanship. O'Day was a great director. He would force Crespi to work harder, to confront himself.

And Vicky Pierce. To work with that most lovely and sensitive of actresses, one of his boyhood passions. What a thrill it would be.

But so much was going wrong. The changes in the script. Under the most perfect circumstances, Crespi hated change, feared the demands of the unknown. These changes, forcing him to alter his character, to enact a person he could never become, to become so . . . physical. He had never put his body to much use in performing, working instead out of his emotions, bringing them forth as precious gifts to the audience.

Those stinking boats. The pervasive odor of fish.

Something strange and reminiscent about it, terrible, forbidden. He turned his mind away from that, almost able to recapture the smell of the draggers, afraid he might become sick again.

Nor was he happier at this party. Among all the strangers. Each concerned only with himself, his immediate needs, desires, rutting passion. Was he any different? Loneliness had driven him to put himself in this surging mob scene, the wistful hunger for a companion. Some sympathetic and receptive person to whom he could talk quietly and feel at ease with.

He held a glass of ginger ale in one hand, a cigarette in the other. He took up a somewhat languid, almost insolent stance, a worldly man slightly better than all around him. All a pose. A shell assumed to conceal his fears. Another job of acting. Done well, admittedly, yet it always left him with bad feelings about himself.

Out of the crowd appeared a great quivering mound of flesh, rolling forward like a moist ball of pallid clay. Crespi shuddered and sought an avenue of escape. There was none.

"Ah," said a melodious voice, coming out of a small pink mouth. "Mr. Joe Crespi, in the flesh. I thought it was you. I'm intruding, I know, but please forgive. There are limits to every man's self-control. People undoubtedly press themselves at you constantly. Autographs, a few precious words, a lock of your lovely hair. You do have lovely hair. Would you believe that I . . . I am a fan. A fan of yours. Come to bask in your hot glow. Oh, Mr. Joe Crespi, you'll never know, to stand this close to you, in the flesh, so to speak. Your talent. Your stage presence. Your incredible beauty . . ."

Crespi's mouth moved in an approximation of a smile. A sad, small suggestion of gratitude, appreciation, masking the rising panic he felt.

"I am Harvey Hunnicut," the fan declared. "Would you believe Harvey Hewes Hunnicut, my mother's maiden name. Hewes, that is. My mother believed in women's rights. And alliteration, as you can so plainly see. My father believed in the Protestant work ethic and the accumulation of large amounts of money. Cheapest son of a bitch you ever saw." Hunnicut emitted a succession of wheezing gasps as if under bodily attack. He was laughing. "We all have burdens to bear, do we not, Mr. Joe Crespi? But not you. What a marvelous actor you are, sir! Olivier. Brando. Poor Monty Clift. In all factors, you surpass them all. The gift is great. The voice resonant, pure. The technique refined and subtle. You are a genius, sir. May I shake your hand?"

Crespi's fingers were swallowed in Hunnicut's fat wet palm, and he made an attempt to free himself.

"In you, Mr. Joe Crespi, I detect some of the same qualities of alienation and apartness which I myself experience so painfully much of the time. Shall we step out on the deck? Cape nights are fantastically beautiful . . ."

Crespi shuddered. He refused to accept Hunnicut as an emotional blood brother. He was his own man. Not bound to a band of misshapen spirits. He wanted no cult to cheer his every move. No company of insiders to elevate him onto a rhinestone pedestal of their own making. He should not have come, he told himself. Not to the party. Not to Provincetown.

"I am waiting for someone," Crespi managed to get out.

The lie lodged in his throat like a monstrous fishbone. Hunnicut's acceptance of it was no less false. He shuffled in place with all the ambulatory grace of a beached whale. "I," he whispered with harsh intensity, "run a little antique shop. Do come and see me, my wares. Anytime, day or night, I'd make you welcome.

I am, if you'll forgive a certain immodesty, the best blow-job in P-town. Ask around, if you don't take my word for it." He rolled away as he'd come, leaving behind the noxious sweet odor of decay and deceit.

Crespi wanted to cry.

John Patrick Michael O'Day felt like a maypole. Around him a score of men and women stomped and skipped and stepped in an ungainly hoedown, as he called the tune. Assholes all, he thought.

Men he had never before seen called him Little John and made rough jokes and told him stories of war and street fighting and fornication as if they were of a kind. They envied his roughneck charm, the easy sophistication, the unpretentious wisdom and culture he displayed. They hoped some of it would rub off.

Women twitched and giggled and inched closer, maneuvering into his line of sight. They puffed themselves up. They sucked themselves in. They sidled and shifted, offering themselves silently and sometimes aloud like sacrificial virgins fearful and proud of their fate at the same time.

O'Day stayed aloof. Kept his distance. Distributing attention fairly but in small amounts. He encouraged no one. Provincetown was, for an interval, his *buena mesa*; O'Day was careful not to shit where he ate.

A convoy of familiars had accompanied him to the party. Jacoby, Klein, Downing with the new girl, Hayden, a squad of assistants, gaffers, electricians, helpers with one skill or another. For a drink or two, they hung on until, their sucking dues paid for the evening, they drifted away in search of goods and services.

O'Day spotted Joe Crespi moving up to the outer edge of his audience. Hesitant, slightly unfocused, afraid. There he was, a beautiful man with a growing celebrity, stooped, diffident, with downcast eye.

O'Day had known them like Crespi before, emotional beggars seeking alms from those whose pockets were full. O'Day, having little of that particular coinage to spare, closed Crespi out, directed his attention elsewhere.

Crespi, an expert in recognizing rejection, soon faded away, making hardly a ripple as he left.

The pool was shaped like a huge daisy. A central fountain spewed multicolored water to varying heights, to the exotic pings and plucks of electronic music.

The pool was creatively lighted, heated, treated. On the bottom and along the sides, hand-painted tiles formed erotic displays. The deeper you went, the dirtier the pictures.

A gentle pumping action kept the water in constant flow, a sensuous and distorting shimmer, giving the illusion of a convex glass.

Junie Wheeler sat on the low diving board, legs reaching toward the water at the deep end of the pool. She wore a tight white jumpsuit that contrasted with her deep, even tan, and sipped chilled white wine and listened to a Harvard Ph.D. hold forth on various cosmic questions.

"I give you the composition of literature," he intoned in a nasal voice that had a soporific effect on his students.

Junie told him that she loved to read, that she belonged to three book clubs. "I join the public library wherever we happen to be," she declared sweetly. In addition to the house in P-town, the Wheelers owned a co-op apartment in New York, a chateau in the south of France, a house on the Appian Way in Rome, a flat overlooking Hyde Park in London, and a Mexican-style hacienda in Santa Barbara. "I can read in four languages," she lied lightly.

The Ph.D. gave no indication that he was impressed. "Aren't all books one book?" he asked rhetorically. "All authors one author?"

Junie gazed into his eyes. "My shelves are loaded with thousands of books. Don't you just adore brightly colored dust jackets? I do," she ended ingenuously.

The Harvard man could not be diverted by trivialities. "The man who reads Shakespeare, the man who speaks a single line from Shakespeare, isn't he in fact William Shakespeare?" His voice rose up to a clear note of triumph.

Tom Reynolds came out of the house onto the pool terrace. He was alone, and Junie waved at him. She came off the diving board, standing very close to the Ph.D. "You are truly an original thinker."

"A gift of the gods."

"No, I mean it. Superb. To hear you carry on is a unique human experience. See you around, chum." He frowned and watched her go.

Junie went up to Reynolds. "Tommy, how handsome you look. Where is Wanda?"

"Around. Who is that?" He indicated the departing Ph.D.

"A Professor Something-or-other. A genius, I think. Spends summers in P-town contemplating."

"Contemplating what?"

She shrugged. "Who knows? He's one of the world's great idiots." Her fingers played a riff down his middle, hooking onto his belt. "Did you come looking just for me? How dear you are."

"I wanted to talk about your little beach trip."

"Wanda is lovely, my dear. A perfect body. How lucky you are."

"I dig your body."

She laughed and stepped back. "Now, now, we must abide by the rules, mustn't we?" She stroked his cheek reassuringly. "When the moment is right, it's party time, the Wheelers and the Reynoldses. See you anon."

She floated across the veranda and disappeared into the house. Reynolds, irritated and dissatisfied, followed; she was gone, lost in the human flow, in the mass of structural twists and turns. He helped himself to some hors d'oeuvres and picked his way along a dimly lit passageway. In a small book-lined room he recognized Sandy Hayden surrounded by a number of young men, all trying to look down the front of her loose peasant blouse.

"Oh, God!" he groaned. She raised her eyes and smiled, waved, and came over to where he was standing.

"What the hell are you doing here?" he gritted.

"Having a marvelous time, Tommy. All these lovely young men."

"I want you to leave at once."

"You don't own me."

"Don't you understand? My wife is here."

"I'm an invited guest. I am not going."

"What if Wanda finds out? What if—?"

"Don't be a fool, Tommy. Why should I screw up your marriage? This is a chance for me to get to know O'Day a little bit. To make him remember me."

His face seemed to melt. "You intend to fuck him?"

"You have sex on the brain, Tommy. I want to make sure O'Day makes me look good. I want all the screen time I can get. My career's involved here."

"You selfish bitch."

"I'm not terribly smart, Tommy, and I'm not terribly talented. But I'm pretty, and my ass is round and my tits are good. A girl's got a right to look after herself in whatever way she can. Isn't that right, Tommy? You wouldn't want me to work the streets. You have a good time for yourself, and let me do the same. And,

Tommy, don't worry about Wanda. I've never even met the lady."

He watched her march away, all parts meshing smoothly. His fear was diluted by memories of her in bed, and by a revived desire. Her logic, he conceded reluctantly, was unassailable.

Vicky Pierce came in disguise. She might have been anybody. Or nobody. Perhaps a middle-aged matron out for a night on the town by herself. Or a widow looking for some quick action. Her appearance drew no special notice, and that jolted her confidence, even though she was pleased to be left alone. She had put on no makeup and wore her hair in a bun at the nape of her neck. She drew only casual interest; no one recognized her.

Unable to locate O'Day, she made her way through the heaving mob to the nearest bar. She found Sexton prepared to serve her.

"Your pleasure, ma'am?"

"A new line of work?"

"Man learns by his failures."

"That was temporary. It will change. I like you a lot, Sexton. Maybe it was my fault, something I said or did."

"*Mea culpa, mea culpa.* How could it possibly be? You are one of the world's great sex symbols. The gentleman is a bust, madam. Damaged goods. The flesh is fatigued, and nothing can fix that."

"I don't want it to be over for us, Sexton. I like you a lot."

"You're repeating yourself. It never really began."

"What's wrong with your wrist?"

"There is only one thing wrong with me, and we've exhausted that as a topic of conversation."

"Break down, Sexton, take a girl out."

"Find another playmate."

"Ah, Sexton . . ." Her voice was heavy with regret.

"Go away," he said. "Have some laughs. You don't need me."

After she was gone, a kind of impotent rage surged through him. He was furious with her for stirring up ancient emotions better left to expire quietly. And angry with himself for treating her badly, angry at his self-pity, his weakness and cowardice. He took a long drink to wash his mind clean; it didn't work. He kept remembering that he had never become the man he wanted to be.

A voice broke in, summoned him back to the present. A young woman confronted him.

"May I have a glass of tonic?" she said.

"That's not a drink." His voice was harsher than he'd intended.

"I'm not a drinker."

"I never socialize with temperance ladies. You are dismissed."

Pale spots developed at each corner of her mouth. "You have a very bad memory."

"Find someone else to service you," he said thinly, wishing he could stop.

"That's nice," she said, walking away. "That's very nice."

She watched Kiley with the glaring intensity that a jungle predator watches his prey. She inspected his various parts with a clinical eye—the wide strong shoulders, the torso lean and hard, the tight ass, the crotch bulge. She watched him move. As big and as strong as he was, he picked his way around the room as if fearful of being damaged, making physical contact with no one. He glided past clusters of people as if on the prowl for some particular victim, eyes malevolent and defensive. What a fantastic brute!

He came to a stop, and she rapidly closed the space

separating them, looking up into his rocky face. He returned her gaze. He grunted, he belched, he licked his lips.

"Your move, lady."

She liked that. A concession to her obvious authority. Even this animal recognized the implicit power of her personality. She made her round eyes rounder, kept the muscles of her face still. Brando had described it as "the face with nothing behind it."

He wasn't the first to call her names. Someone had once termed her a barracuda who "nibbled around the edges of the lives of her betters, working up nerve enough to kill."

And Jackie O. had said she was "the most awful woman I've ever known."

She adored such compliments. After all, her function was to provoke, antagonize, to make the people she wrote about angry and irritated while entertaining her readers. Nobody did the job better. Compared to her, Rona and Rex were minnows, small fish in a very large, rough ocean.

"I know you," she said to Kiley in a serrated whisper that had been likened to the warning of an unhappy cobra.

Kiley stared past her to where Joe Crespi stood. The dirty little fag was cruising. He disgusted Kiley, made him want to puke.

"Lee Downing pointed you out," she said, making it sound like a crime.

Kiley wished Crespi were gone. Dead. Buried. Removed as an obstacle to his own considerable dreams of fame and glory.

"I'm Letita Belmont."

Being a movie star was like being a king. He'd buy himself a castle on a hill and spend his time balling all those great-looking actresses.

"You've seen me on television, I'm sure."

An absolute brute, she thought. Crude, loutish,

without any of the trappings of civilization to get in the way. A true primitive, the rough edges plain to see.

"Of course, you've read my column."

He wanted what Crespi had. All of it—the wealth, the notoriety, the servants, the cars, the clothes. He wanted all of those Hollywood big shots sucking around, working their butts off to get him into their pictures. Offering him anything. *Everything.* Only Crespi stood in the way. Goddamn . . .

"Crespi," he said aloud.

She looked over at the actor. "Sweet little lamb. I can't blame him for going with men. I prefer men myself. I don't find many like you. Downing says you do stunts."

He looked down at her shining face, the pink mouth agape like that of a voracious sparrow in its nest.

"I could be a star."

Her brows rose. "Of course you could."

"I've got what it takes."

Across the room, Crespi was talking to a large round man. A pair of queens, swapping tales of assholes they had seen.

"What it takes is influence."

"You've got influence. You're the most important writer in Hollywood."

"My, you do know who I am. Kiley. The name fits. Hard, mean. I like a mean man."

"Listen," he felt compelled to say, "I am no kind of a weird case."

She shivered. "But you *are*. Weird and wonderful, I hope. Come with me."

He held back. "I need help."

"I can help you. I know many important people." Holding his hand, she led him down a long hallway. They turned a corner and went into the bathroom. She locked the door and sat down on the toilet. "Come to me, beauty."

"I should be doing Crespi's part."

"Crespi's doing it." She unbuckled his belt.

He stopped her. "What if he wasn't?"

"O'Day would get somebody else."

"Talk to him for me."

"O'Day can be a very difficult man."

"Try."

"I'll try." She unzipped his fly, dragged his jeans over his knees. "My God! I've never seen anything like it." Her face came forward.

He held her head between his hands, keeping her away. "You take care of O'Day, and I'll take care of Crespi."

"I will. I promise. Let me, please, let me."

He released her. "Why not?" She was, he thought as he watched her, a little old for this kind of work. But, what the hell, everybody made compromises.

Letita Belmont drew Kiley out to the pool area. Her round face glowed like an incandescent lamp, and she licked her lips with satisfaction.

"There he is," she said.

O'Day stood alongside the pool, people flaring out around him like a human skirt, a couple of dozen in all. He said something, and they all laughed. He spoke again, and they moaned; a few of them applauded.

"I always keep my promises," Letita said. "Little John!" she called imperiously, advancing at a rapid tilt, her natural gait.

The human wall gave way before her. "Little John," she gushed, offering her cheek for his kiss. "It's been too many years."

He ignored the cheek. "Downing warned me you were here."

"Warned! How droll. You know Kiley, of course."

O'Day nodded, muttered, and opened a new deck of Gitanes.

"He's magnificent, Little John. Look at that size. That face. Those muscles. With the right director, he could become the hottest thing in pictures. A star."

"Is that what you want, Kiley?" O'Day lit a Gitane. Tobacco would destroy him yet, he warned himself. Unless the Pikes and the Belmonts and the rest did it first.

"Sounds okay," Kiley managed. Men like O'Day troubled him, left him unsure of how to act, what to say.

"Help the boy, Little John. Give him a part in the picture."

O'Day fingered his mustache. "I've got nothing to give."

"Create something, Little John. You're a very creative director. You can do anything you want to do."

"You flatter me, Letita."

Kiley wanted to get away, to remove himself from O'Day's bright condemnatory gaze. "We just came over to say hello, Little John," he said, feeling stupid.

"Call me Mr. O'Day."

"Mr. O'Day." Kiley raged silently at a world he had never before encountered, a world that kept him always looking in.

O'Day said, "You may go now."

Kiley spun on his heel and strode away.

"There was no need to humiliate the boy," Letita said.

"It was you I was after, not him. Go, Letita, soothe his shattered ego."

"You made a mistake," she said before she left. "A very serious mistake."

O'Day put her out of his mind, sidestepping over to the edge of the pool, staring across the lighted waters to where Sandy Hayden stood alongside the diving board.

She'd been waiting all evening for a chance to capture O'Day's attention and interest. She'd watched him, trailed after him, discarding plan after plan.

And at last O'Day riveted his eyes on her, and she didn't know what to do.

Her knees were weak. A rush of nausea flushed her middle. Her brain pitched and yawed, and her vision blurred. She had to do something, and so she did the first thing that came into her head. She took off her clothes.

Deliberately, slowly, she climbed to the high board. Tested it with remembered skill, and went off in a twist-and-a-half with a tuck that was worth at least a solid seven points. Underwater, knowing that all eyes followed her, knowing how good she looked, she swam with studied grace. After this, O'Day could not ignore her.

She surfaced with hardly a splash, searching for O'Day. He was gone. With his entourage. She was alone in the water. It had all been for nothing.

The sound of hands clapping drew her around. A man stepped out of the shadows, superbly turned out in a white linen jacket. He crouched at the water's edge. "Not a false note. You did very well, Sandy."

"Who the hell are you?"

"More subtlety is required for someone like O'Day. Surely he's seen every trick there is, including your best. Try a different approach."

"How do you know my name?"

"My dear, I am your host. Now, do come out of the water so that I can get a good look at you." He offered his hand, and she took it, climbed out. "Very nice," he said. "Very, very nice. Do you ball?"

Armed with a nearly full bottle of bourbon and an empty glass, Sexton went out onto a small balcony that faced the harbor. He arranged himself on the two-by-four that served as a safety rail, feet dangling, and filled the glass. He drank, and drank again, determined to keep his mind empty of all thoughts, memories, emotions, permitting nothing to intrude on this pure and perfect moment. It was not to be.

"I accept your apology," a voice, tinged with irony, said. The chick from the bar.

He made no reply.

She came up behind him. "Long way down."

"Keep your distance."

"If you fall, you'll hurt yourself."

"I know how to fall."

"I'll go with that."

"Saracasm is the language of the devil."

"You didn't just make that up," she said accusingly. "You stole it."

"Paraphrase is not stealing."

"Hah!"

He took a good drink of bourbon. "Why are you following me around?"

"Just being friendly."

He considered that for a moment. "Have a drink."

She drew a leather cigarette case from her pocket. "Grass," she said. "Want to light up?"

"I don't use drugs."

"It's only grass."

"You're a hophead."

"You're a virgin! You've never smoked."

"I am not an addict."

"Grass is not addictive."

"Why don't you quit?"

"I don't want to quit."

"See what I mean?"

"Oh, boy."

He turned his attention to the harbor. Running lights marked the track of a ship moving out to sea. Headed where? England? The Med? Maybe he'd do the same, split for the Continent. Spend a year just hanging out. Painting, drinking, living good.

"Why don't you like me, Sexton?"

"Go away."

"I don't understand you."

"There's nothing to understand."

She lit up.

He was appalled. "What if a cop walked in?"

"People smoke grass all over P-town."

"It's against the law."

"So was booze during Prohibition. Never stopped people from having a drink."

He decided that talking to her was a waste of time and energy.

"This is excellent grass, Sexton. Try it."

"No way."

He swung off the rail and went back inside the house. She finished the joint before going after him. He was, she was convinced, without knowing quite why, someone special.

Mario felt a kind of helplessness, much as he felt on those occasions when the engine on the dragger failed him. A ship without power or direction, just drifting.

Around him, the milling crowd. All shoulders and elbows, shoving hands. He was propelled up against Vicky Pierce. He pulled back as if pained by the encounter.

"Sorry," he said.

She smiled vaguely at his obvious discomfort. He was shy in her presence, and that was a novelty. She tried to remember when last she had met a shy man.

"I didn't hurt you?" he said.

"I'm fine."

"All these people, it's crazy."

"It is, a little."

"If my father could see, he wouldn't believe it."

"Why?"

"Me, with all these famous people. Me talking to Vicky Pierce."

Had that stopped Sexton? Vicky Pierce, movie star. A special and imposing personage. Oh, God, she didn't want that.

"I'm just like anybody else."

"I hope not."

"What do you mean?"

"If I were a movie star, I wouldn't want to be like other people. What the hell, if you're up there, why not enjoy it?"

"I see."

"My father would be impressed. Not that he'd let on. The old man is too cautious for that. I guess I'm keeping you . . ."

"What from?"

"That Miss Belmont or Mr. O'Day."

"I've been around movie people all my life. A duller lot you'll never meet."

He didn't know how to respond. "Personally, I like movies a lot. The theaters in P-town are closed off-season. They'll open them soon."

"Summer means movies to you."

"And tourists. Too many of them. Gets so, in order to have a little room to yourself, you have to go out to sea."

"It's dull during the winter, then, and too crowded in the summer."

"I hadn't ever thought about it that way. I guess you're right."

"Why not leave, go to another place?"

He seemed surprised. "I could never do that. This is where I live."

Jerry Wheeler said it with an ingenuous smile. "Wanda, meet Sandy."

Wanda said, "Nice to know you, Sandy."

Sandy said, "Gosh, you sure are a good-looking chick, Wanda. You must be fighting 'em off around here."

"Wanda's got a loving husband," Jerry said blandly. "Tom Reynolds, the man who did the script for your picture."

"Oh, are you in the picture, Sandy?"

"Just a small part."

"I'd say Sandy's headed for great things," Jerry said. "Sure stardom. All the equipment, right out in front."

"You're beautiful, Sandy."

Sandy performed a brief curtsy. They all laughed and felt friendly.

"You'll like Tom," Jerry said to Sandy.

"Will I, Wanda?"

"I wonder where Tommy is?" Wanda said.

Jerry put an arm around each of them. "This is so much fun," he said. "So goddamn much fun."

A fight broke out. Two men battling over prior rights to a pretty girl. Blows were thrown, and one man went down, the other beating on him. Somebody screamed, and somebody else began to cheer. The winner took the girl by the arm and left.

Crespi decided it was time for him to go home. All those people, and so little human exchange. No affection, no warmth, no real communication.

Outside, he made his way downhill toward Commercial Street, his step heavy, sad. If only life were different. If only people were kind and more loving to each other. If only life made sense. But it was a cruel, random affair that seldom came out all right in the end, as in the movies.

"Pike phoned this afternoon."

O'Day put it out casually, as if mentioning an old

friend. As if the content of any conversation he conducted with Hillary Pike would not acutely affect Vicky's life. As if she were in no meaningful way involved.

She said, "Oh!" Giving no excessive value to the word. A voice lively, interested slightly, her true reaction disguised behind an actor's skillful defenses.

"Try this one," O'Day said, brushing his mustache, trying to be amusing, the eyes lost in their hollows, avoiding her. "All telephones are eliminated. Destroyed. What happens to a man like Pike? He fades away into the sunset."

"From your tongue to God's ear," she said.

"Pike," O'Day said, "is unhappy."

"I will try not to laugh."

"Is it funny?"

"Men like Pike are genetically deprived. They are conceived in dissatisfaction. They are born with no talent for contentment. Pike is disposed by nature and by choice to criticize, to complain, to render ugly what may have some beauty." She laughed, a short, mirthless laugh and peered into her own restless soul. "Pike doesn't know how to be happy."

"I wish I'd never left Ireland," O'Day said presently.

"Why did you?"

"Would you believe money?"

"No."

"It was money, in part."

"The other part?"

"I was an exile among strangers. Who wants to use up his days being a foreigner? Anyway, living in a castle is not all it's cracked up to be. You ought to see it. Outside of Dublin, halfway up a long hill, very green, very picturesque. Like a Barry Fitzgerald movie. From my window, you can see the sea, watch the clouds form up low and gray. Marvelous light in Ireland, but the weather stinks. You have to wear heavy wool sweaters in August. Why did I come back? Because I left something behind. I have to get it back."

"With this picture, Little John?"

"Why not?"

"Because Pike won't let you. It isn't in his character. He's a destroyer, not a creator."

"Maybe," he said after a while. "Pike can put the parts together—the property, backing, distribution, you and me. But he can't make a film. That's where I come in. Every day we expose some film, I stamp my mark on the project. By the time I'm done, nobody will be able to erase it. Pike may find some way to butcher the final cut. But my signature will remain in every scene. People will come to see what I've done. They'll appreciate it."

"And give you back your career?"

"Yes, dammit. Now, let's talk."

"About Pike's phone call?"

"Pike doesn't like the dailies."

"What does he want?"

O'Day ground out the cigarette. "My mouth tastes like a cesspool. I'm going to give these up, a dirty habit. The second beach scene . . ."

"It was good, Little John. You handled it delicately. Crespi and I worked so very well together in it."

"It isn't right."

"You told me . . ."

"I know what I said, that I liked it. Well, I was wrong. I've changed my mind."

"What does Pike want?"

"He feels it lacks excitement."

"It's a love scene."

"It just lies there. Too heavy, too . . . old-fashioned. Out-of-date. It needs . . . should be more . . . graphic."

"Graphic!"

"More provocative, visual interest. . . . I agree with Hillary," he ended lamely.

"Exactly what do you expect me to do, Little John?"

"Pike says get more sex into it. We'll reshoot the entire scene. At night, I think. With a greater amount of body contact, more . . ."

"Visual interest," she supplied.

He nodded.

Her mouth shifted, the corners turning up, and a casual onlooker might have believed she was amused or pleased. It was no smile.

"At my age?" she said.

"Pike says . . ."

"It must be a joke."

"No joke."

"Vicky Pierce in the nude?"

"That's it."

"And Crespi?"

"Both of you."

"That's crazy."

"Making love. Tastefully, of course, but—"

"No."

"Listen, Vicky—"

"No."

"Pike wants the flesh."

"Fire me, Little John."

"Don't be a fool."

"No."

"I told you, at night. A skeleton crew, just old hands. No outsiders, no voyeurs . . ."

"Except a hundred million moviegoers. Thanks."

"I've given it a great deal of thought. I've got some good ideas. It will be a beautiful cinematic moment. No one will be offended."

"No."

"You're a beautiful woman, with nothing to be ashamed of."

"No."

"Trust me, Vicky. . . ."

13

Letita Belmont was delighted with herself. Kiley was a find, a stroke of good fortune. Already she was putting together plans for him. She would bring him back to the West Coast, establish him securely in her Bel Air mansion, keep him dependent until such time as she grew bored with him. Eventually that would occur, she knew, since it always had before. Until then, he would provide her with a succession of good and full nights, to the raw envy of some of her so-called friends.

She stroked his hard bicep, scratching lightly.

"Mama's got to make," she cooed. "Want to come along, do again what we did before?"

"You're too greedy, Letita."

"Yes," she drawled. "Can't get too much of a good thing, and you've got such a good thing." Pleased with herself, she went off in search of an unoccupied bathroom.

Kiley looked over to the spot where he had last seen Joe Crespi. The actor was gone. Kiley shuddered, charged with dark and conflicting needs. He wanted to do nothing to damage this new relationship with Letita Belmont; she could do him a great deal of good. But he couldn't stop thinking about Crespi, couldn't stop resenting the obstacle he presented. Kiley went outside.

No sign of Crespi anywhere. Reflexively, Kiley headed downhill toward the harbor, trying to anticipate Crespi's route. He cut behind a white-and-yellow house, making up ground, going through an alley. He moved swiftly but without sound, not wanting to attract attention. He went on, his resentment at Crespi's good fortune growing, transforming itself into a crimson rage that pulsed wildly in his eyes. He came out of the alley and looked down the hill. Less than fifty feet away, Joe Crespi. Stooped, slight, without any of the heroic proportions lavished upon him by the silver screen.

Kiley ducked out of sight and advanced behind a number of houses until he came to a point ahead of Crespi. He crouched silently in a darkened corner, muscles taut, his eyes fixed on the oncoming actor.

Crespi was past Kiley by a yard or two when the biker attacked. He hooked Crespi around the throat, effectively silencing him, and dragged him back into the shadows. Crespi was helpless in the grip of the larger man. When he felt safe from prying eyes, Kiley flung Crespi to the ground. Gasping for air, Crespi came up into a sitting position. And as he did, Kiley struck.

He pounded relentlessly at those soft girlish features until Crespi, moaning and coughing blood, lay huddled on his side, eyes already swollen shut. Kiley stared at the still figure on the ground. What kind of a man made no effort to fight back? Refused to protect himself?

Kiley yanked off Crespi's pants, his shorts, rolled him onto his face, his buttocks soft pale mounds in the darkness. He pulled down his own jeans, and the night air caressed his engorged rod like a cool kiss. His knees began to tremble and grow weak, and that brought his anger back up to the boil. He mounted Crespi and spread him apart, then drove forward with all the force and manly power he could muster. Crespi stiffened, but offered no resistance. After a moment, he began to weep.

It was soon over. Kiley stood up and adjusted his clothes. "Goddamn queer," he muttered before kicking Crespi in the face. "Party's over."

"What the hell am I doing here with you?" Sexton said.

"You picked me up at the party."

"Ella," he muttered. "What's it stand for—Cinderella?"

"Just plain Ella."

"You picked me up."

"I did, didn't I? You don't get picked up easily, mister." She lay back on the sand. "I love the beach at night."

They were at Herring Cove, where the sea broke in small phosphorescent waves.

"Why do you fight so hard, Sexton?" she said.

He decided it was a mistake to allow her to get even this close. He didn't want anybody intruding on his life, and certainly not this freaked-out drug fiend.

"Fighting's what I do best." He said it lightly, not intending to make any additional explanation.

"Why?"

"Why?" He was stalling for time and knew it. "Damn fool question," he growled. "I'll take you back."

"I'll let you know when I'm ready."

"You're wasting your time with me. Find somebody younger, more agreeable to your weird ways."

She shook her head from side to side. "You're a fine-looking man, you know. A little worked over, but with good character lines. I like the grooves you've developed. I imagine you were too pretty for your own good when you were younger."

"You are weird."

"You still haven't answered my question. Why do you fight so much? And please don't tell me that you're good at it."

Life is a jungle, he almost said aloud, a hot war with nobody around to depend on or trust. He said none of it, however, embarrassed by the thought, believing it and disbelieving it at the same time. He thought about Mike Berger, dying alone for a few lousy bucks.

"You gotta fight," he muttered.

"Why?"

The anger rose up in him. "Survival."

"Cooperation can do it."

"Fantasies."

"Your way leads only to death."

He wanted to shout at her. Punish her for causing old hurts to flare alive again. For pushing him too close to the tender places.

"You don't know a goddamn thing."

"Tell me, why don't you?"

"Smart-ass chick. It's the way of the world. The way people are."

"The way you are."

"The way I am."

"I don't believe you enjoy fighting. There's a sensitivity to you, to your face. Life has created your face, and I can read it clearly. You don't like to fight."

"Show me a better way." He felt oddly docile, not beaten, but passive with unexpected gentleness.

"Give me time, give me the chance. I would like to, very much."

The anger drained away and left him weak and uncertain. What the hell! He had come out to the beach with her, had in fact invited her to join him. It would cost him very little to be polite, make small talk before sending her back to wherever it was she came from. "Next question. What are you doing here?"

Her grin was a quicksilver flash in the darkness, a sardonic gleam, a prod, a flirtation. "Just trying to see if I can turn you on."

"Knock it off."

"There it is again, the tough guy."

"You wait tables. It doesn't fit."

"I'm meant for better things, you think?" Still an undertone of mockery. He decided not to respond. "I wait tables in order to make bread, enough to live off."

"You came to P-town for the summer?"

"I've been in P-town for nearly two years. You might say I've been living here. Part of the swinging scene."

"I never saw you before I came in the restaurant."

"I saw you last summer. We spoke, in the gallery. It was not what I would call a terrifically successful encounter."

"No sparks?"

"Cold and distant."

"It's the way I am."

"I was beginning to believe that. A lot of dudes come into the restaurant, they're after more than just a meal. Not you. You didn't give me a first glance."

"Maybe you don't get to me."

"Ah, you don't mean that—do you? That day at the beach . . ." She saw the puzzled expression on his face. "There, you don't remember that, either. It was raining, my car broke down . . ."

"That was you?"

"That was me. Well, I forgive you all your transgressions."

"I don't deserve forgiveness."

She measured him speculatively. "What do you want in a woman, Sexton?"

"Consider this. I don't want anything in a woman."

"A man like you, you need somebody. I can tell. What are your requirements?"

"How about deaf and dumb, oversexed, and the owner of a liquor store."

"Very funny. You know what I think?"

"You're going to tell me."

She drew a joint out of her purse, lit it. "I think you're not as tough as you make out." She offered him the joint.

He drew back in alarm, and she laughed. He took a pull on the bottle he had lifted from the party.

"There's no room in my life for a woman, least of all a crazy young chick. You're half my age."

"I'm twenty-one."

"You look sixteen."

"You look . . ." She eyed him speculatively. "What's wrong with being young?"

"Stay in your place, you'll be all right."

"My place! Times they are a-changing, Sexton."

"Not for me."

"Haven't you ever heard of the women's movement?"

He punched shortly at the night air. "Take that, Betty Friedan."

"See, you're not so tough."

He leaned back on his elbows. "What are you after?"

"You."

"Don't be stupid."

"I'm not."

"You don't know a damn thing about me. Wise up, kid. Fling your butt at somebody else."

"Okay, okay, don't get mad." She sneaked a look in his direction. His profile might have been chipped out of rock. "Afraid I'll fall in love with you?"

"Happens all the time."

"I believe it."

"I'm an old man. I drink too much."

"You can always quit."

"I like to drink."

"You're an alcoholic."

"No," he said thoughtfully. "I just drink a great deal."

"Haven't you ever been married, Sexton?"

"You're changing the subject."

"Booze is a bummer."

"And marriage isn't? I've been there. Oh, hell, you couldn't know."

"I been married."

"What happened, he walk out on you?"

"Oh, wow! Maybe I split on him. Stir that around in that piggish mind of yours."

"Okay, you left him."

She sucked on the joint. "He got snuffed."

"I'm sorry. In Nam? I was there. A lot of good guys bought it in Nam. Is that why you came to P-town, to work it out?"

"My old man wouldn't go to Nam, wouldn't wipe out peasants. He hated soldiering and he hated killing. The poor bastard just died on me. Got himself a cancer, and it took him all the way down. It's part of why I'm here."

"That's rough."

"There was a lot of pain and a lot of fear, and there was no way I could help him. He hung right in there, the poor bastard, right to the end."

"Good man."

"Dumb. He should've let go, died easier. But he didn't know how. Everything he ever did was hard."

"Everything is shit," Sexton said.

"I don't believe that. I hope you don't, either"

"Maybe I do, maybe not. I can't be sure. I'm forty years old . . ."

"Ancient."

". . . I'm not sure what to do with the rest of my

life. O'Day, the movie director, wants me to work for him. I used to be in the business. I paint. Lately, I've found a new way—style, content, all of it new. Nobody is painting the way I am now."

"I was in the gallery," she said softly. "You've got choices, and not everyone does."

He took another pull on the bottle.

"Before you get zonked out of your skull," she said, "let's go back to my place."

"Don't get sexy with me."

She stood up, and so did he. "Sexton, for an old guy, there's a lot you don't understand."

Outside her rooming house, he offered his hand. "Hope I wasn't too rough on you."

She stood on her toes and kissed him on the cheek, her fingers drifting tentatively across his chest. "I can handle it."

He wasn't sure whether it was a compliment or an insult.

14

"The pleasure principle," Jerry Wheeler said. "There is no other worth abiding by."

The master suite was on the second floor of the house. It contained four rooms, each designed for a different purpose. The sitting room contained no furniture. The floor was covered with a variety of Oriental rugs of different sizes, and a scattering of immense pillows. In the center of the room, a single candle flickered in the crimson glass chimney of a hurricane lamp. Out of concealed speakers came the driving beat of Ravel's *Bolero*. Sprawled around the candle in positions of repose were four figures. Each of them had a brass pipe filled with marijuana to suck on, each of them a goblet of chilled white wine.

Reynolds let his eyes go over to Junie Wheeler. She sat up, was doing something to the shirt she wore. She was on her knees facing him, and somehow, magically, in that soft crimson light, the shirt fell away. Her enormous breasts were fully exposed, the nipples pink and appealing.

"See," she murmured. "Tan all over."

She hovered over him, and as she moved, her nipples brushed against his cheek. She lay back and pulled off her slacks.

"Take something off," she urged. "Take everything off."

Beyond the candle, but within range of the crimson nimbus, Reynolds was able to make out Wanda and Jerry. They were locked in a tight embrace, mouths fastened together, and Jerry's hand was busy manipulating his wife's breasts. Reynolds sat straight up.

"Listen to them," Junie whispered. "Sucking tongue." She positioned herself in front of Reynolds, pressing her breasts against his face, forcing him back down on the pillows. He felt himself smothering in that powdered flesh as she writhed and humped against him. Her hands worked at his zipper. "Ah, there it is, the cute little devil. Is it broken?"

He came up into a sitting position again. He blinked to clear his eyes. Wanda was naked from the waist down, and Jerry, also naked, shifted around until he was situated between her thighs.

"Beautiful," Junie cooed. "Wanda is fantastic, look at her go."

Reynolds moved closer on all fours, Junie hurrying to catch up. "Look here," she cried. "Look at how it happens. The way she moves."

Reynolds quivered and became afraid in ways he had never before been afraid. He stiffened when Wanda cried out and urged Jerry on. Jerry coughed and shouted and groaned, his body in spasm, until he pitched forward. Reynolds sat in place, unable to move or speak, unable to tear his eyes away.

Junie assisted him back down to the floor, working hard to make him respond. He felt nothing except a serrated terror that tore up his soul and unloosed a blinding white wash that blanked out the rest of his life.

15

The bedroom of her hotel suite was a sanctuary. No one could reach her here. No one could harm her, frighten her, tell her what to do. There was no one she would let get close enough. Sexton—he had rejected her. Consciously or otherwise, his flesh had turned her away. And she felt some shame, guilt; as if, in a way she could not isolate and name, she had done something wrong.

She undressed. And stood naked in front of the long mirror on the bathroom door. The body she saw reflected in the glass seemed balanced, all parts in harmony, the legs long and tapering.

Were her breasts too heavy, sagging more than ever? She was no longer a girl, and had to expect such changes. Time worked its mischief on everyone.

The hips were still good, smoothly rounded, the hips of a woman made for childbirth. Not that she had ever managed that. She had wanted a child, a family, a normal life; it had been denied her.

One small benefit of that deprivation—her belly was unmarked, a gentle rise, smooth, firm.

She cupped her breasts and closed her eyes, and it was almost as if Tony were holding her, rubbing against her, licking her neck and speaking of his feelings. Most of the pain about Tony was submerged now, surfacing only at rare and unexpected moments.

Years had passed since Tony, and there had been no one else since. Sexton would have been nice. Very nice. Poor, poor Sexton.

Poor Vicky. Was her time for men ended? Was she fated never to feel the hardness of a man inside her again? Never to enjoy that peculiar mix of strong male odors? Never to love, and never to be loved again?

Perhaps it was just as well. Men had given her a great deal of pain, more pain than pleasure. Even Tony, sweet Tony, at the end; it had not been easy.

She hoped, just before she fell asleep, that it was not over. Not yet. Please, not yet.

16

Two joints.

Two by two, the pairs entering old Noah's ark. Was it in fact some cosmic design for people to proceed along in complimentary pairs? Weird Ella, one of life's incurable romantics, had slipped a couple of joints into his shirt pocket. That kiss, those skillful fingers on his chest. She was a kook, a fanatic intent on converting him to her freaky ways.

Before he got into bed, he arranged the joints neatly on his night table. Behind the bottle of bourbon. He lay in the dark and sparred with the rapid-fire thoughts coming aggressively at him.

Hopheads, sex fiends, dropouts, deserters. Let it all hang out, chicks out front. Living in a world without right or wrong. Everything goes. Anything goes.

Bullcrap.

They didn't know how delicious it could be to do what was *forbidden*. Break the rules. Sneak around. Sin.

Bootleg booze tasted sharper than any other kind. Cop one of your old man's Luckies, if you wanted a really fine smoke. Screw your best friend's wife.

He'd never done that. Though more than once he'd wanted to, and more than once had the chance. Why not? Only a warped and false moral system would keep a man from getting all the good pussy that came his way. The idea of right and wrong—whose right and whose wrong, he kept trying to discover—was a puzzlement.

Those joints. Creepy numbers. A cunning creature, that Ella. Bent on hooking him. No way she'd get her way. He had her action wired all the way.

A lost soul, that girl. A lost generation, hers. What was she truly after? Twenty long and hard years of living separated them, and always would. Still she came sniffing around, persistent, sneaky in her aims, tricky in her ways.

The pleasure he experienced in thinking about her was abruptly transformed into resentment. Resentment that she believed he was so easily manipulated. Resentment that she believed him to be so indecisive and weak that he could be drawn into her freaky world via the lure of her fine young body and the promise of grassy dreams.

Her subterfuges were flimsy and obvious, and he would not allow himself to be so used. He took a long swallow of bourbon and then another. The liquid scorched his throat, heated up his stomach, gave rise to the old vague dissatisfaction with things. The old uneasiness. He came off the bed in a quick, smooth, feline movement, a creature on the stalk.

Bottle in hand, he made his way down to the beach, pacing along like a hunting animal, pausing only to drink, until the bourbon encased him in its spreading amber glow. To drink was good, he told himself, examining the diminished level of bourbon in the bottle. To drink until all memories were blurred and all emotions were anesthetized was good. Until the swelling bubble of rage in his gut fizzled into nothing. Or burst.

He recalled those four boys who had hoped to work him and O'Day over, their mean soft faces. How he wished they would appear now. He wanted to destroy those hostile visages, to draw blood and deliver pain. To punish.

He killed the remaining bourbon and let the bottle fall to the sand. He picked his way along the beach, past a couple rolling in sexual embrace under the rotting pier, going up to Commercial Street. In the first bar he came to, Sexton ordered a double bourbon, knocked it back, and called for a refill. Through a descending haze he examined the room, the slow-moving figures, the pale featureless faces giving forth empty words and loud laughter. His anger reached out. . . .

He became aware of the irresistible pressure in his bladder, and went weaving toward the men's room. Someone spoke to him, said his name. Sexton went on without replying. He stumbled into a chair, and there followed a cry of dismay over a drink spilled, a dress stained. A man rose up in Sexton's path, demanding an apology, complaining of the cost of a new dress for his wife. Sexton placed his hand on the man's chest and shoved hard. The man went over backward in a clatter of chairs and hoarse protests.

Sexton made it to the men's room. A small cubicle with only a single urinal and a single stall. The stall was in use, the door securely bolted. A large man in patchwork jeans and a workshirt blocked the way to the urinal.

"Shake it, pal," Sexton said. "This is an emergency."

"I'm not your pal, pal," the large man said, not looking back.

"Hurry it up, will you?"

"Drink it," the large man said. He laughed, pleased with his retort.

Sexton tapped the large man on the shoulder. "I'm desperate, pal," he said. The finely etched features were without expression, the far-seeing eyes lidded and still, the resonant baritone voice lifeless.

The large man made a quarter-turn, placed his massive hand on Sexton's shoulder, and pushed hard. Sexton stumbled backward. "Fuck off, pal. I've staked my claim."

Sexton came back fast. Faster than the large man imagined he would. His right hand traveled only a short distance, hooking into the large man's kidney. There was a scream of agony and anger as the man pivoted, fists coming up. Sexton stepped inside and hit him twice in the face. The large man began to bleed from the nose even before he fell to the floor.

A frightened voice inside the stall cried out, "What's going on out there?"

Sexton gave no answer. He stepped over the fallen man and emptied himself into the urinal. When he left the men's room, he felt neither relieved nor satisfied, his rage a lingering force that drove him out into the streets and into the late-night parade of grotesques and ordinaries.

A trio of glamour queens decked out in tight French jeans and satin shirts open to the navel got in his way. He sent them spinning to the side like three blond bowling pins. A hooker looking for an easy victim to roll tried to keep up with him. He left her behind.

He never saw the crew-cut man from Idaho. Crew Cut was bigger than Sexton, with immense shoulders and powerful arms. Pale of cheek, with yellow hair that almost glowed in the night. He wore red Bermudas, black tasseled loafers, and tartan knee socks. With him, his wife and his nine-year-old son. Crew Cut, wife, and son all agreed, nothing like Commercial Street existed in all of Idaho. Determinedly taking in the human sights, none of them saw Sexton careening along.

Nor did he see them. His hard shoulder landed heavily on Crew Cut's chest, sending the man from Idaho reeling backward. He managed not to fall.

"Watch where you're walking, fella," he said.

Sexton froze in place, zeroing in on Crew Cut. Not thinking, trapped in his own alcoholic emotions.

"Get out of my way."

Crew Cut was a former varsity fullback, a former college wrestling champion, and had had many fist-fights in and out of the ring. They had all been conducted according to a certain set of rules that everyone understood and gave silent service to. He had never encountered a man like Sexton, however.

"You might apologize," Crew Cut said.

Sexton glared and leaned, focused at a point between Crew Cut's pleasant blue eyes. Sexton recognized his enemy and moved to wipe him out. He advanced, fists cocked.

"Don't you hit my daddy!"

The boy, his slender, unformed face drawn up in a ferociously protective mask, had stepped between Crew Cut and Sexton, small hands raised to do battle.

"I'll beat you up!" the boy cried.

All rage drained out of Sexton, leaving him trembling and ashamed. "Oh, Jesus," he muttered, before he turned away. "Oh, Jesus . . ."

Back in the apartment behind the art gallery, back in his bed, Sexton felt all the controls fade away, and he began to shake violently. The springs creaked under the fierce assault. He waited for the tempest to pass.

He continued to see Crew Cut and his son, aware of how much he had wanted to hurt the stranger, to use him as a target for his anger. But he couldn't do it. Couldn't humiliate the man in front of his son, his wife.

What he had done, what he had almost done, frightened and dismayed him. He sat up and tried to clear his head. There was so much to think about, to rethink. His eyes came to rest on the night table, and he saw the two joints at rest there. He brought one of them up to his mouth, let it hang between his lips.

He imagined it lit. Imagined dragging the sweet

smoke into his lungs. Something new and better might result. Some monumental implosion that would rock his mind. Shatter all the old, bad ways. Change him irrevocably. Make him a member of a small and secret club. Well, he amended in rueful reflection, not so very secret these days. Not so very small.

Just before he fell asleep, it came to him that he was not nearly as good as he wanted to be. But he was not so bad, either.

17

Carlos Sauza was more than a year away from reaching his seventeenth birthday. Officially he was still in high school; but only officially. Like many of his friends, Carlos attended class only on Fridays, when the draggers laid up, or on those other days when weather prevented them from going out. Carlos came from a family of fishermen. He worked on his father's boat, doing the same things that his father and his older brother did, and as befit his junior position in the family, a little bit extra.

Among his many tasks was to see to the coffee. Ashore and on the boat. Every morning Carlos rose thirty minutes before his father and brother did. He made the coffee and prepared the breakfast. Only then did he wake his father and brother. While they were getting dressed, Carlos ate his breakfast. By the time the others came downstairs, Carlos was out of the house, on his way to the town pier.

There were no women in the Sauza house. Carlos' mother had died of heart failure when he was eight years old. His two sisters—both older—had left home as soon as they could. One had married; she was since divorced and working as a sales clerk in Filene's in Boston. The other dealt blackjack in a casino on the strip in Las Vegas. Carlos believed, as did his father and his brother, that both sisters were whores; it was what girls became when they left home.

His morning walk to the pier was the only time that Carlos had to himself. No one to interrupt his thoughts. No one to order him about. No one to call him lazy and stupid.

Walking along, head down, his mind drifting through misty corridors, Carlos almost missed Joe Crespi. But not quite.

He stopped and stared at the unconscious man. There was blood on his face, and he was naked from the waist down. Carlos put it together without difficulty. The man on the ground was probably a fag, and mugging fags was a way of providing entertainment for Carlos and his friends, especially during the long, dull off-season. But they never hurt anyone, not this bad.

Carlos looked around. Nothing moved. But soon, other fishermen would stir, head for the boats. He didn't have much time. An alley led off the street, and halfway along, he spotted a pair of pants. He searched the pockets and came up with a wallet. It contained more than two hundred dollars. Carlos pocketed the money and left the wallet; credit cards only meant trouble. Then he continued down the hill.

When he came to a pay phone, he called the police, reported what he'd found. Satisfied that he had performed a good deed, he went cheerfully on his way.

The police took Joe Crespi to the medical center on Bradford Street, where a fat, bearded doctor determined that Crespi had suffered a concussion of some severity, a broken nose, a fractured jaw, plus assorted bruises, cuts, and welts. He was, the doctor announced, in lousy shape.

A policeman, having identified the actor from his credit cards, phoned Lou Klein to report what had happened. Klein thanked the policeman and suggested he come around when he was off-duty so that he might be suitably rewarded. Then Klein called O'Day, who went immediately to the medical center.

"You're going to be okay," he assured Crespi.

The actor kept his eyes closed. He was in considerable pain and even greater mental torment. He felt completely exposed, used up, violated, and wondered if in all the world there was not a safe place for him to hide. He wished he had never left the small house he owned on the beach in Venice. He wished he had never become an actor. He wished he had never been . . . born.

"Do you know who did this to you, Joey?" O'Day said.

Crespi shook his head once. But he knew, he really knew. In the end, he had only himself to blame. He was guilty, he was his own worst enemy.

Back in his hotel room, O'Day ordered breakfast sent up, asked Klein and Jacoby to join him.

"No luck," Klein said when he arrived. "Some pictures are cursed."

"Too bad," Jacoby said. "I got some good film on Crespi."

"I've got a list of possible replacements," Klein said.

O'Day accepted the list without looking at it. Crespi was finished; the decision had been made by that unknown assailant. No one would ever be able to accuse O'Day of buckling under to Hillary Pike.

Jacoby said, "Crespi's gonna be okay. I mean, he'll recover. Might need some plastic done later on to fix up his face. Remember the way it was for Monty Clift after the car wreck?"

Klein sighed. "Mugging has become the national pastime. The star-spangled sport."

"They raped the poor guy," Jacoby said.

Klein spread his hands. "We all knew that about Joey. He must've enjoyed that part of it."

O'Day lit a Gitane. "Get Pike on the phone for me, Lou." His voice was dull and low.

"It's a three-hour difference to the Coast, Little John. Pike's probably bedded down, sleeping off last night."

"Get him, goddammit, and don't say another fucking word."

Klein flung up his hands in surrender. "Coming right up. Whatever you say."

Pike came on the wire, irritable and unfocused, complaining that he'd been awakened. O'Day ignored the complaint, told him what had transpired. When he was finished, there was a brief silent interval before Pike spoke. "How much film is there of Crespi?"

"Maybe twenty percent of what we've shot so far."

"Can you salvage any of it?"

"A couple of long shots, not much else."

"Insurance will cover it."

"Do we cancel?" O'Day said, deliberately shifting additional responsibility to the producer.

"Cancel! Are you kidding! Push ahead. Replace Crespi, just like I wanted to do before. This is the best thing happened to us. Let's get somebody in there with balls. Kiley, go with Kiley, I say."

"He can't act."

"Who cares about acting? John Simon, maybe. Kael. Nobody pays attention to them. You can make Kiley look good, Little John. Work in some really rough footage."

"I want to close down for a few days."

"Close down, why? There's a whole company on payroll. The budget—"

"I have to study what we've got. Go over it and make changes. This will mean more rewriting."

"Just get it moving."

"I still need a man to head up the second unit."

"It's those damned cop shows on the boob tube. They use up all the stunt directors. Call down to New York, Little John. You'll come up with somebody. By the way, you talk to Pierce, like I said?"

"I spoke to her."

"Well?"

"She won't do it."

"The hell she won't. She needs to be reminded about the facts of life. She's no kid anymore. Nobody's breaking down any doors to hire her. Come down on her—heavy. Make her know she's got to do it. You understand me?"

"I understand."

"Good." Pike sounded pleased suddenly. "Things are going my way now. Everything's gonna be all right. When do you figure you'll wrap it up, Little John?"

"Two weeks, more like three."

"That's too long. Let's get it in the can. I give you two more weeks. Stay in touch. I want to know what's going on."

O'Day hung up the phone. "We're closing down for a few days. A paid holiday for all hands. Get Reynolds over here. Frank, you stick around. There's work to do."

Klein said, "What've you got in mind, boss?"

O'Day showed his annoyance. "Same as before, to make the best sumbitch of a picture you ever saw."

Reynolds woke with a start. His head throbbed, and his mouth tasted horrible. He forced his eyes open and saw Wanda sitting at the end of the bed staring at him.

"Oh, God," he said. "I feel awful."

"I feel great."

"I'm hung over. Too much booze."

"Last night," she said.

"I don't want to discuss last night."

"I loved it."

"It happened. It won't happen again."

"You were the one kept talking it up."

"It's over, I said."

"I know how you feel . . ."

"You don't know. You can't know. Seeing you, seeing him in you, seeing you enjoy it . . ."

"I've never been so excited. Next time it'll be good for you."

"No."

"You'll be fantastic, better than Jerry. Once you relax. Next time."

"There isn't going to be a next time. I was disgusted."

"It didn't disgust me, Tommy. I dug it a lot. I want to do it again, lots of times."

"No."

"Maybe I disgust you now?"

"Don't be dumb. I admit it, it was all my fault. I kept pushing it. Okay, it was a mistake. I recognize the mistake. There's no point in repeating it."

"Just talking about it gets me worked up. Jerry said he's planning another little get-together. He promised me a surprise. What do you think it will be?"

"We're not going back."

"I am."

"You'll go by yourself."

Her face pulled together darkly, and she selected her words with care. "Jerry says everyone must contribute. No freeloaders. It is a community affair, family style. You fizzled out last night, Tommy. Jerry gets upset when Junie's disappointed. He really cares about her, you see."

"I am not going there again."

"Oh, yes you are. You're going, and you're going to perform."

"And if I can't?"

"In that case, I'll find somebody who can."

It was early afternoon when O'Day and Vicky Pierce went walking, ending up on MacMillan Wharf. Except for Mario's two draggers, the fishing fleet was still at sea. Mario was repairing his nets.

O'Day waved, and Mario lifted one hand in response, went back to his work. "Nice guy," O'Day said.

She gave no reply, as if to speak would be a commitment, would involve her in matters beyond her control. She approached this day in anticipation of a hostile act.

"Pike wants me to give Crespi's part to the stunt man."

"Kiley?"

"Pike wants more muscle in the picture."

"Won't that throw the story out of balance?"

"It's Pike's picture."

"I thought it was yours," she answered in a very small voice.

On the dragger, Mario sat with his back toward them. He was hunched over, shaggy hair falling down his neck onto the collar of a worn sweater. Even in repose, he looked graceful and slightly vulnerable.

"What about him?" O'Day said.

"Mario?"

"Why not? He's even better-looking than Crespi. Got a lot of the same qualities."

"Keep hiring nonprofessionals, you'll have the Screen Actors Guild on your back."

"I can handle them. What about you?"

She shrugged.

"Can you work with him?"

"You said it—he's a nice guy."

"Then it's settled."

"Pike won't like it."

"I'll handle Pike."

"No," she said. "Not anymore, Little John."

He followed her off the pier, guided her into a small dark bar with an old jukebox in the rear, out of which came the tinny sounds of a bossa nova. They sat at a corner table and sipped cold draft beer.

"We've got things to talk about, Vicky."

"My mind's made up."

"This is show business, Vicky."

"It's my life."

"For people like us, there is no difference."

"You mean life is like show business. Or is it the other way around?"

"You're a living legend, Vicky. Nothing can hurt you."

"I'm lonely and I'm frightened. Everything hurts me."

"You've got to do it. Give me one night to shoot in. It won't take long. It will rejuvenate your career, Vicky. I'm sure of it."

"Oh, God, this business is obscene, everything about it. Nobody wants to see a middle-aged woman in the flesh."

"Everybody wants to see Vicky Pierce. Trust me, Vicky."

"Oh, God!"

"Everything in the best taste. I'll protect you, Vicky."

"Oh, God!"

"You're too serious. Just do it, get it out of the way, take the money and run."

"One night," she said finally, not looking at him. "I'll do it. But, please, don't ask me to trust you."

Purple shadows across Commercial Street signaled the oncoming night. Sexton stood in front of the gallery watching the tourists on parade. All the shops were open now. All the restaurants and bars. Sleeping space was at a premium.

Customers appeared more frequently in the gallery, and each day he sold more paintings. Seascapes, as usual, were selling well. He made a mental note to phone Novick in the morning, put in an order for more. Sexton decided to close down for an hour or two; he needed time to figure out what he was going to do.

He locked the front door and hung up the "Closed" sign and went out onto the tiny back deck with a glass half full of bourbon. He sat quietly staring down at the harbor, drinking occasionally. He heard somebody pounding at the front door but made no move to accommodate whoever it was. He struggled to clear his mind of all distractions, to deal directly with the problem at hand, to think in a straight line.

"Hey! Up on the deck!" Her voice came drifting up from the beach below, instantly recognizable. He took another sip of bourbon.

"Closed for repairs. Nobody home. Gone fishing."

A moment later Ella, looking incredibly young and cheerful in faded jeans and a black wool sweater, climbed over the guardrail.

"Hi, Sexton!"

"Beat it."

"You sure know how to make a girl feel at home. Keep it up, Sexton." She indicated the glass in his hand. "Having a party?"

"A *private* party."

"Beautiful, the way you stroke me. Make me feel wanted." She held up a hand. "Don't say I'm not wanted. It would trouble me. Take me for a walk on the beach, Sexton."

"Can't you see I'm busy?"

"You call that busy?"

He raised his glass. "I'm drinking and thinking. And you are trespassing. This country is founded on property rights. A man's castle is his home, so watch your step."

"Be warned, Sexton, I can get tired of you."

"No staying power, that's the trouble with young people today. When you go, take those poisoned cigarettes of yours along."

"Didn't you try one?"

"No way."

She went into the apartment, returned moments later, grinning. "Almost did it, didn't you, Sexton?"

"I don't know what you're talking about."

"Right next to the bed. Matches at the ready. You're gonna make it, Sexton, I believe in you."

"Kiss off."

"Come on, how about that walk?"

He appraised her solemnly. She was, he had to admit, a great-looking girl. With a certain style, a relaxed way, the quick smile, the bright dark eyes that seemed to miss so little and enjoy so much.

"A little walk can't hurt."

They tramped over the dunes, stumbling in the dark over low shrubs, finally settling down to gaze out at the ocean.

"I think I'll light up," she said.

"You're going to get me busted."

She dragged. "Try it, Sexton. Let the magic smoke take you through the door."

"What door?"

"Whatever door you want to open. Unlock the secrets of your mind."

"O'Day came to see me a couple of hours ago."

She waited.

"Offered me the job again."

She smoked the joint.

"Part of me wants to take it. Part of me wants to leave things as they are."

"How are they, Sexton?"

"No sweat. No big problems. No big responsibilities."

"And no big rewards, either."

"When did you become a missionary for upward mobility?"

She grinned and looked away. "Why do you work at the gallery?"

"For bread, that's all."

"Wouldn't you make more, and quicker, making pictures?"

"You're good, you are. More in a few weeks than Novick pays all season."

"That answers it?"

"You decide."

He lay back on the sand, staring up at the high speckled sky.

She bent over him, extending the joint. "Try, Sexton."

He stared up at her, but in the darkness her face was a shadowy mask, without features. He grew afraid and sat up.

"A man can only do so much."

"Cross over, Sexton."

"Give it up, will you?"

"One drag, and you'll never be the same."

"You think I'm afraid."

"Everybody's afraid of something."

He removed the joint from between her fingers, put it to his lips. He spoke around it. "I want to tell you, I couldn't help noticing that you are one sensational-looking chick."

"I noticed you were noticing. Smoke."

He dragged slowly. "Just a trial run."

"Hold the smoke in, don't waste it."

He dragged and held. "Nothing."

"Give it time. You've got all your defenses up."

"In my head, I'd really love to do it."

"Make it, you mean?"

"Yes."

"In your head?"

"I can't."

"Smoke some more." She watched him closely. "Have you got a late date you're saving yourself for?"

He felt strangely out of synch, tingling from the knees down, disconnected from everything he'd ever experienced. "Can't you understand what I'm saying to you? I can't get it up!"

"You don't have to shout."

"I'm a boozer, dammit. Booze busts a man up that way."

"Ah, you're not busted, Sexton, just out of practice."

"And you are going to get me back into shape?"

"Right on."

"You dames are all alike." He fell back on the sand, laughing softly. He sucked on the joint.

"Wrong again," she said, coming down to him.

"What?"

"We're not all alike."

"You're so damned sure."

She touched his cheek with her fingertips. "Hopeful."

This release is printed in its entirety and without comment, courtesy of Hillary Pike Productions, Inc., Lee Downing, publicity director.

FOR IMMEDIATE RELEASE

Mario Costa, the former Cape Cod fishing captain, who zoomed to stardom in his first movie, *Provincetown*, and has since made two still-to-be-released pictures, announced at a press conference today (9/17) that he intends to produce and direct, as well as act in, his next motion picture.

The new movie, entitled *Man or Beast*, will be based on the soon-to-be-published novel by Thomas Reynolds. Reynolds, who will author the screenplay as well, concluded transfer of all dramatic rights to Costa Film Company two days ago.

Said Costa: "Only by exercising the power inherent in the roles of producer and director can an artist retain complete control over his work. Acting is simply not sufficient in and of itself. The public is entitled to the full sensitivity of a performer, and in this way, and this way alone, that debt can be dispatched."

Negotiations for a leading star to play the feminine role opposite Costa are now in progress, and an announcement is anticipated within the week. Costa indicated that he has several fine actresses in mind, both American and foreign. Mentioned have been Liv Ullmann, Sophia Loren, Barbra Streisand, Faye Dunaway, and newcomer Sandy Hayden.

Said Costa: "My friend Tom Reynolds has composed an especially fine and sensitive novel which concerns itself with some of the central moral issues of our times. Here we have the story of an individual man who, in order to survive, must deal directly with criminals. Yes, in answer to the inevitable question, there is violence in this tale. But then, isn't life itself violent? I will portray a man who follows his conscience, which is all any person can do, to the obligatory conclusion. Can any of us do less?"

Production of *Man or Beast* will begin as soon as the screenplay is ready. During the interlude, Mario Costa will act in another Hillary Pike production, entitled *The Hunchback Returns.*

18

They gathered in the conference room in Zeke Bechtol's midtown Manhattan office. Amidst the ledgers and accountancy library and gray file cabinets, business could be discussed in a businesslike manner. That was Pike's idea; Bechtol was all for meeting in a private dining room at 21. Bechtol appreciated the conversion power of glamorous frills. In the end, Pike had his way, making a concession to the early-morning hour by allowing coffee in Styrofoam cups to be served with jelly doughnuts, Danish pastry, and an almond ring from Sara Lee.

Pike got them situated around the coffin-shaped conference table, Bechtol at the far end. Pike, standing until everyone else was seated, lean, white, swayed slightly, as if about to go on the attack. He sat down, adjusted the sharp creases in his spotless trousers, cleared his throat, gazed at his guests until they squirmed uncomfortably.

"Okay," he said. "You want to know why you're here."

A man named Max said, "We know why we're here, to give you a crack at our dough. Now, tell us why we should cough up, Hillary."

"Max, you're a winner, straight from the shoulder, that's you. How would you like to get in on a can't-lose proposition?"

"Can't lose," Max repeated. He leaned back in his chair.

The sole woman in the room, bright-eyed and smoking energetically, waved a bony hand as if to wipe away an offensive thought. "I don't know about these fellows, Pike, but nobody dumps on me. Can't lose, that's crap."

Pike glared at her. He couldn't even remember her name—Martha Something-or-other . . . Keenan. Who needed her? He arranged a pleasant white smile on his pale lips.

A stubby little man with a red toupee groaned. "That worries me, Mr. Pike. Money is accumulated by discovering ways in which it may be lost, then assiduously avoiding them. Sure things are never sure things."

"Nothing's sure, not even a fixed horse race," one man said.

"Cows are better than horses," another man said soberly. "A few cows and the right property, you got yourself a shelter the IRS can't crack without going up against the farmers. What politician wants to do that?"

"You're headed in the right direction," Pike said. "Let's talk about my movie."

"Show biz," the woman snarled.

"Hah!" said a large heavy man. "Not since *Guys and Dolls* have I made a nickel in show business, and what did I have there—one point is what."

Pike ran a hand over his smooth skull. "Let me tell you about my picture. John Patrick Michael O'Day is—"

"Is it done?"

"Another few days, a week maybe."

"Can you be sure?"

"O'Day tells me—"

"I heard of him," the heavy man said.

"I thought he was dead," the woman said.

"He's a very great talent," Pike hissed.

"All of which," the man in the red toupee said, "means what? There's scoring, dubbing, editing, titles, maybe even retakes, still to come. Let's talk facts. What's the budget?"

Pike looked over at Bechtol. The accountant avoided his eyes. "Eight hundred thousand," Pike said. "Originally."

Three or four voices sounded at once. "What is it up to now?"

"Two-million-three," Bechtol put in quietly.

A moan went up. "Such insanity. A waste of good money."

Pike said, "Probably end up around three-million-plus, before it's over."

The woman waved her cigarette at Pike. "And that's a can't-lose deal? Include me out, as the saying goes."

"Wait a minute," Pike said. "The work goes on, the costs go up. It's perfectly natural. Perfectly legitimate."

"Incompetent."

"Nobody," Pike said slowly, "can ever point a finger."

His words were weighed in silence.

"Sounds," Max said, "like you invented something new."

"Not new," Bechtol replied.

"A sure thing," Pike said. "A can't-miss."

Bechtol lifted his feral face as if he were on display in a museum's glass case. "Gentlemen and lady, you're here because you are special people."

"Hit me but don't shit me," the fat man said.

"I strive for obscurity," another man said. "How else can you hide larcenous intent?"

"Special," Pike said, "because each of you is an independent operator. Four of you are doctors. Doctors, as we all know, are very good with money. A lot of them get paid in cash."

"Wait a minute!" three doctors cried at once.

"Let me go on. You, dear lady, own a boutique, a leather shop, a dress factory. Two of you own three car washes between you, a health-food restaurant, two singles bars, one Plymouth dealer, there's the cow farm, and you, Max, raise bees for honey."

"What's wrong with—?"

"Nothing wrong, just an indication."

"Pike, you do your homework."

"Each one of you has a large personal income, a highly taxable income."

"Tell us what we don't know."

"Do any of you know what an amortization purchase is?" Bechtol said.

No one answered. Pike said, "In this case, this group is being offered the chance to buy a completed movie."

" 'Completed' is the operative word," Bechtol put in.

"I get it," the man with the red toupee said. "You got yourself a lemon, and you want to squeeze the rotten juice on us. Deal me out."

Pike said, "It works this way. A production service company is created—a limited partnership. Which means you have no liability beyond your investment. The company buys *Provincetown*, putting up no more than one-fourth of the full production cost."

"And," Bechtol said, "that final cost should not exceed four million dollars."

Max laughed humorlessly. "Keeps getting higher every time anybody opens his mouth."

The woman lit another cigarette from the one she was smoking. "Okay, supposing you raise one-quarter in this room, where does the rest come from?"

"Banks."

There were moans, laughter, cries of derision and disbelief. "What bank will lend money on such a deal? What banker in his right mind . . . ?"

Bechtol waited for them to grow quiet before speaking. "It is called a nonrecourse loan. The bank will get its money back out of box-office receipts, without recourse against individual investors."

"The picture itself is collateral?" Max said.

"Isn't that beautiful?" Pike said.

Nobody spoke for a long time.

"No personal liability?" the woman said thoughtfully.

"None."

"What if there are no box-office receipts?"

"You're concerned about the banks?" Bechtol sat back and looked around. "Banks have a way of taking care of themselves."

"It's beginning to sound better," the woman said.

"Wait until you hear the rest of it," Pike said.

Bechtol tapped the table with a pencil. "Though investors put up only twenty-five percent of the total investment, they are able to deduct a prorated share of the full production costs."

"The entire amount?" a doctor said.

"All of it."

Another doctor began writing figures on the back of a prescription pad. "One-quarter buys a hundred-percent tax shelter, is that it?"

"That's it," Pike said.

"Explain, please."

"Cash-accounting methods are utilized," Bechtol said. "For example, let's say one of you puts up one hundred thousand dollars. You may, if there is a loss, make a deduction on your tax returns of four hundred thousand dollars."

"Four for one."

"I like that."

"From current income?"

"From current income, income from any other source."

"Please, go on," the man with the red toupee said. "Doesn't he speak well, for an accountant?"

"Very well indeed," the woman said. "Don't stop."

"Let's place our imaginary investor in the fifty-percent bracket. The extra three hundred thousand dollars deducted as a business loss would mean additional income—I repeat, income—to him of approximately a hundred and fifty thousand, spread out over a few years."

"Spendable money," a doctor said.

Bechtol nodded. "Think of it as a tax-free loan."

"Courtesy of Uncle Sam," Pike said. "And yours truly, if you care to come aboard."

"The company is formed," Bechtol said. "Everything is in order. I am the packager of record."

"Do go on, Mr. Bechtol," the woman said. She dipped her chin cutely in his direction.

Bechtol ticked it off in a nasal drone. "One. Each of you would be able to deduct the interest paid on your share of the bank loan, again proportionately.

"Two. During the first year, you will be able to take two-thirds of the ten-percent federal investment tax credit, a little icing on the cake, so to speak.

"Three. On the entire amount, there will be a depreciation write-off. Eighty percent of that to come during the initial eighteen months."

"And so on and so on," Pike said. "The more you put up, the more you save."

"There must be a catch," a doctor said, hoping he was wrong. He owned five nursing homes with his brother-in-law, the dentist, and the amount he paid in taxes was a shame. A shame.

"Aha," Max said. "You haven't even got a releasing deal for your picture, I bet. That's it, no?"

"Max, you're a pessimist," Pike said. "One theater is set in New York, on the East Side, naturally. We got another in Los Angeles."

"Two houses! That's all?"

"You can't make much money from two houses."

"Let me remind you," Bechtol said. "Making a profit

isn't the goal. We need only a minimum amount of income in order to qualify for tax shelters."

Joy reigned around the coffin-shaped table. All the doctors were making notes now, and the woman wrote in a red diary.

"Suppose," Max said gloomily, "the picture is a hit. And makes a lot of money?"

Pike said, "I was wrong about you, Max. You're an optimist."

Bechtol waited for the laughter to subside. "If that happens, people, you will all get very, very rich."

19

Even as Hillary Pike plowed his way through financial seas in New York, his yacht moved with slow purpose through the water off Cape Cod. The Trumpy rode low and easily, her classic profile enhancing the horizon. Nearby, Mario Costa's rented draggers maneuvered into proper shooting position.

In the bow of the yacht, Kiley posed, resolute, powerful, emanating courage and determination, your everyday red-white-and-blue hero about to launch himself into action. But he stumbled about in the dark caverns of his mind after something precious lost and badly missed.

Soon it would be over, the picture finished. And he would remain as anonymous and unrewarded as before. Nothing had gone right for him. Not the business with Joe Crespi. Nor his attempts to suck up to O'Day. Not even servicing Letita Belmont, right up to the moment she had taken off for Hollywood, paying him off with empty promises. Promises, Kiley understood, didn't buy shit.

His eyes shifted step by step over to the nearest dragger. Sexton was issuing orders. Who was he to tell Kiley what to do, how to do it? He's come out of nowhere to take over the second unit. Without a word of warning, Sexton had showed up, begun sounding off. Gotten on Kiley's ass, riding him hard, never satisfied. Screw him.

And Mario. A fisherman. Jesus fucking Christ! Curly-headed and too damned pretty. No different than the other one. Fags were what they wanted in pictures, not real men. Kiley couldn't believe it when word reached him that O'Day had replaced Crespi with Mario. A stab of acute pain had erupted in the center of his brain, dug into the space between his eyes, made him almost cry out in anguish and protest.

Strangers were killing him. Shattering his dreams of glory. Destroying his hopes. By what demonic device had his destiny passed into their soft, weak hands?

He heard his name spoken in the impatient voice of a disapproving parent. He dragged his attention back to the dragger, back to Sexton. Strangers . . .

"Snap to, Kiley! This is a run-through for the camera. Step through at half-speed. Mario will do the same."

Mario.

His role had gone to Mario. His chance to hit it big. His future ripped off by Mario. By Sexton. By O'Day. They had ganged up on him, and he swore to get even. To punish each of them, as he had punished Crespi. To make them experience the same pain he felt. To destroy them.

"Got it this time, Kiley?"

There was scorn in Sexton's voice. A serrated taunt, opening Kiley up to further embarrassment and shame. His failure was public property now, and he understood that all of them were laughing at him behind their hands. A man could take only so much.

"Got it," he said.

It occurred to Kiley that he had never commanded such obedience. He could never remember being put in a position of authority. Not in the marines; he'd been just another faceless uniform. In the slammer, he'd been an outsider, never a member of the gangs. The Straight Arrows; he was a member, but that was all. Do this, do that; well, he was through with that. Up to here shit-eating.

Mario came out of the main cabin of the Trumpy. His curly hair glistened in the sunlight, the smooth dark cheeks shone with good health, the large eyes were luminous. He was slender and well-muscled, yet delicate, with a subtle catlike grace.

"Hello, Kiley," he said cheerfully.

Kiley muttered a greeting. Tension seeped into his limbs. His gut tightened, and his fingers balled up into fists. He knew the feeling—as if about to go into combat or swing with the Straight Arrows. Battling and balling brought out the best in a man. The *best*.

"Okay!" Sexton yelled. "Stand by, we're going to run it through." Sexton waved his hand, and Mario spoke the lines he had memorized.

"I say we let him go. Otherwise, there's going to be trouble."

Kiley, following Sexton's instructions, shook his head, shoved Mario away. He shoved harder than he had intended, and Mario stumbled backward an extra step before recovering.

"I'm warning you—"

"The hell you say."

"Get out of my way."

Kiley shoved again, and Mario threw a punch. A good mock blow. Kiley staggered as if hit, thinking how easily he could take this pretty spic apart. Spider-man was a spic, and Kiley had taken care of him with very little trouble. A real man could always wipe out a spic.

From his place on the dragger, Sexton watched the action with a detached professional eye. Not great, but it would do. Neither of them was a pro, and it showed. They'd run it a few more times, smooth out the rough spots. Maybe spread the draggers apart a few more yards, get a better angle on the two men. He'd work with Kiley and Mario for a while before shooting began, show them how it should be done. After all, he had been one of the best. He laughed silently at himself, amused at how involved he had become, and how quickly. After all those years, he still enjoyed the work. Hell, he loved it.

Jerry Wheeler designed each day of his life for maximum results, all good. No margin for error; no errors occurred. Life was a downhill ride.

In the morning, he and Junie took ten leisurely laps in the pool. Wearing thick terry-cloth robes, they breakfasted on the terrace. Shirred eggs, Canadian bacon and link sausage, biscuits, orange juice, melon, an abundance of strong coffee.

The next few hours were devoted to business. Jerry took care of this by direct telephone wire to his New York office. He solved problems, answered questions, bought and sold, hired and fired. He made a great deal of money every day with very little apparent effort, having organized everything. Jerry's greatest talent lay in his organizing ability.

Meanwhile, Junie wrote letters in a fine, flowing hand before settling down with Kafka's "Metamorphosis." Junie had planned a summer reading program that included every book she had never understood during her undergraduate days at Smith.

They lunched together, a salad usually. And afterward went horseback riding along the dune trails. By four they were back at the house for martinis and another swim, followed by a nap, exactly one hour long.

At six they played tennis with Susie and Fred McGloughlin. He was a psychiatrist out of Boston who spent his summers in P-town. At forty he had taken up tennis, taking a lesson a day for one year. He played a slashing game, determined to grind his opponents into the ground. He won often, but never the close games. He always beat Jerry, but Jerry didn't care about winning at tennis. He just liked running around for a while.

After dinner—a delicate chowder, shrimp with an exquisite lemon sauce, broiled cod—they smoked marijuana on the balcony outside their bedroom.

"I've arranged it all," he said to Junie.

"Oh, you are a devious fellow."

"I'm worried about Tommy, though."

"Poor Tommy. I'm sure he'll come around."

"I hope so. After all, it's no fun for me if it's no fun for you."

"Sweet man."

"Are you ready?"

"Oh, yes, always."

They went to bed and made love, and afterward congratulated each other for being superb and considerate lovers. Each was, they agreed, the most satisfactory partner the other was likely to have.

"Still, let's keep looking. . . ."

For Vicky Pierce, it was going to be another bad day. One of her worst. Almost as soon as she woke, the pain came alive in her middle and a sour taste rose up in her throat. She tried to numb the pain with gin, but it didn't work.

Sometime during the day she let herself down to the floor and began to exercise. Sit-ups, leg-ups, rolls, and twists. All designed to tighten the muscles, firm the flesh, recapture the perfection of her youth.

She stood naked in front of the mirror and examined herself. There was no change. The glass once again showed a woman sad and soft, a woman who had gradually surrendered to time, all dreams cruelly terminated in a lonely, bitter end. She left the glass and drank some more gin and waited for the terrible night to come.

Kiley squinted against the glaring points of light that danced off the choppy sea. His headache had grown worse, and there was a strange roaring in his ears.

Mario came out of the main cabin of the yacht and took up his place opposite Kiley, who barely noticed him.

"All the way this time!" Sexton shouted from the dragger. "An unbroken shot. Both cameras will follow you guys, so keep up the action until I tell you to stop."

Orders. Kiley clamped his teeth together to keep himself from shouting back. He rolled his shoulders, but the tension was bunched up in hard lumps. He flexed his hands.

"All right!" Sexton cried. "This is a take. Give us the cameras! Let's have the sound! On the yacht . . . action!"

Sexton was pleased by what he saw. His work with Kiley and Mario was paying off in good footage. There was hostility in the angle of their bodies, big men in conflict, ready to fight. They were shoving each other, and soon the punches . . . There, good! Good, keep it up. Sexton had choreographed the fight with the mathematical precision of a ballet master. The old feeling for stunts was still in him, and the work excited and satisfied him. It was good to do something you were good at and be able to see the results.

The actors were mixing it up. The blows came faster. Their grunts drifted across the water.

"Nice work," Jacoby whispered.

Sexton gave no sign he'd heard. Mario threw a combination, two lefts and a right, according to plan. Kiley fell back, returned to the attack.

"Christ," Jacoby said. "That one landed. He belted the crap out of Mario."

Sexton straightened up.

On the yacht, Mario doubled over as Kiley kept punching away at him. The fisherman stumbled up against the rail, lifting his hands as if to fight back. Or protest. Or surrender. Kiley hit him high on the head, and Mario tumbled backward into the water.

"What the hell is going on!" Jacoby husked.

"Keep shooting, dammit!" Sexton went up into the bow of the dragger for a better look. He was being paid to get some good film, not stop a fight.

Kiley, as if following the script, dived into the Atlantic after Mario.

Sexton signaled Paulo, in the wheelhouse, to move the dragger closer in. From his position, he could see blood seeping out of Mario's nose. Kiley surfaced a couple of yards from Mario, thrust himself forward, and the fight continued. They thrashed water, and for a brief interval Mario held his own. Until he took a heavy blow to the side of his head. He fell back, and Kiley went after him. The two men disappeared under the water.

Jacoby came up behind Sexton. When neither man surfaced, he could contain himself no longer. "What do we do?"

Sexton kicked off his shoes. "Shoot whatever you see. Don't stop those cameras." He went over the side, pumping up his lungs, diving steeply. He began an ever-widening search until he found them, locked in a deadly embrace. Mario was struggling to free himself, to rise to the top; Kiley refused to let go.

Sexton came up behind Kiley, hooked him by the chin, jerking his head backward, breaking his hold. Mario shot toward the surface. Sexton gave him a beat or two, then followed. As soon as he broke water, Sexton sucked air and kicked away. Not soon enough. Kiley was right behind him, throwing punches. Two or three landed, and pain radiated through Sexton's skull.

He twisted back, managing to get a hold on the other man, dragging him underwater. Kiley tore lose, and for the first time Sexton became aware of the tremendous strength of the man and the murderous rage that drove him. He kicked out for the surface.

This time Kiley came up in front of Sexton. In his right hand he carried an open gravity knife. He slashed at Sexton, missed, and slashed again. Sexton grabbed for the knife hand, failed to get it, and felt the blade slice into his left shoulder. He drew back and launched a short right hand at the middle of Kiley's face. It landed, and Kiley's nose gushed blood. Sexton hit him again, and Kiley went limp, began to sink. Sexton got a grip on his hair and pulled him over to the dragger.

"Beautiful," Jacoby said when the men were aboard the dragger. "Couldn't've done it myself."

Sexton lay facedown on the deck, waiting for the pain in his lungs to go away. His shoulder began to throb, and his skull ached. He wanted to sleep, to rest, couldn't remember ever being this tired.

"Got some beautiful stuff," Jacoby boasted.

"Jesus . . ."

"Absolutely got to win an Academy Award for this."

"Jesus . . ."

"The truth is, Sexton, I deserve it."

"Jesus . . ."

Reynolds watched Wanda get dressed. Finished at last, she turned to him.

"How do I look?"

"I can see your bikini through the pants."

"Kind of kinky, isn't it?"

"Put on a darker pair of slacks."

"What do you think of this tank top? I bought it today."

"Your nipples show."

"I know. Are you coming or not?"

"O'Day's shooting the love scene tonight. He wants me there."

"Jerry said he's going to have a surprise for us. I wonder what it can be?"

"It's the final scene."

"O'Day doesn't need you."

"Always supportive, that's my Wanda."

She stared blankly at him. "Come over when you're done."

"Wait for me. You won't miss a thing."

"I don't intend to," she said before she left. "I've missed too much already."

Darkness closed in on P-town, and people began parading along Commercial Street in protective groups and pairs, exchanging hostile glances. Men in plaid Bermudas. Women in wash-and-wear dresses, carrying shiny white purses. Children, up past their bedtime, shrilling out their demands and crying. Hard-eyed young women in boots, and soft-faced young men with shirts open to the waist. Girls wandering, waiting for life to catch up. Men seeking someone to take care of them.

Kiley's world. He had always functioned in it with modest competence. Getting along. He understood the rules and knew when and how to break them with impunity. But not tonight.

Frustration clogged his tubes. His nose burned. Fury inflamed his membranes. Pressure pushed at his eyeballs. He snorted, he hawked, he spit. The killing rage took hold of him, and he gave himself over to it.

He leaped on his Harley and busted out into the dark. A rough ride, a series of smashing jolts. The roar of the headers deafened him, and he heard only the distant small cry of disappointment.

He aimed the Harley at the sea, drove it up the face

of the dunes. The machine bucked between his legs until his genitals grew hot and hard. At full throttle, holding nothing back, he went on, until the bike skidded—another failure—and he was flung aside, no longer useful, unwanted, without hope. He screamed his hate at the sky and ran, struggling up the great sand mountains.

20

Work lights lit up the beach. Stanchions and platforms, booms and dollies, wires and cables, turned the area between dune and ocean into a surrealistic jungle. Hoarse commands caused a light to be lit or a reflector to be moved. From behind the shooting site the hum of generators could be heard. Men laid wooden tracks down so that the Arriflex could be dollied in and out, as O'Day might wish.

Three times O'Day had rehearsed the actors, making slight alterations here and there. Everyone agreed that the scene played well, that it possessed sensitivity and delicacy, that it would look good on film.

"People are going to love it," Reynolds said to O'Day following the last rehearsal.

The director stared at him.

"I agree," Jacoby said. "Good visuals."

The director walked away.

"What's wrong with him?" Reynolds said plaintively.

Jacoby shrugged. "Head honcho. It can be hard on a man."

O'Day went over to the commissary wagon and asked for a cup of tea. He lit a Gitane and looked around. It was all set up and ready for him to say the word. To put them all to work, the craftsmen and skilled workers and actors. He was the boss, the power, the ultimate creator, the major force in deciding what course the film should take. Its final success rested on him alone. They were all waiting for him.

Sexton appeared out of the darkness, and O'Day was surprised at how pleased he was to see the other man. Pleased and relieved, as if by his presence Sexton might answer some of the questions, lay to rest some of the nagging doubts.

"You did good work earlier today," he said in greeting.

"Kiley went ape, that's all."

"Keep your back to the wall, man, it's the only way you can be sure."

Sexton grew thoughtful. "I'm tired of it."

O'Day showed his surprise. "Not you, tough guy. The heroics, that's your line of work. You're built for it. You're good at it. I saw you in action, I remember."

"No, no more. I have had it. A few days ago, I almost busted up some poor sucker in the street."

"A bad guy?"

"Just a guy. I was drunk and pissed off at the world, and he happened to come along. I was going to take it out on him. Work him over in front of his wife and kid."

"What happened?"

"The kid stepped in, defending his daddy."

"Good kid."

"Real good. But me—I was going to humiliate that man in front of his family. Get rid of my problems that way. No, no more. I'm not like that. At least, it's not the way I want to be."

"I think, Sexton, you are a very human guy, better than most of us."

"Save it, Little John."

"I mean it. In your heart, you are a gentle man."

Sexton started to answer, thought better of it. "What about Kiley?"

"The sumbitch is going to the slammer, that's what

about Kiley. Attempted murder with a deadly weapon. If it hadn't been for you—"

"Let him off, Little John."

"The bastard's no good. He would've killed Mario. Killed you."

"Maybe not."

"You wouldn't have done it."

"There's more of Kiley in me than I'd like to admit."

"You're no killer."

"When I had to, Little John, I killed."

"You must've had good reasons."

"The point is, Kiley didn't really damage anybody."

"Thanks to you."

"It's hard for me to think of his action as a crime."

"It is."

"Take him off the hook."

"To hell with him. He goes for the full ride—arrest, trial, jail."

Sexton exhaled. "Maybe you're right. It'll bring a lot of publicity your way. Make the picture famous before it's in release. Of course, who can say how the public will react? A potential murderer on your payroll. . . . What the hell, Little John. You're the expert about pictures, you know what you're doing. You know best."

"Sexton, you dirty dog." O'Day grinned mirthlessly. "You play me like a fiddle. Okay, so I protect the picture. I have to do that. But what about Kiley? He just gets off?"

"You fired him?"

"Bet your ass I fired him. Is that enough?"

"It's enough."

O'Day gave a short, harsh laugh. "Stay around and work for me, man. I need you."

"You're a good man, Little John." Sexton turned his face toward the high dunes. "Now, if you don't have something for me to do . . ."

"What's up there?"

"A girl."

"Your girl? That's nice."

"She's younger than I am. A lot younger, a lot different."

"Pretty?"

"Beautiful."

"That helps. Smart also, I bet."

"Also a little strange."

"That's not so bad. I envy you."

They strolled toward the dunes, side-by-side. "I meant what I said about working for me, Sexton. The word is out. The phones are ringing again. From the Coast, Europe. Offers are coming my way again. Like in the old days."

"Congratulations, if it's what you want."

"Hell, yes, it's what I want! To climb back where I belong. When I put all the pieces of film together, this is going to turn into one hell of a movie."

"If you say so."

"You disputing me?"

"Not for a minute."

O'Day drank some tea, smoked his cigarette. "Just in a hurry to get up there with the girl?"

"Like that."

"Some big deals have come my way. Firm offers. My lawyer's talking to the people at Paramount, and De Laurentiis wants me for something. Two projects in Europe are pretty hot, too."

"You can pick, that's good."

"Come with me, Sexton. First assistant. Screen credit. You'll never have a better teacher, and I guarantee top money. Don't answer right away. Think on it. Two, three years, you could be on your own. I'll give you whatever help you want."

"My head's a little unhinged right now, Little John. I don't know what I want."

"Talk it over with your girl."

"Yes. I will do that."

O'Day strode back to where Jacoby and the others waited. "Okay! Kill the works and show me the lights one more time, please!"

Three very carefully located lamps glowed and grew brighter. Stand-ins took up their positions where later Mario and Vicky would perform.

"I like it," Jacoby said. "I've got no problems. We won't get too close . . ."

"To hell with that," O'Day said, voice suddenly harsh. "Get in there. Shove the damned lens right up Vicky's crotch. You see a pimple on her ass, you show it to us. Warts and beauty marks. Make us smell her."

"You know Vicky, Little John."

"Do it."

"Whatever you say. With these lights, we won't miss a thing."

"Maybe," O'Day said, almost to himself, "maybe there is too much light. Kill the booms, let's go with a single source."

Jacoby was startled. "Little John . . ."

"Do it, damn you. One source, narrow, soft."

Jacoby issued the appropriate orders. "Two naked actors with lots of shadow," he pointed out. "People aren't going to know what they're looking at."

"Let 'em use their imaginations."

"Pike won't like it. Pike wants explicit nudity."

"Get your camera ready."

O'Day watched Jacoby walk away. A cool breeze caused him to pull up the collar of the old suede jacket he wore. A stooped, solitary figure staring out at a horizon he knew was there but couldn't see.

"Gonna be a beautiful scene," a voice said at his back. Reynolds, O'Day said to himself, go away. Fade into the night and leave a troubled director to his unresolved miseries. O'Day preferred writers out of sight. They talked too much and were usually much more impressive on paper than in the flesh. They possessed all the shortcomings of ordinary folk magnified by their literary and intellectual arrogance. He came around to Reynolds, tugging at his mustache.

"That's your opinion?"

"Absolutely. Sexiest scene I ever wrote."

"You think so?"

"Oh, I do. This time I've put some first-rate words on paper for you. Can't-miss stuff."

In a vacant region of O'Day's mind, there was a lazy stir.

"Can't miss," he muttered.

"No chance. Just follow the words, it's all there."

"The words . . ." A picture came into focus.

"You won't be needing me anymore," Reynolds said. "I'm meeting my wife and some friends . . ."

"Go ahead," O'Day said. He felt a pale fondness for Reynolds, brief, however, and without depth. O'Day went back to the camera. "Kill the sound," he said with quiet assurance. "Get the mike boom out. We shoot this one dumb."

Sexton found Ella sitting up on the crest of the dune, and took his place next to her.

"Not much going on down there," she said, without complaint.

"Making movies is dull work, if you're not involved. O'Day thinks he's got a winner here."

"Is that good?"

"For him, yes. Producers are after him again, he's in demand."

"That's his number, making pictures."

"Yes. He's invited me to go along. First assistant, all the goodies that go with it. What do you think, shall I take the job?"

"It's your life." She brought a joint out of her pocket and lit up, handed it over.

"You've turned me into a dope fiend."

"You're a boozer," she said, not unkindly.

"I've got a hold on it now, thanks to you."

"I didn't do a thing, Sexton."

He thought: She, who had given him so much, brought his dormant manhood back to life, would not interfere at this moment. Any decision he made had to be his own. A hardheaded lady, this one, in touch with the center of her own being. He gave her back the joint.

"I'm running out, Sexton. You wouldn't happen to have a connection, would you?"

"Only in liquor stores." He rummaged among his memories, his dreams, in pursuit of an answer. "The bread's good."

"Money's not everything."

"Everything costs." Resentment ran out to his nerve endings and expired almost at once. "Ah, maybe I don't even want the damned job."

"Maybe. You ought to be sure."

"If I took it, would you come with me?"

"Whatever you decide, that's okay. Take it or not, either way it's cool with me. But don't hang it on me. You live your life, I'll live mine."

He stood up, walked in a small circle around her, and sat back down. "You should've been there this afternoon, seen it."

"You're all hero, Sexton. I knew that from the start. You could've been killed."

"Somebody had to stop Kiley."

"I'm proud of you."

He decided she meant it. "The point is, there we are in the water. Mario's half-dead. Kiley trying to cut me. My lungs are about to pop, and it looks like I'm about to drown, and what do I think about?"

"Me?"

He squeezed her knee. "I kept hoping that Jacoby was getting it all on film."

"That's your way."

"Craziness." He tried to penetrate the shadowy glaze that separated them, to know exactly what she thought and felt. "My way? I can change my ways. I don't have to make movies. I don't have to drink. I don't have to be by myself all the time. I'll tell O'Day to shove the job."

"Your choice?"

"All mine."

"And if I take a walk in a week or two? What then?"

"Same decision. I'll cry a lot."

"That'll be the day," she said softly. "One great day, when you let yourself cry." She uttered a pleased laugh. "What will you do, Sexton? No way you can just hang out."

"Paint."

"I've seen your painting, Sexton. You'll never get rich."

"That bad?"

"Not bad, but not commercial."

"The movie money will stretch a long way. I know a couple of places in Europe where living is cheap. I could paint and . . ."

"And what?"

"And screw."

"Dirty old man."

"Will you come along?"

"Yes."

"We can get married!"

"It's okay to screw without getting married, Sexton. Nobody died from it."

"Sounds good to me."

"And if I split on you one day?"

"No strings, no hard feelings."

"Well, okay."

"How's Italy sound to you? Someplace in that direction. Water, sunlight, some open spaces."

"Wherever we can flow with the life."

"That's great, just great. Now, let's go back to my place and celebrate."

She let herself fall back on the sand, arms outstretched. "Can't you dig the great outdoors, old man?"

They were both laughing as he went down to where she was.

Vicky, trembling under a layer of rough blankets, sat in her tent alternately drinking gin and lime juice from a Styrofoam cup and steaming coffee from a tin mug.

"Are you ready?" O'Day said.

"We've done a dozen takes already."

"Four," he corrected mildly, patiently, wishing she would drink more coffee and less gin.

"This is the last one, Little John."

"You must trust me, Vicky."

"You should be a presidential candidate. You sound like one." She stood up, took a last drink of gin.

"Are you ready?"

"I'll never be ready."

She went outside and took up her position. The cold night air seeped into her flesh, made her bones brittle, caused her teeth to ache. Was there anyplace anywhere for her to hide?

Mario came out of the tent that had been provided for him, stood opposite her. He smiled. "Here we go again."

She made no response.

"I thought it would bother me," he said cheerfully. "It doesn't."

"Being naked?"

"Acting," he answered. "I want to be very good."

"O'Day will make you look good, it's his gift. You enjoy this?"

"Maybe I'll go to Hollywood when this is over."

She almost forgot the cold, her fear, the misery. "You want to become a movie star, is that it?"

"You think I could?"

"I think . . . make up your own mind."

He stared boldly at her. "Will you go back to Hollywood? You're a beautiful woman, with a beautiful body. I'd like to see you again."

Under other circumstances, she might have been flattered. Or at least amused. "We're strangers," she said. "Playing parts. When it's over, we go different ways."

"Just like in the movie."

"Ironies within ironies."

"Stand by!" came the warning cry.

A dresser removed the blankets, and Vicky had to struggle not to crouch, not to shield herself, not to run.

Alongside the camera, O'Day studied the actors.

"You think there's too much shadow?" Jacoby asked.

"It's fine. We'll establish from back here, Jacoby. When I signal, you dolly in, very slowly. As we move up on them, fix on Vicky. Give me a run over her body, whatever we can see. Hold on her face."

Jacoby whispered, "She's scared silly, trembling like a leaf."

"That's okay. On film it'll register as desire, desperation. The critics will love it. No sound, no words to screw it all up. Let's go with it. All right!" he shouted. "Actors, we are beginning. Camera, Frank . . ."

21

Reynolds planted himself at the front door of the Wheelers' house, unable to make up his mind. He liked to think of himself as a man of character and strength, decisive, forthright, able to consider all possible alternatives objectively, to choose a course of action without hesitation. He had virtually convinced himself a man could shape his own destiny, could withstand the incidental buffetings of life and proceed courageously against the storm. Look how much Tom Reynolds had accomplished. How much still lay just ahead. Triumphs of willpower and hard work, of intelligence and determination. There was nothing to be frightened about.

Yet he was afraid. Afraid of what he would find behind that closed portal. Afraid of what he would discover about himself, about his marriage, about his future.

But why? Hadn't he imagined all manner of weird engagements for himself and Wanda? What was it he had told her? "It's incorrect to surrender your freedom to the physical and moral fetters of a restrictive society." And he had believed it then. Still believed it. Why, then, did he stand frozen in place like some terror-stricken adolescent on his first date?

It was absurd to question himself in any way. He was attractive, desirable, young, extremely sensual.

He'd been told, many times; and no complaints. Never. Not one time. He knew what he was doing in the old saddle, was good at it, strong, controlled, and women turned on to him. Then why this sense of inadequacy? This weakness, as if failure was fated to be his constant companion. He grew angry, longed for a specific target at which to direct it. It seemed to Reynolds that unknown forces conspired to deny him the rewards he justly deserved.

He rang the doorbell. A silent servant directed him to the playroom with no hint that he comprehended what went on behind those finely carved double doors.

Reynolds slipped inside and stood in place, struggling to make his eyes adjust to the shifting light in the room. Pink and amber flashers sat in opposite corners, turning lazily. The soft thump of a jazz bass, the weary moan of a tenor sax, the gentle whir of brushes on drumheads, seemed to encase him in sound. He shivered and was afraid.

Jerry Wheeler materialized. He carried a crystal goblet in one hand and a burning joint in the other. He wore a Cheshire smile on his face, and nothing else.

"You made it," he said in a thin voice, neither glad nor sad.

"I had to work," Reynolds said.

"There's Courvoisier and Colombian. Take your choice. Hope you don't mind, but we started without you."

"Not at all." Reynolds recalled his mother fondly; she had always insisted on good manners. "Good manners," she liked to say, "are all that separate us from the beasts." He smiled agreeably and felt out-of-place with his clothes on. "Where is everybody?"

Jerry drew him toward the center of the playroom. There, on a pile of plump cushions, was Junie. She reclined with feline grace, one knee raised and rocking gently from side to side. Reynolds forced his eyes to her face.

"Darling," she drawled, "how good of you to come."

She seemed almost disappointed to see him. Or so he suspected. He delivered what he meant to be a confident smile in her direction.

"You look great," he heard himself say.

She blew a kiss in reward, and he immediately felt better.

"Which?" Jerry said at his shoulder. "Brandy? Pot? Both?"

Reynolds accepted a joint and lit it.

"And for God's sake, darling," Junie said in a voice too loud and too affected, "take off your clothes before we all get a complex."

Reynolds hesitated. "Isn't Wanda here?"

"Here," Junie said—she raised one leg and pointed her toes—"and there."

From out of the undulating beams of colored light came a muffled sound. Moist, ripe, tinged with amusement. Reynolds brought his eyes around to where a pale sculpture of some size and indeterminate form sat in the middle of the room. Amber crevices and pink mounds turned and shifted in slow motion as Reynolds watched. His brain functioned ponderously, clogged with sensory information that possessed no logic, no history. He grew confused and weary.

"Where," Reynolds asked, gripped by a spreading panic, "is Wanda?"

Wheeler laughed, a taunt full of raw pleasure. "Surprise!" he cried.

"Isn't he too much!" His wife giggled. "Take off your clothes."

"Wanda . . . ?"

The sculpture rolled and tumbled and came apart with considerable reluctance and whispered promises. One of its two parts came up into a sitting position.

"My God! Wanda!"

"Hello, Tommy."

Horror and revulsion crept up Reynolds' neck, and he twitched and shivered.

"What are you doing?"

"Silly," Junie murmured. "Didn't you see?"

"A great natural talent, your wife," Jerry said. "All she needed was to have the way pointed out. One of the world's great heads."

Reynolds groaned.

"Get undressed," Wanda said. "You look silly with everything on."

Reynolds pointed. "Who is that?"

The second half of the sculpture sat up, and he saw the foxy face of Sandy Hayden. Somehow it came as no surprise.

"Bitch!" he cried.

Sandy licked her lips in satisfaction.

"Get your pants off," Jerry commanded.

Reynolds took a backward step and tripped and went down. He scrambled back to his feet. "Why," he wailed in his wife's direction, "are you doing this to me?"

Sandy said, "Actually, she's been doing it to me, Tommy. Very nicely, too."

"Join us," Wanda said. "You'll be surprised how much I've learned."

"My God!"

"When she's finished with Sandy, she's promised to do me," Junie said.

"What happened to you?" Reynolds screamed.

Wanda spoke in a mild voice. "I've become the wife you've always wanted me to be."

On the Harley, Kiley charged across the blowout area. Up one dune and down another. The grade steepened, and the bike came up on its spinning rear wheel. Kiley roared out his rage and leaned forward, putting his face across the handlebars, down, until his chin almost rubbed the front tire. No good. The bike went over, and Kiley tumbled, rolled, scrambling to avoid the bike.

When everything stopped bouncing, Kiley picked himself up and stalked over to the Harley. He righted the bike and planted one heavy boot on the kick starter, came down with a powerful jump. The engine exploded into life with a raw boom that shattered the still night. He set himself into the saddle and gripped the handlebars tightly. He gritted his teeth and squeezed the clutch lever hard. He kicked the bike into gear, and a twist of his right hand gave the Harley full throttle. At the same time, he let the clutch lever spring out. *Wham!* Off again, bursting ahead as if in search of enemies. Faster he went, back up the dune, this time making it to the top, riding blindly down the other side, the pounding saddle arousing him.

He went down again, and he lay with his engorged penis in the sand, wondering what it would be like to fire his sperm off into the earth itself. *Fuck you, world!* He went back to the Harley and gunned it back up toward the sky. The machine bucked and fishtailed, leaped wildly, the spinning wheels spraying sand in stinging clouds.

Down. This time the Harley fell across his legs. He struggled to free himself. His legs were stiff at the joints, and oddly weak, unsteady. Pain stabbed into his thighs. He glared at the Harley, a dormant monument to his dreams and to his failures. He left it behind and picked his way up the nearest incline, advancing slowly until he stood alone at the top of the world. Below, the endless white strand of beach, and beyond it, the infinite black sea. He started down toward that soft and vulnerable streak in search of . . . what?

Halfway down the slope, his knees gave way and he

fell forward, out of control. At the bottom, he lay without moving. Time passed unmarked. Finally he raised his head as if seeking something.

He squinted along the beach. A ghostly blue figure materialized, was coming his way, intent on his destruction. The enemy at last. With animal cunning, he drew himself together, eyes locked in place, not moving, hardly breathing. Patiently waiting. Kiley knew exactly what he had to do.

O'Day rented the Harbormaster for the night. A private party for cast and crew, and wives, lovers, casual acquaintances. All available spaces were filled, and the air was thick with smoke and various scents and sounds. Another picture done, let's celebrate.

"Party time!"

O'Day chose his place carefully. A large round table set deep in a corner, his back to the wall. In case the urge to depart should suddenly come upon him, he mapped out escape routes to the left and to the right. Charged by completion of shooting, he rode through the tinges of depression and felt almost good. Smug, but not satisfied.

He smoked and sipped Chivas Regal over ice and accepted congratulations from one and all. He allowed no one to stay too long, for fear of being bored or propositioned or asked a favor. Movie parties were like flea markets; everybody had something to sell. O'Day had learned the hard way, no bargains anywhere.

"Where's Vicky?" he asked periodically. No one had the answer.

"Send her over when she comes," he commanded, and knew she wouldn't arrive. "Great actress," he declared, to widespread accord. "Great woman."

He was relieved by her absence. Even talking about her gave him moral indigestion. He smoked a little more and drank a little faster.

"Anybody seen Sexton?" he asked.

O'Day wanted Sexton to accept the job. Needed him around. As if Sexton's presence would provide affirmation of O'Day's own drives and unresolved cravings. His once and future life.

Ah, Sexton, come aboard, man.

Reynolds squeezed out of the crowd and presented himself at the big round table in the corner. His eyes made mechanical starts and stops, cranked from corner to corner, unable to stay long in one place. His hands washed the air with apprehension, fighting off evil spirits. He sat unbidden at O'Day's table.

"I," he announced portentously, "am extremely disappointed in you."

"Take aspirin. Two," O'Day replied reasonably. "Get a good night's sleep."

"This is no joke."

"Of course not. What hurts?"

A young woman with spectacular breasts outlined under a torquoise tank shirt made it over to the round table. She rested one breast on O'Day's shoulder and murmured into his ear. He worked his shoulder out from under her.

"Sure you would," he told her.

"I'm good," she said.

"Sure you are."

"Later?" she said, and returned to her starting point.

Reynolds began again. "I had a lot of respect for you, Little John."

"I've failed you?"

"Massively."

"Poor Reynolds. What a sober man you are. So serious. So disappointed. A heavy burden to carry around."

"That's it, make fun of me."

O'Day offered him a Gitane. It was refused. O'Day lit up.

"Ford," Reynolds intoned. "Wyler, O'Day. Those were my heroes."

"Don't leave out Huston, Wilder, Welles."

"Enjoy yourself at my expense, that's okay."

"What gave you the idea that I'm enjoying myself?"

"It was my book."

"You'll feel better when the picture is released."

"I won't. You ruined my script. Cut the heart out of it."

"They say 'balls.'"

"What?"

"Writers usually claim I cut the balls out of their scripts. Castration, y'know."

"It's not funny."

"Look at it this way. A script is a production schedule. Something to keep in mind but not to stay married to."

"You're old!" His face flushed, Reynolds pushed himself erect.

"True. Still, Reynolds, I've made you look like a winner. Later, take all the credit you can."

"I'm going to demand Pike take my name off the picture. You've ruined me."

"Oh, I wouldn't think so."

"Without young talent like me to feed off, you'd fall flat on your face."

"You've got a way with words, kid."

"My words made the picture."

"It's all wrapped up. There are no more rewrites."

"What the hell does that mean?"

A sprightly blond girl bounced out of the crowd, put herself onto O'Day's lap. "Oh, Mr. O'Day, can you find some time for me?"

O'Day set her back on her feet, gave her a brief smile. He turned to Reynolds. "Life is an enigma, as you surely have discovered. What do you mean, what do I mean?"

"Jesus!" Reynolds said, and marched away with canine pride in every jerky step.

O'Day watched him go.

The sprightly blond said his name, and he gave her his attention. "You want something?" he said.

"Do you?" she replied happily.

"You honor me. But as host, social duty binds me to this chair for the remainder of the evening."

"I," she whispered, "won't be far away, if you want me."

"Lovely creature," he said in dismissal.

Mario was next. O'Day invited him to sit.

"How'd I do?" Mario began.

"You did very well, Mario."

"I mean my performance."

"You gave me what I asked for."

"Acting is hard work."

"But fundamentally dishonest."

"I don't follow you."

"Fishing is honest work."

"There's no future in fishing."

O'Day fingered his mustache; it needed trimming. Perhaps he would allow his beard to grow, become grizzled and gray, a father figure, in fact. "You've become infected, Mario. That's bad."

"I thought I'd give New York a whack."

"You've seen the future, have you? Believe me, it doesn't work."

"I could be an actor."

"Follow the yellow-brick road . . ."

"I could study at the Actors Studio."

"You've contracted a really virulent strain."

"I suppose I'll need an agent."

"Mario, get drunk. Get stoned. Get laid. Hide on your boat and wait for it to go away."

"I can't do that."

"Talk to your father, he'll straighten you out."

"My father thinks I'm crazy."

"True wisdom, that."

"I could use some help."

"You want help, go to a priest."

"I don't believe in that stuff, do you?"

"I believe in a great many things."

"Like what?"

"On the other hand, I believe in very little."

"You confuse me. Can you recommend a good agent?"

"That's a contradiction in terms. There are no good agents."

"I need somebody."

"So do we all."

"You could help me, Little John."

"The picture's over, kid. The dream's all washed out."

"No, I can make it. Big."

"Oh, shit."

"Miss Belmont, she said I had what it takes."

"She tells that to all the boys. Go home. Go fishing."

Mario stood up. "A man like you, you ought to understand. But you don't. Well, nothing can stop me. I'll do it on my own."

"Whatever you say, Mario."

Mario went away, and O'Day finished his drink. A pervasive weariness clutched at his body, and suddenly he felt old and empty. There was still so much to do. All the bits of film. He had to examine and assess them, patch them into a coherent piece of work, get them scored, dubbed. Do all the things that he did so well in order to make one damned fine movie.

That was all for later, however. For now there was only the sadness for what he was incapable of doing. Remorse for those he had inevitably failed. But it was late, too late. He was tired, too tired. The fire was out, the embers cold, the nighttime long and lonely.

Enough.

Last August, Joe Bob Alderman, intrepid investigative reporter and free-lance film critic, worked his way inside the heavily guarded Dunn, Aronson studios, where John O'Day was editing and scoring the final version of his picture Provincetown. *The following exchange took place, as reported in the November issue of* Way to Go *magazine. In the interests of truth and accuracy, no changes have been made in the text.*

DIRECTOR TRAPPED IN LAIR
by Joe Bob Alderman

THE CINEMA CAPITAL OF THE WESTERN WORLD: There he was. The Great Man himself. Little John Michael Patrick O'Day. Hero to hordes of cinema buffs. America's randy contribution to the auteur theory. Subject of doctoral theses, white papers, reviews, lofty criticisms and assessments, endless speculation. And your reporter had him dead to rights. Cold in my journalistic sights.

Look at him. Hunched over a movieola just like your everyday, normal movie mole. Puffing a smelly French cigarette just as if tobacco hadn't gone out of fashion, and in violation of the big red sign: NO SMOKING. Fire hazards and health warnings don't exist for Great Men.

He senses my presence and looks up. That handsome, perfectly-groomed-by-generations-of-poetic-Irishmen face. Sumbitch, as Little John himself might say, he's wearing specs.

Glasses on a Hero. Some kind of a comedown.

He sweeps them off the bridge of his classic nose. He pulls at the bushy mustache. He glowers with eyes grown a mite rheumy with age. He frowns.

"Who the fuck let you in?"

The voice is low, graveled with threat. He *is* a tough guy, just the way you'd heard. Beautiful. I introduce myself. I wrote to you, I remind him.

"You wrote to me." He couldn't care less.

"For an interview. I never received an answer."

"Get your ass out of here."

I plunge right in, electrified by his presence, full of journalistic daring. "Do you consider yourself to be one of the top three directors of our era?"

"On your way."

"Flannery Gideon wrote that your films are crowded with powerful images of sexuality and death and—"

He stands up. "Out!"

I back up. "As one of America's very few mature artists, would you claim to have been touched by the psychic destructiveness of popularity? After all, you've had commercial success as well as—"

"You've got ten seconds."

He reminds a reporter of a tight-bodied John Wayne. One tough old bird.

"Mr. O'Day, how young were you when you first longed to make films?"

"Stupidity . . ."

"With this interview . . . ?"

"There is no interview."

He's counting aloud. "Cynthia McDermott-Jones suggests in *Cinema Galaxy* that you were concerned not with esoteric indulgence but the primacy of the imagination. Would you say—?"

"Who needs this cockamamie horseshit? Three . . ."

"You must admit your films depend to a large extent on a cold authoritarianism. You attack conventional morality and conventional philosophical stances."

"Four . . ."

"About Vicky Pierce. We know how closely you and she worked together, how much you cared—"

"Out, fuckhead."

"One gets the feeling that *Provincetown* was jinxed. The sadness about Vicky Pierce. And, of course, the affair with Crespi. Happily, Joe Crespi is fully recovered now and acting better than ever, I understand, in *Tender Loving Care.* Perhaps at this point you'd care to comment on Crespi's thespic ability?"

"Five . . ."

"Is there any advice you'd care to give to young filmmakers?"

"Six, seven . . ."

"How does it feel to be a legend in your own time?"

"Eight, nine . . ."

"You have been quoted—"

"Ten!"

Not wishing to disturb a Functioning Artist at his labors, the reporter departed. Encounters with Great Men are often trying experiences.

Sumbitch.

22

She moved without purpose along the empty beach. Occasionally she would pause as if trying to reach a decision, then go on unsteadily. A faint montage went stuttering through her mind—events barely remembered, faces without names, quick shocks of recognition and shame.

She tripped on a piece of driftwood and fell, remained kneeling in place. A scouring wind off the sea made her shiver, and she clutched at the blue terrycloth robe. The blanket? What had she done with the blanket? Left it behind in the dressing tent, she supposed. Or lost it. No matter.

She continued on, an aimless amble. She had raised herself up from an ignominious past. Learned to live with pride and self-respect, loved and given love. Put the whore to rest. The useless flesh handed from director to agent to producer; no more. She had altered her persona, inside and out, transformed herself by a mighty and courageous effort. A chattel no longer.

But the system would not be denied. The system had given her everything, it deprived her of everything. The system had pumped her full of lies until she had believed in her own invulnerability, her own immortality. And when all of it had been accepted fully, become part of her being—The Legend of Victoria Pierce—the system had cast her down onto the cruel shoals of her own hubris.

First, her career began to falter; pictures were fewer, parts less rewarding. Then Tony had been taken from her. And finally, the money, as if fate intended to put her into an intolerable position once more.

Tony. None of it would have mattered if Tony were still with her. Not that he was the man of her girlhood dreams. No, he was the man of her mature years, the man who pleased her in so many ways, at night and during the day, the man she needed and wanted and loved. In spite of what he was not.

She had never expected it to go on forever. That was the way the movies told it. Life was different. Life terminated relationships for its own capricious reasons, without explanation, without pity. Another woman had come along, a younger woman, a prettier woman, a woman Vicky Pierce had never seen or heard of or known about. A woman Tony desired more than he desired her. He went, he left her alone.

At the shore, she allowed the small night waves to lap at her feet and ankles. The sea was mother of us all, she reminded herself. It circulated life without consideration of good and evil. It shattered rocky shores and smashed stone to fine grains and delivered the sand to other shores and made beaches. It was where the big fish ate the little fish, and so it always was and always will be. She, Vicky Pierce told herself silently, had begun as a very little fish, had grown into a big fish, and had completed the circle. Vicky Pierce was a very small fish indeed.

She let the robe fall away and stepped tentatively into the sea. To what purpose? In order to play out the absurd drama her life had become, provide an ending suitable for the Great Coast-to-Coast Audience. She envisioned the headlines: MOVIE STAR TAKES PLUNGE. Suicide suited her not at all.

She backed out of the water and stood on the beach, the cool night air caressing her skin. She would return to the house in Connecticut. She would find ways to support herself. Her needs were not great. She had known luxury, extravagance, and required neither of them. With luck, she would meet a man one day. A kind and gentle man. She was sure it would happen.

"You're looking good, Vicky." The voice was rough, without kindness or gentleness. Without turning, she knew who it was, and a stab of fear reached into her middle. She looked around for the robe. "Is this what you want?"

She came around and faced him squarely. The robe hung from one of his big hands.

"Give it to me, Kiley."

In the darkness, his features shifted, and for a moment she imagined she was able to glimpse into his skull.

"I like the way you look."

She held out one hand. "The robe, please." She warned herself to remain calm, not to do anything foolish. In a moment or two, this would be over, just another unpleasant incident soon forgotten.

"I spotted you coming up the beach," Kiley said, inspecting her with idle curiosity. "I watched you all the way. I didn't want it to be you, y'know. I wanted it to be O'Day. Yeah, O'Day would've been really good."

"Please, I'm cold. Give me my robe."

He shook his head.

"I have to go," she said.

"Sexton would have been okay. Both of them shafted me. But you'll do just fine." He took a single step forward, and she retreated a step. "Come and get it."

She turned to run, but her feet refused to function efficiently, and she went down. Before she could get up, he was at her, planting one boot in the middle of her back, holding her in place.

"Nobody," he grunted, tugging at his jeans, "nobody shits on me."

He rolled her over and went to his knees. She kicked out with both feet, catching him on his injured nose. He hit her in the stomach, and she gasped. He beat her around the face and chest. She screamed, but that seemed to infuriate him, and he struck out harder until she lay still. He put her onto her back and spread her legs.

"Here's yours, cunt. Here's what I've got for all of you. Nobody fucks Kiley."

23

O'Day was still asleep when the phone began to ring. He stirred, rolled over, but was unable to bring himself to full wakefulness. He'd drunk too much the night before, smoked too much, and then been unable to fall asleep. It took two Valiums to ease the tension in his body, to quiet his restless mind. Now he felt thick and heavy, unwilling to make the effort to answer the phone. It stopped ringing.

And immediately rang again. He located the offending instrument, brought it up to his ear. "O'Day here."

It was Lou Klein. "Little John, are you awake?"

"What . . . ?"

"I've got some bad news, Little John."

"What . . . ?"

"It's Vicky. They found her out on the beach. She's dead."

O'Day lost his hold on the phone and began to cry.

Kiley fought against the panic. Fought the urge to run. Running would be a mistake, a virtual admission of guilt. Better to stay, to gut it out.

He laundered everything he had worn the night before. And using a stiff brush, he scrubbed the black engineer boots he had stomped Vicky Pierce with. Using the garden hose, he washed the Harley, polished the paint and chrome to a high luster. Satisfied with his work, he went out and ate a good breakfast.

At a few minutes after nine, he phoned Lou Klein. He identified himself and told Klein he intended to leave P-town that afternoon.

"Any chance of getting the rest of my money?"

"You haven't heard?" Klein said.

"Heard what?"

"Somebody killed Vicky Pierce."

"Jesus!" Kiley said. "That's terrible. Anything I can do?"

"Raped her, the cops say, and kicked her to death."

"The dirty bastards," Kiley said. "Who'd do such a terrible thing?"

Klein said he didn't know.

The police questioned Kiley on and off during the next three days. The same questions repeated, and Kiley supplied the same answers each time.

One detective, with a neck like a turkey's, put his bony face close to Kiley and said, "I think you did it, fella."

"I liked the lady. Why would I do a terrible thing like that?"

"You wanted to get into her pants, and she wasn't having any, so you decided to take it. You got scared and stomped her so she couldn't make a complaint against you."

"Nah," Kiley said. "She must've been forty, too old for me. I dig young chicks."

Turkey Neck examined Kiley's room. His clothes. He wanted to know why Kiley's boots were damp, and Kiley explained that his job as a stunt double demanded that he spend a certain amount of time in and around the water. Turkey Neck checked with O'Day, who corroborated Kiley's statement.

"I still think you did it," Turkey Neck told Kiley.

"I'm innocent, officer. Never laid a glove on the lady. She was good to me, considerate, kind, you see."

"Awright," Turkey Neck said finally. "You're clean for now. Leave an address where I can get in touch."

Kiley provided the street number of the Straight Arrows' clubhouse.

Lou Klein advanced him two hundred and fifty dollars, saying the rest would follow by check. In about a week or ten days, Klein said. Kiley thanked him, strapped his gear onto the Harley, and took off.

Feeling fine.

Earlier that same morning, Reynolds loaded the trunk of the Eldorado with his wife's Gucci bags and his own luggage from Hunting World. With Wanda beside him, he headed down the Mid-Cape Highway.

"I'm glad we're going," he said as they rolled past Truro.

"You said that before," Wanda said. "Twice before."

"Sorry."

"Turn the air-conditioning down. I'm cold."

"It's on low now."

"I'm cold, I said."

"I'll turn it off. You want to roll down your window?"

She offered no reply.

"I'm glad you changed your mind," he said.

"All the fun is gone, after what happened. Jerry said he'd have to play it cool, all those cops sniffing around."

"Well, I'm glad it's over, the business with the Wheelers."

"We'll see them in New York."

"No," he said without much force.

"I want to. And others, too. I like it."

"I'm your husband. You have a responsibility to me."

"You're invited, darling. If you can handle the action. Your choice."

"What's going to happen to us?"

"Fun and games, for the rest of our lives. . . ."

Only positive omens. Kiley sensed it. His luck had turned, and good things were coming his way. Getting it off with Vicky Pierce like that, wasting her. No way the cops would tag him for it. He was clear. Clean. Going home. Underneath the plastic shield of his shining black helmet, he laughed long and loud, pleased with himself. He gave the Harley a turn of the throttle, felt the big machine shudder and leap ahead.

He knew how to play this hand. Once back in the East Village, he'd get off a letter to Letita Belmont. He'd remind her of how it was when they were together in the john, how she'd gone ape over his tool. He'd tell her he wanted to give her more of it, wanted to come out to Hollywood to see her. For sure, she'd send him the air fare.

He'd service her for a while, go neat and cool, until he was settled into a solid movie career. A stud with his natural gifts, his guts and good looks—how could he miss making it big!

He steered the Harley in long graceful loops around the squares in their station wagons and comfortable sedans, shooting ahead, reveling in the fierce roar of the bike.

Ahead, just this side of Sandwich, an accident happened. An elderly man wearing thick glasses tried to make it onto the highway in his Valiant. The old man was intimidated by the rush of traffic and slowed the Valiant, changed his mind, and decided to chance it. A camper coming fast made him nervous, caused him to go for the brake. The camper slowed about the same time, and the old man went back to the accelerator, a little heavier than he'd intended. The Valiant leaped ahead. He never did see the 1966 Thunderbird pulling out from behind the camper, speeding up in order to make its pass.

The driver of the Thunderbird spotted the Valiant coming out and smashed his brake, twisted his wheel. But oncoming traffic kept him from going into the other lane. He fought the wheel, and the Thunderbird went into a screeching spin, tail trying to catch up with the front. He crashed into the Valiant, driving it into the concrete abutment that spanned the overpass. The Thunderbird came to a rest, completely blocking the off-Cape lane. Traffic ground to a halt, a long line of cars rapidly overheating in the hot sun.

Seeing the cars backed up, Kiley put the Harley on the center line at full speed, glorying in his ability to get where he was going, untouched by difficulties that stopped ordinary men. He felt powerful. And free.

He spotted the Thunderbird. To avoid it, he slowed briefly, picking up speed as he went around it. He failed to see the black oil slick until it was too late.

The Harley skidded, the drive wheel spinning. Kiley fought for control as the bike bucked and twisted, rose up like a wild horse. The bike shot across the highway and slammed into the concrete abutment. The Harley came to a dead stop. Kiley kept going, a human missile, tumbling through the air to the road below. He lay where he landed, unable to move.

At that exact moment, a truck carrying a load of watermelons rumbled out of the underpass. The driver hit hard at his brake, but before the heavy vehicle could stop, the right front wheel had passed over Kiley's chest, crushing his rib cage, killing him instantly.

Authorities agreed, upon investigation, that no one

was to blame for the unfortunate sequence of events that caused Kiley's death. Except Kiley, of course.

O'Day claimed the corpse. No one else seemed to want it. He arranged for transportation to the West Coast and burial. Forest Lawn had never been Vicky's style, but O'Day intended to plant her with all the pomp and circumstance befitting a True Movie Star.

Two weeks after the funeral, public television ran a week-long Vicky Pierce film festival, with appropriate commentary before and after by well-known critics. Pauline Kael held forth on the "Star Personality" and the sad demise of the "real matinee idol with all his glamour and popular appeal." Andrew Sarris said that stars were only an albatross to a serious film director and serious filmmaking and serious filmgoing. John Simon allowed as how Vicky Pierce had always been a little too big in the bosom for his taste, putting it down to a lack of genetic refinement. Rex Reed said that if he could find a woman like Vicky Pierce, he'd marry her in a minute. Letita Belmont mourned the passing of the old Hollywood and predicted that *Provincetown*, a jinxed picture, could not possibly show a profit.

Coincidental with the national release of Provincetown, *the following item ran in Letita Belmont's syndicated column.*

BURNT-OUT STAR

Look for Alex Kiley in *Provincetown.* You can see this magnificent physical specimen in the very exciting water scenes late in the picture. It is Kiley who rescues a drowning Vicky Pierce. It is Kiley who made those fight sequences so true to life. It is Kiley who is in the water when the whales appear.

Kiley was the stunt double for Mario Costa. With a little bit of luck, Kiley would have become a star in his own right. He was a man, and that's more than can be said for most actors these days. Too bad, but Kiley's luck ran out on a highway up in Cape Cod.

He will be missed.

24

Sexton and Ella traveled across Europe without haste. They visited museums and ruins and cathedrals. They ate in inexpensive restaurants or nibbled cheese and bread and fruit while trying to hitch a ride at roadside. When they could, they crashed. Or else slept in the fields. Once in a while they cadged a joint. Sometimes they drank wine with their meals. It had been almost a year since Sexton had taken a real drink.

In Greece they explored Athens and the remains of classical Greece before going by boat to the island of Skiathos. They took up residence in a large bright room, bath down the hall, with an unobstructed view of the harbor.

Here Sexton began to paint again. He worked mornings, and in the afternoon they went swimming at one of the beaches outside of the town. They dined at night in the taverns overlooking the water, observers of the passing parade of ships and people. They ate souvlaki, and mussels with rice and pine nuts, and fresh fruit and cheese. They sipped small cups of thick sweet coffee. And on special occasions they treated themselves to baklava.

On this particular night they strolled along the quay examining the boats that had docked during the day. Tied up was an old three-masted schooner, a fifty-five-foot Burmeister, a sleek oceangoing yacht that reminded Sexton of Hillary Pike's. For a moment he longed for what he had given up, for what had been within his reach. But only for a moment.

Ella said his name, and he looped his arm around her shoulders as they walked. "There's something I feel you should know," she said.

A spasm constricted his chest. He feared the day she would tell him it was over, that she wanted to move on. He was certain it would come one day, but not yet; he wasn't ready for it to end.

"Yes," he said.

"I am going to have a baby."

He stared blankly at her.

"It's true."

"But how?"

"I don't know, an accident. I must've forgotten . . . Maybe I really wanted to get knocked up. Anyway, there it is, Sexton."

"A baby," he muttered.

"You sore, Sexton?"

"No, I'm not sore."

"Well, that's good," she said a little more aggressively than she'd intended.

"I guess it's time," he said, taking her arm. "We better get married now."

She yanked her arm away as if burned. "Married! "What for?"

"Dammit! It's what people do. When they're knocked up."

"No way," she shot back, and strode down the quay in that free-swinging stride of hers, drawing admiring glances from a number of tables.

Sexton caught up. "Okay," he said. "No wedding."

She stopped and confronted him challengingly. "You mean it?"

He shook his head. "What are we going to do?"

"Go on living, of course." Her expression softened, and she touched his cheek. "And have that baby. A fine, healthy baby."

He took hold of her arm and this time she made no objection. Without urgency, they went on their way.

ABOUT THE AUTHOR

BURT HIRSCHFELD is best known for his bestselling novel, *Fire Island.* A native New Yorker, Mr. Hirschfeld was born in Manhattan and raised in the Bronx. He left school at the age of seventeen and took a series of menial jobs. Immediately after Pearl Harbor, he enlisted and spent three of his four years in service overseas. After the war, he attended a Southern college for several years. For the next fifteen years he worked on and off for movie companies and also did some radio and acting work. Burt Hirschfeld did not write his first novel until he was in his early thirties. He worked on it for three years and, when it only earned $1,500, he abandoned writing for several years. At thirty-seven, he decided to find out once and for all whether he had the makings of a successful writer and began to freelance. He wrote everything—from comic books to movie reviews. He also wrote numerous paperback novels under various pseudonyms and eleven nonfiction books for teenagers which were very well received. *Fire Island,* his first major success, was followed by *Aspen,* the twelfth novel he has written under his own name. *Provincetown* is his most recent book. Burt Hirschfeld lives in Westport, Connecticut, with his wife and two sons.